Algrove Publishing Limited
1090 Morrison Drive
Ottawa, Ontario
Canada K2H 1C2

Canadian Cataloguing in Publication Data

Main entry under title:

    Popular mechanics shop notes

(Classic reprint series)
2nd ed.
Includes index.
Originally published: Chicago : Popular Mechanics Co., 1905-Compiled from the
    Shop notes department of Popular mechanics magazine, and Written so you can
    understand it : tells easy ways to do hard things.
ISBN 0-921335-74-1 (v. 1) - ISBN 0-921335-76-8 (v. 2) - ISBN 0-921335-78-4 (v. 3) -
    ISBN 0-921335-80-6 (v. 4) - ISBN 0-921335-82-2 (v. 5)

    1. Do-it-yourself work. 2. Industrial arts. I. Windsor, H. H. (Henry Haven), 1859-
1924. II. Title. III. Title: Shop notes. IV. Series: Classic reprint series (Ottawa, Ont.)

TJ1160.P66 1999   600   C99-900763-7

Printed in Canada
#10799

Publisher's Note

Virtually every woodworking magazine in the English-speaking world has a shop notes section and has published an accumulation of them in book form. This was all started in 1905 with the first annual issue of *Popular Mechanics Shop Notes*, a compilation of advice on jigs, fixtures, methods of work, processes and projects. The earlier issues focussed primarily on metalworking, but with tips for a variety of other trades liberally sprinkled throughout. As years went by, the contents shifted more and more to woodworking and handyman projects. Each book is profusely illustrated. The line drawings of the earlier issues were supplanted by superb engravings until photographs started to creep in during the 1920s. Each year has its charm but all issues share the attribute of being clear, concise and widely informative.

Leonard G. Lee, Publisher
Ottawa
September, 1999

WARNING

This is a reprint of a book compiled in the early 1900s. The book describes what was recommended to be done in accordance with the knowledge of the day.

It would be advisable to treat all corrosive, explosive and toxic materials with much greater caution than is indicated here, particularly any materials that come in contact with the body.

Similarly, some of the recommended projects were dangerous then and remain so now. All of this material should be regarded with a judicious eye and necessary precautions taken.

POPULAR MECHANICS

SHOP NOTES

FOR

1908

EASY WAYS TO DO HARD THINGS

OF DAILY USE TO EVERY
MECHANIC

Volume IV—Table of Contents, Pages 809-816

Price 50 Cents

POPULAR MECHANICS, CHICAGO

This Volume is Reprinted from the

Shop Notes Department
of Popular Mechanics

As Published Monthly During 1907

Edited by H. H. WINDSOR

SHOP NOTES

Unloading Big Revolving Field

The revolving field for a 6,600 k. w. alternator was shipped on a special flat car having an opening in the middle which allowed the bottom of the field to come 3½ ft. below the surface of the car. The field weighed 42 tons and it would have been necessary to raise it 3½ ft. in order to clear the car in unloading, which involved the erection of powerful hoisting apparatus.

Instead, one end of the car was lifted from its truck to a sufficient height and the field, which was 13½ ft. in diameter, was rolled out from under the car.

To Make a Round Leather Belt

Cut the leather into long strips, having a square section, and then draw through a die made by drilling holes in a piece of steel, as shown in the illustration. The holes should be drilled of different sizes and the belt

Making a Round Leather Belt

should be drawn through the largest hole first. To polish and smooth the belt draw it through a tapered hole, having the belt enter at the large end. —Contributed by A. W. Griggs, 955 Market St., Kenosha, Wis.

Hydrogen Generator

A good hydrogen generator for furnishing a non-oxidizing flame can be made, as shown in the sketch. A tall bottle, A, is fitted with a perforated cork which has a small glass tube in-

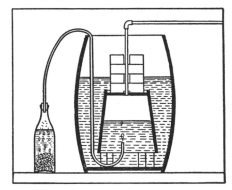

Hydrogen Generator

serted to connect the rubber hose, B. Dilute sulphuric acid and bits of zinc are placed in the bottle, and the resulting reaction liberates hydrogen gas, which passes through the hose, B, and bubbles up into the receiver, C.

The receiver consists of an inverted butter tub, D, placed in a barrel of water and held down by bricks, E. A ⅛-in. pipe, F, is connected to the bottom, as shown, and carries the gas to the burner, which can be placed in any convenient location.

Pure hydrogen without air will not burn, but when mixed with air an explosive mixture is produced. For this reason the air space in the top of the bottle should be relatively small, and it is well to let the gas generate a minute or two before connecting the hose, in order to drive out the air.

The inverted tub should be entirely filled with water in order to prevent air becoming mixed with the gas. If it is desired to increase the pressure, pour more water into the barrel. It is well to construct a small generator first, if one is not familiar with the properties of hydrogen, as an explosion would then be less dangerous.— Contributed by A. G. Ward, Peebles and Edgerton Aves., Wilkinsburg, Pa.

Gas Burner for Melting Lead

Having occasion to melt a large quantity of lead in a pot 16 in. in diameter and 10 in. deep, a piece of ¾-in. pipe was bent in a circle and

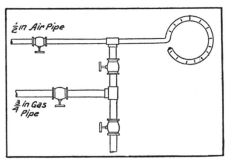

Gas Burner for Melting Lead

the end capped, says the Journal of Electricity, Power· and Gas. Slots were then cut with a hacksaw. To this a ¾-in. gas pipe was attached with gas under 5 lb. pressure, and a ½-in. pipe from compressed air tanks. By regulating the air and gas valves, 10,000 lb. was melted and poured in four and one-half hours.

Crankshaft Made Without a Lathe

A crankshaft which will run true and serve a practical purpose may be built up as follows:

Mark off two centers, E and F, the distance apart of the throw-off crank on a piece of mild steel, A, and drill holes B and C. Cut out the portion D by drilling a hole at the bottom and sawing down to it. Drive a piece of rod—a tight fit—through B to form a crankpin; drive a longer piece through C to form a shaft. Secure these rods at the joints by brazing,

and put a safety pin, G, through. Saw away part H, then file the crank and round it off. A double crank

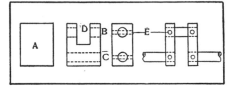

Crankshaft Made Without a Lathe

may be made in this way, but all depends on the holes being drilled parallel and true.

Making a Temporary Piston

One of our water service pumps failed, and an examination of the piston showed that it had been broken beyond repair, writes a correspondent of Power. No spare pistons were on hand, and the pump was needed. The sketch herewith shows how a temporary piston was made. A wooden disk, W, was turned, faced and bored to fit over the piston rod; this was reinforced by two steel plates, SS, about $\frac{1}{16}$ in. thick, that were in stock. One plate was bored smaller than the diameter of the piston rod, fitting the small end of the taper part as shown

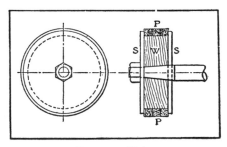

Temporary Piston

in the sketch. Square packing, P, was put between the plates, and the piston was completed. This piston gave no trouble, working all right for several weeks, when the plant shut down; then a new cast-iron piston took its place.

Drill Press Made from a Vise

An ordinary bench vise with a small hole in one of the jaws makes a very good drill press for small work. The work is placed against one jaw and the end of the drill placed in the hole in the other. Round shank drills may be turned by means of a small pipe wrench or gas pliers and square shank drills may be turned by using

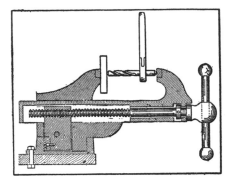

Vise Used as a Drill Press

a monkey wrench.—Contributed by Reader, Chicago.

Home=Made Power Transmission Device

Anyone desiring to pump water, or perform some other operation with the power from an engine some distance away, can easily do so by means of a rope drive. Where little power is required, a rope 3/8-in. or 1/2-in. diameter will be large enough and the power may be easily transmitted to a distance of 100 ft. or more.

In the device I made, which is used for pumping water, a wooden frame, A, supports the sheave, B, which is connected by the rope to a similar sheave on the engine shaft. Both sheaves are made of wood and have sharp V-grooves which prevent the rope from slipping. The spur gears, C, while not absolutely necessary, are useful in reducing the speed and save the extra work of making a larger

sheave which would be required if the gears were omitted. A crank on the shaft of the larger gear operates a

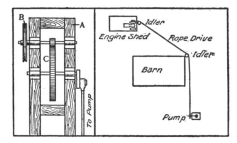

Pump Operated by a Rope Drive

connecting rod, which is attached to the pump rod.

It will be noticed in the plan view that the barn comes between the pump and engine. In order to make the bend around the corner, I used idlers, the bend from the engine being made in the same way.—Contributed by Harry E. Fillberg, Taylors Falls, Minn.

Obtaining Correct Pipe Bends

For bending 3-in. pipes, one a little shorter than the other, so that they can be located one under the other, the drawing shown in the sketch will

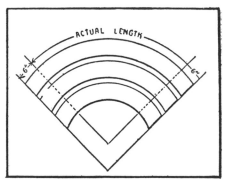

To Make Correct Pipe Bends

be found to give accurate results. The drawing should be made accurately on the machine shop floor, so that it can be used at any time. About

6 in. is allowed for cutting off at the ends. The drawing, says the Practical Machinist, shows how to find the correct length of pipe to be used and the radius of the required bend.

How to Make a Continuously-Ringing Plunger Bell

The continuously-ringing bell is constructed so that wire, A, from the right-hand solenoid crosses to the left-hand contact piece, B, and the wire, C, from the left-hand solenoid crosses to the right-hand contact piece, D. The switch is pivoted at E, and when the plunger is in the position shown it is attracted toward the right-hand end. When it moves to the right-hand it touches the contact, D, and closes the circuit for the left solenoid and opens the circuit for the right solenoid. Then the left solenoid drives the plunger, P, through to the

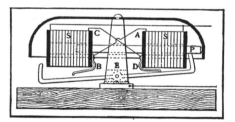

Continuously Ringing Bell

left and strikes the bell. The plunger is then an electromagnet because of the action of the coil and draws the left end of the switch toward it, the switch being made of iron. The switch then touches the left contact piece and closes the circuit for the right-hand coil and opens the circuit for the left-hand coil. The plunger then flies to the right and strikes the bell. The switch is hung so as to be slightly unbalanced, says Machinery, thereby securing contact to one of the coils and enabling the plunger to start.

The University of Wisconsin will use phonographs in teaching students at their homes.

Wasting Water

Where water is sold through a meter, landlords are wise enough to have spring closing faucets on all bathroom fixtures especially. The practice of washing the hands with running water causes a greater waste than if the water were caught in the bowl for use. This is not the case where the hands are only to be rinsed or damped.

A faucet may leak slightly, yet waste a large amount in the 24 hours. One was leaking at a rate of over 60 drops a minute, and it was found to fill a pint measure in 10 minutes, making a waste of 3/4 gal. per hour, or 18 gal. a day.—Contributed by W. D. Browning, Collinwood, O.

How to Open a Book

Hold the book with its back on a smooth or covered table; let the front board down, then the other, holding the leaves in one hand while you open a few leaves at the back, then a few at the front, and so on, alternately opening back and front, gently pressing open the sections till you reach the center of the volume. Do this two or three times and you will obtain the best results, says Modern Bookbinding. Open the volume violently or carelessly in any one place and you will likely break the back and cause a start in the leaves. Never force the back of the book.

"A connoisseur many years ago, an excellent customer of mine, who thought he knew perfectly how to handle books, came into my office when I had an expensive binding, just brought from the bindery ready to be sent home; he, before my eyes, took hold of the volume and tightly holding the leaves in each hand, instead of allowing them free play, violently opened it in the center and exclaimed: 'How beautifully your bindings open!' I almost fainted. He had broken the back of the volume and it had to be rebound."

Home=Made Automatic Gas Regulator

Fit a 1-in. brass pipe, A, 12 in. long, into a T reduced for a ½-in. pipe, B. Fit the other end with a coupling, C, into which screw a ¾-in. angle valve, from which the stem and valve disk have previously been removed. In place of the valve stem fit in an iron rod of the same size as the valve stem and having the top end, D, looped as shown. Thread the bottom end and put on two washers, E, between which wind hemp packing. Hold this in place with a nut. The steam connection to the boiler is through the pipe, P. This brings the steam pressure on top of the piston, says the Engineers' Review, and necessitates that the stuffing-box of the valve be packed. Run the cord over pulleys, so arranged that convenient connections are made with the valve levers on the gas burners.

Fig. 2 shows the position of the burners and the gas supply as arranged on the front of the boilers. Fit valves V V V V (of the straight

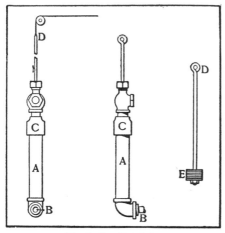

Fig. 1--Gas Regulator

way type) with levers about 8 in. long and connect each of the first three levers to the other by means of a rod long enough to extend from the first valve to the third. The fourth valve is not operated by the regulator at all,

but is always left burning at its full capacity while the boiler is in operation.

The valve levers are connected to the rod R so that when the regulator operates them the valves do not all shut off the same amount. For instance, if the valves are open full and the regulator operates, the rod R is

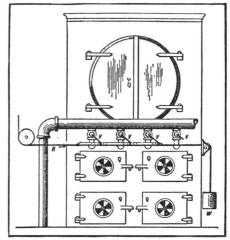

Fig. 2--Burners and Supply Arrangement

pulled to the left in the direction of the arrow. This closes the first valve a certain amount, the second valve a little more and the third valve still more. In this way the gas is not all shut off, but enough to permit the steam to drop. When the piston of the regulator is relieved of the excessive amount of steam pressure on the top side of the plunger, the weight, W, pulls the rod, R, to the right, opening the valves wider, permitting more gas to enter the cylinder to be burned. This pulls the plunger of the regulator up, and when the steam pressure again reaches the desired point the plunger is forced down and the gas is once more partly shut off.

Steam hose containing rubber should always be heated until pliable before uncoiling, says the National Engineer. If this precaution is taken the rubber will not crack, and the hose will last longer.

Practical Mechanical Movements

Every mechanic or inventor should study to avoid clumsiness in the construction of his model or machine and so arrange the several parts as to produce the result desired with the least number of parts possible. He should, therefore, be very careful to select as far as possible the simplest and best forms of mechanical movements. Some of the more common movements are here illustrated, and the following is a brief description of the various movements as numbered:

1. Pulleys with a belt passing thereover.

2. The ordinary sliding clutch and pinions.

3. Means for imparting a jumping motion to a horizontal arm. A cam secured to a cog wheel alternately lifts and drops said arm.

4. Elliptical spur-gear for securing variable speed.

5. Beveled gears.

6. Means for imparting an alternate rectilinear motion to a rack-rod by a continuously rotated mutilated gear.

7. Means for transmitting motion from one shaft to another, said shafts being in the same plane but at right angles to each other.

8. Pulleys for lifting weights.

9. An eccentric upon a revolving shaft adapted to impart a reciprocating movement to a yoke strap.

10. Two forms of universal joints.

11. Differential gears. The inner and outer gears move in opposite directions at different speeds.

12. Different kinds of gear for transmitting rotary motion from one shaft to another arranged obliquely thereto.

13. Means for imparting a partial revolution to a ratchet-wheel at the completion of each revolution of the main wheel.

14. A tilt-hammer. The wiper-wheel lifts the hammer four times each revolution.

15. Means whereby a reciprocating rectilinear motion of a vertical rod transmits an intermittent circular motion to a toothed wheel.

16. An ordinary sliding clutch and pinions.

17. Sun and Planet motion. The outer gear is fixed to the connecting link and moves around the axis of the fly wheel.

18. Means whereby the reciprocating motion of a jointed rod produces an almost continuous rotary movement of the ratchet-face wheel.

19. Gearing for transmitting a continuous rotary motion to a vertical shaft from a horizontal shaft, by the alternate revolution of gears upon said horizontal shaft. These gears are loose upon their shaft, and have ratchets which are engaged by pawls fixed to the shaft.

20. Means for transmitting rotary motion from one shaft to another at right angles thereto.

21. Multiple gearing. The triangular wheel drives the large one.

22. A simple ore stamper or pulverizer. The plunger is raised and dropped twice for each revolution of the shaft.

23. Variable rotary motion produced by uniform rotary motion.

24. Ordinary crank-motion.

25. Air pump; piston motion. The racks are moved in opposite directions by the revolution of the gear.

26. Crank motion. The wrist-pin upon the disk works within the slotted yoke.

27. Centrifugal governor for steam engines, etc.

28. A lower fixed rack having a gear mounted thereon and meshing with an upper movable rack. As the pitman secured to the gear reciprocates, said gear revolves and imparts a movement to the upper rack which is double that of the gear.

29. Means for imparting a reciprocating rectilinear motion to an upright rod by rotating an upright shaft having an oblique disk secured thereto.

30. A heart-shaped groove engaged by a lever, is adapted to impart an

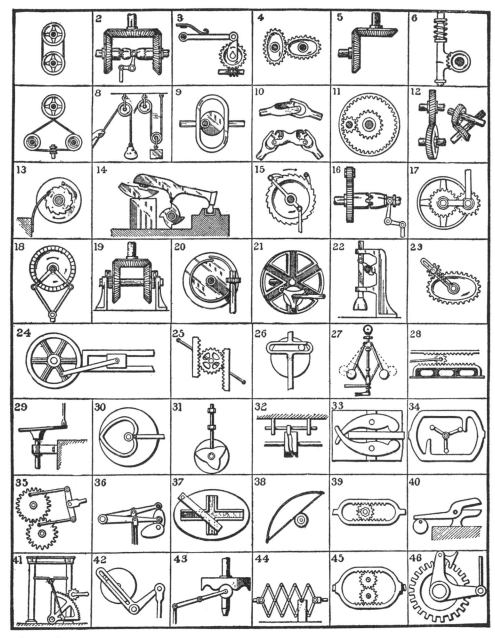

irregular swinging motion to said lever.

31. A triple cam adapted to lift the rod three times at each revolution of the disk to which said cam is secured.

32. Means for producing a uniform reciprocating rectilinear motion by the rotary motion of a grooved cam.

33. A carpenter's bench clamp. By pressing a strip against the crossed ends of the dogs, the rounded heads thereof will clamp said strip.

34. Means whereby a reciprocating motion is imparted to a frame by a continuously rotating shaft. This shaft has three wipers adapted to

contact with inwardly extending arms within the frame.

35. Means whereby the rotation of two spur gears having crank wrists produces variable alternating traverse of a horizontal bar.

36. Means for converting uniform circular motion into alternating motion. Cams are mounted upon a revolving shaft and alternately lift and drop levers to which are attached rods.

37. An ellipsograph. By attaching a pencil or other instrument to the cross-bar ellipses may be readily drawn. Studs upon the bar engage the grooves.

38. A fiddle-drill. A strap is secured between the ends of a bow and encircles a shaft or drill which is revolved by the back and forth motion of the bow.

39. A crank substitute. Two loose pinions with reverse ratchets are attached to the shaft, with pawls on the pinion ratchets. Each rack meshes with the reverse pinion for continual motion of the shaft.

40. Metal shears. The arm of the moving blade is raised and lowered by the revolution of the cam.

41. A vertically movable presser platen. This platen is secured by a rod to a toothed sector pivoted within a frame and which receives motion from a small pinion meshing therewith.

42. Means for converting circular motion into variable alternating rectilinear motion. A wrist-pin upon a revolving disk works within a slotted lever.

43. Means for converting circular into rectilinear motion. A waved wheel mounted upon a rotary shaft rocks a lever upon its fulcrum.

44. "Lazy tongs." A system of crossed levers pivoted together by which the amount of a rectilinear motion is increased by the proportional number of sections in the tongs.

45. A rack adapted to receive rectilinear motion by the rotary motion of toothed wheels meshing therewith.

46. Means for converting reciprocating rectilinear motion into intermittent circular motion.

(Continued next month.)

Relay Saves Battery Current

By using the device here shown, a very weak line current may be used. The relay, A, is connected with the main circuit and operates the local circuit, which may contain a bell, telegraph sounder, or any other electrical device by making a contact at the armature and completing the circuit of the local battery.

The relay may be made from an old bell magnet, B, rewound with fine wire about 28 or 30, single covered, and should be mounted on a wooden base, with the armature in position, as

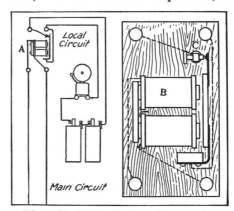

Wiring Diagram and Construction of Relay

shown. The contact, C, can be made from the circuit breaker of the bell and should be so adjusted that the point nearly touches the contact when no current is flowing. Then the least current flowing through the magnet will cause the armature to move and make contact, thereby closing the local circuit. Relays of a similar nature are in common use in telegraph and fire alarm lines and can also be used for battery call telephones.— Contributed by A. G. Ward, Peebles and Edgerton Aves., Wilkinsburg, Pa.

How to Make An Alcohol Lamp

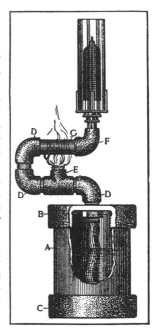

An alcohol lamp, which will prove very useful to the student draughtsman, or mechanic, is shown in the accompanying illustration. A piece of 2½-in. pipe, A, about 3½ in. long is fitted with caps, B and C, the cap B being tapped for a ⅜-in. pipe in the center. Three ⅜-in. ells, D, one ⅜ in. by ⅛ in. tee, E, and one ⅜-in. by ⅛ in. ell, F, are connected with ⅜-in. nipples and arranged to support the incandescent burner as shown.

A cotton wick extends through all the fittings and terminates in a knot at the end of the long nipple, G. If it is found difficult to pass the wick through the fittings, they may be strung on the wick in the proper order, before being screwed together.

A portion of the wick is pulled up at E and is used to furnish the necessary heat for vaporizing the alcohol in G. If desired, a small metal cap can be made to cover the wick at E and thus prevent the evaporation of the alcohol when the lamp is not in use.—Contributed by a reader, Chicago.

How to Make an Emery Wheel from an Old Bicycle

The illustration shows a home-made emery wheel, which was constructed by a correspondent of the American Blacksmith, and is described as follows:

The parts were procured from an old bicycle. If these are not at hand, they may be purchased at a very small cost. The frame is of course a double one and is constructed throughout of 1¼ by ¼-in. stock. The two parts of the frame are put together by means of bolts run through pieces of gas pipe. By this means it is possible to tighten and brace the frame so as to allow little or no give or spring. The seat for the operator may also be taken from the old bicycle. I used an old seat from a binder. This answers the purpose very well. The top end of the longest piece is fitted with a T which is babbitted and in which runs the spindle for the pulley and the emery wheel. The bicycle part consists of the hind wheel, the sprocket, chain and pedals. The wheel from which the tire has been removed, is hung in the frame by means of a large axle bolt. The crank is then hung as shown and the bicycle chain used to connect the sprocket attached to the wheel and that of the crank. A belt is now used to connect the pulley with the driving wheel and the machine is ready for work. By using the bicycle bearings in the three boxings, an easy running and very serviceable emery stand will be the result.

Emery Wheel Made from Old Bicycle

A Home=Made Jack of All Trades

The illustration shows a very handy device, which can be made of a piece of ¾-in. round steel, A, about 8 in. long; one stationary nut, B, riveted on

Handy Device with Many Uses

and one movable nut, C. Turn threads on one end of the rod and turn a handle near the other end, making a screwdriver point at the extreme end.

With both nuts screwed up tight the device makes a very good hammer for driving tacks and small nails and the screwdriver end is very useful for opening boxes, pulling tacks, etc. By loosening nut C and adjusting the distance between the two nuts the implement is converted into a very effi-cient wrench. The device is also useful as a hand vise for filing small articles which may be firmly held between the two nuts. The illustration was made from a "shadowgraph" contributed by Dr. C. E. Warren, North Easton, Mass.

A Quick Setting Cement

One of the best cements that can be found for fastening tools into handles, or uniting small parts of metal or other material, is common orange shellac dissolved in sufficient alcohol to form a paste. To use, place the required amount in a small tin (the top of a baking powder can will do) and set fire to it. As soon as the flame dies down, use immediately before it has a chance to get cold.

When fastening tools into wooden handles it is well to heat the tang over the flame previous to fastening in the handle. This cement is strong and waterproof.—Contributed by E. V.

Lifting Water By Suction

The right method of connecting a pump in order that it will lift water 40 ft. and deliver it to the boiler is shown in the accompanying sketch from the Practical Engineer. A suction pipe, A, extends into and within 1½ in. of the bottom of an air-tight tank, B, holding say 1,000 gal. and situated midway between the water level and the pump. Another pipe, C, in which there is a check valve, D, connects the tank with the water.

Thus far, there is simply an air-tight suction line 40 ft. long, the tank, B, being merely an enlargement of the pipe half-way up. E is an air pipe extending just through the top of tank and is connected with the upper suction pipe, A, by means of a by-pass, F. A globe valve, G, is placed in the by-pass and one is also placed in the air pipe, E, above the by-pass connection, designated at H.

In starting, close valve H and open valve G; this allows the air to be exhausted from the lower suction pipe, C, and the air-tight tank, B, through the air-pipe, E, and the by-pass, F. Of course, in starting up, and until water has attained a depth of 1½ in. in the tank, some or all of the air may take a direct course up through the upper suction pipe, A; but

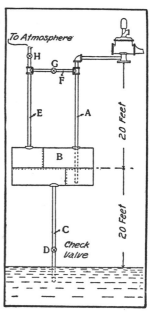

Pumping Water 40 Feet

after it has reached a depth sufficient to submerge the lower end of pipe A, the rest of the air will be exhausted through the by-pass; hence the necessity of the by-pass or some similar arrangement.

As the air is exhausted, the water will be forced up the suction pipe, C, into the tank, B, until it is full, and possibly a short distance up the pipes A and E; then open valve H and the air rushes in and destroys the vacuum, which is holding the water up this far, and the water starts back down the suction pipe, C, when the check valve, D, closes and we have the main body of water trapped 20 ft. from the pump with atmospheric pressure on it. Then by closing valve G in the by-pass, the pump will lift the water the rest of the way and deliver it into the boiler.

To Find the Clearance of an Engine

A good way to find the clearance of an engine, especially when the cylinder heads are provided with indicator connections, is to place a strip of lead inside the cylinder and then turn the engine over the center. The thickness of the lead should be greater than the clearance, so that the piston will compress it against the cylinder head, thus giving the true clearance. This method can also be used to advantage in finding the clearance of an air compressor.—Contributed by A. E. Schutz, Trevorton, Pa.

Lathe Chuck for Small Work

The drawing shows a chuck that I constructed for holding small rods in making duplicate work. A steel barrel, A (Fig. 1), is tapered inside to receive the jaws, B, shown in detail at Fig. 2. The jaws are held apart by the spring C until the barrel is screwed on the lathe spindle, which forces the jaws into the taper and brings them together.

This chuck is not adapted to work where there is much variation in the size of the stock, but is very useful

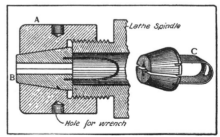

Fig. 1   **Fig. 2**

and convenient for duplicate work. By making several jaws with openings of different sizes they may all be used in connection with a single barrel.—Contributed by Geo. W. Smith, Jr., 122 Genessee St., Marquette, Mich.

To Make Solder Wire

Having used up all my solder wire and having an abundance of stick solder on hand, I used the following method of making it into wire:

Punch a small nail hole in the bottom of a cocoa can and pour the

Pouring the Solder

melted solder into the can. Move the can over a cold flat surface, as shown in the sketch, thus making a long, thin, wirelike strip, which may be rolled up in the form of a ball, for convenience in handling.—Contributed by Chas. Grogan, 295 Bainbridge St., Brooklyn, N. Y.

Raising Device for Wagon Boxes

The accompanying e n g r a v i n g shows a simple device which may be rigged up by most any smith having need of an apparatus of this kind. The

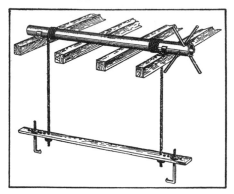

Simple Labor-Saving Device

work of lifting a wagon box becomes mere child's play with a windlass arrangement of this kind, says a correspondent of the American Blacksmith. As seen in the sketch, A is a piece of 4-in. pipe long enough to pass over four of the crossbeams overhead. Our shop in which the wagon work is done has no upper story and we therefore placed the pipe directly on the beams which support the walls and run across just overhead. After securing the pipe and cutting to right length,

drill four holes in one end of it. These holes should be drilled in such manner as to have each set of two directly opposite each other, so that when two pieces of gas pipe are inserted in the end they will pass each other as in the engraving. Before placing on the beams, two holes are drilled in the pipe to receive the rope ends. This will prevent the ropes from slipping around the pipe. The pipe is now placed upon the beams and either brackets placed each side of it or long spikes driven into the beams to keep the pipe from rolling. Two good stout ropes of equal length are now secured and after binding the ends with wire, drive and fasten in the holes made for this purpose. Now secure a good stout plank of 2-in. timber about 6 in. wide and long enough to go across your widest wagon box. In each end of this bore four holes. Now forge two hooks and thread the ends of both of them to receive a large nut. The loose rope ends are now thrust through the two holes nearest the center of the plank and your device is ready for use. The holes in the ends of the plank are for adjusting the hooks to different sizes of wagon boxes. A stop to keep the device from turning after the box has been raised is simply an iron rod which fits loosely into a hole drilled through one of the beams.

To Drive Spikes Under Water

Spikes and nails can be driven in several feet of water at any angle desired by the use of the following method:

Place a piece of gas pipe, B, long enough to extend above the water to a convenient height and just large enough to drop the spike in readily and still keep it upright, in the water, as illustrated; drop in the spike, C; then by using a steel drift, A, and holding the gas pipe at whatever angle required, drive the spike. The steel drift should be long enough to drive the spike down and leave a handhold above the pipe sufficient to hammer on, says the American Miller. This method is of great help in building forebays, pits and bottoms for foundations. The spike will go at whatever angle the gas pipe is held.

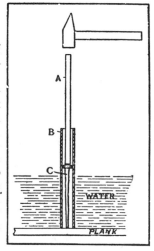

Lantern Glue Heater

This device was contrived by a correspondent of the American Miller for convenience in repairing bolting cloth in cold weather, thin glue being required to make a good patch. It will, however, be found useful in other lines of work also. A canopy made of metal and having four prongs is riveted to the lantern, so it will withstand the heat from the same. A can of liquid glue set on the canopy soon heats to the right degree. For patching bolting glue is always more satisfactory than flour paste and is easier to handle.

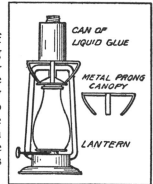

To Preserve Iron Against Rust

To preserve iron against rust, immerse it for a few minutes in a solution of blue vitriol, then in a solution of hyposulphite of soda, acidulated with chlorhydric acid, says the Inland Printer. This gives a blue-black coating, which neither air nor water will affect.

Changing Drawings

Probably one of the most important problems coming up to draftsmen in general is making changes on drawings. The following method is recommended:

From the original drawing make a brown print, using a thin, tough paper. This gives a print with clear white lines on a brown background, the brown being impervious to light. Paint out on this print, with ordinary drawing ink, the lines not desired on the changed drawing, after which make a second brown print from the first. The print thus obtained has dark brown lines on a white background. Draw in on this print the changes and you have the new drawing desired, from which blueprints can be made.

The writer has used this method for some time and finds it a very desirable one.—Machinery.

Fitting a 9 by 16 Board to a 12 by 12 Hole

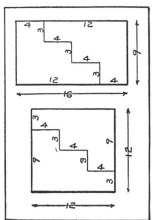

While working for a contractor at one time I had occasion to get out a small job which was to fill up a hole 12 in. square in the floor. As it was on the third floor and all the lumber was on the ground floor except a 9 in. by 16 in. board the boss said, "By cutting that board in two pieces you can make it do." Now the hole in the floor being 12 in. square made me think a while and of course a bet for the cigars was made then and there.

The accompanying sketch shows how I lost the cigars and incidentally gained in knowledge and experience. The board was marked out in two step-shaped pieces which being put together formed a board surface 12 in. square as shown.—Contributed by Geo. P. Schmidt, U. S. S. "Alliance," Culebra, P. R.

Decimal Equivalents of Drill Sizes

The following table gives the sizes in decimals of an inch, of all drills from number 80 to ½ in., and will be found valuable for figuring clearances, driving fits, etc. For example, supposing you want to drill a bearing

SIZE.	Equival't Decimals of 1 inch.	SIZE.	Equival't Decimals of 1 inch.	SIZE.	Equival't Decimals of 1 inch.	SIZE.	Equival't Decimals of 1 inch.
1-2	0.500	G	0.261	5-32	0 1562	51	0.067
31-64	0.4843	F	0.257	23	0 154	52	0.0635
15-32	0.4687	E 1-4	0.250	24	0.152	1-16	0.0625
29-64	0.4531	D	0.246	25	0.1495	53	0.0595
7-16	0.4375	C	0.242	26	0.147	54	0.055
27-64	0.4218	B	0 238	27	0.144	55	0 052
Z	0.413	15-64	0.2343	9-64	0.1406	3-64	0.0468
13-32	0.4062	A	0.234	28	0.1405	56	0 0465
Y	0.404	No. 1	0.228	29	0.136	57	0.043
X	0 397	2	0.221	30	0.1285	58	0.042
25-64	0.3906	7-32	0.2187	1-8	0.125	59	0.041
W	0.386	No. 3	0.213	31	0.120	60	0 040
V	0.377	4	0.209	32	0.116	61	0.038
3-8	0.375	5	0.2055	33	0.113	62	0 037
U	0.368	6	0.204	34	0.111	63	0 036
23-64	0.3593	13-64	0.2031	35	0.110	64	0.035
T	0.358	7	0.201	7-64	0.1093	65	0 033
S	0.348	8	0.199	36	0.1055	66	0.032
11-32	0.3437	9	0.196	37	0.104	1-32	0.0312
R	0.339	10	0.1935	38	0.1015	67	0.031
Q	0.332	11	0.191	39	0.0995	68	0.030
21-64	0.3281	12	0.189	40	0.098	69	0 029
P	0.323	3-16	0.1875	41	0.096	70	0.027
O	0 316	13	0.185	3-32	0.0937	71	0 026
5-16	0.3125	14	0.182	No.42	0.0935	72	0 024
N	0.302	15	0.180	43	0.089	73	0.023
19-64	0.2968	16	0.177	44	0.086	74	0.022
M	0.295	17	0.173	45	0.082	75	0.020
L	0.290	11-64	0.1718	46	0.081	76	0.018
9-32	0.2812	18	0.1695	47	0.0785	77	0.016
K	0.281	19	0.166	5-64	0.0781	1-64	0.0156
J	0.277	20	0.161	48	0.076	78	0.015
I	0.272	21	0.159	49	0.073	79	0.014
H	0.266	22	0.157	50	0.070	80	0.013
17-64	0.2656						

hole for a ⅛-in. shaft. By using a drill 1/64 of an inch larger the hole would be too large and would allow the shaft to run out of true. A ⅛-in. drill on the other hand would make it a driving fit, as the drill is made a trifle smaller than the nominal size. But by referring to the table it will be found that a No. 30 drill is about .008 of an inch larger than the shaft, which is just about the proper clearance.—Contributed by A. Edwards.

A good rust preventive, and one which is extensively used, is banana oil, which can be obtained at any drug or paint store. First polish the article and then apply the oil, using a soft brush.—Contributed by E. V.

Water-Cooled Motors in Winter

For winter use instead of water for water-cooled motors, one of the automobile companies recommends a mixture of 1 part wood alcohol, 1 part glycerine and 1 part water. Get it in early. If the car is laid up for the winter, drain dry, pour two quarts of wood alcohol into radiator and run the car for a few minutes.

Renewing a Gauge Glass

In opening the water glass connections after putting in a new glass, it is generally recommended that the pet cock at the bottom of the glass be opened first and then the steam valve at the top, thus allowing steam to blow through the glass and warm it gently. Next open the water valve and close the drain at the bottom of the glass. If water is admitted first, and then steam, the glass will often break, says the Practical Engineer. This is because the water is much cooler than the steam and there would be a greater expansion in the upper half of the glass than in the lower half.

To Tin a Soldering Copper

Chip a depression in one side of a common red brick and put a few bits of solder and rosin in the hollow. Heat the copper to the usual working heat and rub it briskly in the rosin and solder, holding the handle high so as to work on the point of the copper.—Contributed by Wm. Ed. Jackson, 18 N. Washington St., Tarrytown, N. Y.

To Remove Piston Rod Packing

To remove the packing around the piston rod of an engine remove stuffing-box gland and turn on steam. The packing will then be blown out as slick as a whistle.—Contributed by Fred Eckley, Tekamah, Iowa.

SHOP NOTES

An Automatic Pump Regulator

To regulate the water level in a tank supplied by a pump that is run by a
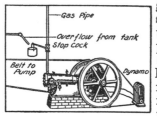
gas engine, simply fasten a tin pail on the stop - cock handle and run an overflow pipe from the
tank to the pail. After starting the engine the operator may leave it and allow it to stop itself, as it will run without attention until the water from the overflow pipe shuts off the gas.—Contributed by Paul Green, R. F. D. No. 5, Columbus, O.

Turning Large Work in a Small Lathe

Having occasion to face up a large casting which was too large to finish in the largest lathe in our shop, we accomplished the job by removing and reversing the head on the lathe and fastening the casting on the face plate, as shown in the sketch. A small lathe

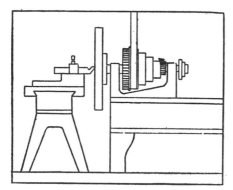

Using Two Lathes on a Large Job

was then moved up and used as a tool holder.—Contributed by C. R. Mc-Gahey, Florence Hotel, Atlanta, Ga.

Reclaiming Thick Tin or Lead

A method of reclaiming thick tin or lead which is used in the majority of establishments manufacturing solder or other white metals, says the Brass World, is both simple and effective.

It is to introduce a stick of green

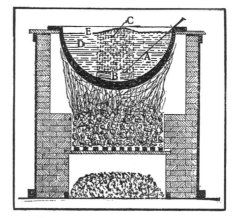

"Boiling" the Metal with Green Wood

wood into the kettle and allow the gases that are driven off from the wood to bubble up through the molten metal. In Fig. 1 is shown a sketch of such a process. The metal must be below a red heat, as the oxidation is very great at such a temperature. It would be impossible to reduce the oxide under these conditions as fast as it is formed. The right heat for the operation is somewhat over the actual melting point of the metal, but below a red heat.

The stick of green wood is used because gases are given off which act beneficially in the reduction of the oxide. Dry wood does not give as good results. By means of a steel rod, A, the stick of wood, B, is pushed down to the bottom of the kettle and the metal, D, allowed to boil through the expulsion of gases, C, until it runs freely. Some considerable dross, E, forms on the top of the metal, but this is readily skimmed off. The operation usually takes several hours for ordinary thick lead or tin.

A Pressure Indicating Device for Boilers

This device is intended to give an alarm when the pressure in a boiler becomes either too high or too low. It is not intended to prevent boiler explosions, as it would be less efficient and dependable for that purpose than the safety valve on the boiler, but in cases where the engineer has many duties to perform and cannot always watch the pressure gauge it will prove useful in preventing the loss occasioned by the blowing of the safety valve and will save many

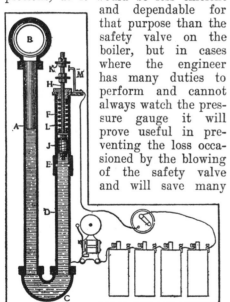

High and Low Pressure Indicator

delays caused by the pressure running down.

A piece of 1-in. pipe, A, is connected to the steam line, B, and is fitted with a return bend, C, at the lower end. Another piece of 1-in. pipe, D, is fitted with a coupling, E, into which is screwed a piece of heavy brass tubing, F. The piston rod, H, is made of ⅜-in. round steel and is threaded at both ends. The piston, J, is made by compressing any suitable packing between two heavy brass washers, held together by nuts on the piston rod.

When the pressure becomes too high or too low the spring, L, is either shortened or allowed to lengthen, thus completing the circuit with the brass contact, M, through the brass washers, K. The object of using two pipes with a return bend instead of a single pipe, is to prevent the escape of live steam around the piston. This construction is also favorable to good lubrication, as a considerable amount of heavy oil may be poured into the pipes, thus keeping the piston well lubricated.

To set the contacts, adjust the upper washer so that it just touches the contact M when the steam in the boiler is at the lowest working pressure. This can be done when first steaming up in the morning. Then run the pressure up until the safety valve is nearly ready to pop and adjust the lower washer to just touch the contact. With the electrical connections as shown the device is then ready for use.—Contributed by A. G. Ward, Peebles and Edgerton Aves., Wilkensburg, Pa.

How to Level Furniture

In setting up bookcases and similar stationary furniture it is almost always necessary to use wedges to square them. A shingle is the best kind of a wedge and the carpenter's method is to drive it under as far as it will go and break or cut off the projecting portion. A better way is to split a hard wood shingle into 1½-in. wide strips and cut these strips into 3-in. lengths, thus obtaining a series of graduated wedges. By driving one of these, which will nearly level the furniture, butt foremost, another thinner one may be driven thin end foremost, which will level the furniture and make the bearing surfaces parallel. If necessary, a small block may be used as a base, or several of the thicker wedges may be used, alternating thin edge and butt and always using two or multiples of two.—Contributed by Dr. Chas. Everett Warren, North Easton, Mass.

Regulation of Fan Blower

It is a peculiar function of a fan blower that instead of always delivering a fixed volume of air, regardless of requirements, it automatically increases the volume as the resistances are decreased. On the other hand, if the blower be in operation with a fairly free outlet, in excess of its capacity area, and that free area be decreased, the pressure produced will immediately rise, thus tending at once to overcome the increased resistance. Therefore, if a certain maximum pressure is known to be required, the fan may be so speeded as to give this at such times as the conditions demand; while at other times, when less pressure or volume of air is required, proper manipulation of the blast gate will economize power.

To Make a Good Rust Joint

Measure by weight 2 parts flour of sulphur, 1 part powdered sal ammoniac and 80 parts iron borings, and mix to a paste with water. This cement will set quickly.

For a slower setting but much stronger cement use 200 parts iron borings, 1 part flour of sulphur and 2 parts sal ammoniac, measuring by weight as before.—Molesworth's Pocket Book of Engineering Formulæ.

How to Set a Planer Bit

A very simple and accurate method of setting planer bits consists in using 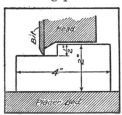 two fiber blocks about 1 in. thick and of the general dimensions shown in the sketch. By placing one of these at each end of the head and raising the bed, the bit may be set by lowering it until it just touches the fiber block at each end.—Contributed by W. J. Rout, 1426 E. Rich St., Columbus, O.

Blacksmith's Device for Holding Work

The illustration shows a handy billy or hold-up recommended by a correspondent of the American Blacksmith.

Counterweight for Heavy Work

It consists of two pulleys over which a rope is passed. A weight on one end of the rope counterbalances the work to be held up. It is a very handy appliance, as work can be so easily manipulated with it and the slightest lift adjusts it on the anvil.

Pipe=Pulling Device

A handy device is a tool for pulling sections of pipe out of the ground. The tool must be made to suit the size

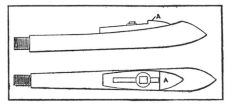

Tool for Pulling Pipe

of the pipe inside and the sketch indicates its construction.

The tool is secured into a piece of pipe of proper length, says Machinery, and pushed down in the hole until the end enters the hole in the pipe to be pulled out. When the pull is made, the part A slips down, wedging in the pipe, and pulls the pipe out.

Electric Window Closer

The sketch herewith shows a device that I have used for the past two years for closing my bedroom window at

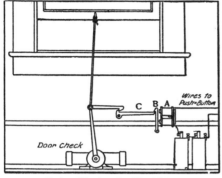

Closing Window by Electricity

night without getting up. An ordinary door check is connected to the window by a small chain and is operated by an electric releasing device as shown. When the circuit is closed the magnet, A, attracts the armature, B, and releases the trigger, C, thus allowing the door check to close the window. The push button for closing the circuit may be located in a convenient position for operating from the bed.—Contributed by A. L. Macy, 231 W. 40th St., New York, N. Y.

Quick Method of Removing Paint From Buggy Body

Mix equal parts of turpentine and kerosene oil and put the mixture into a spring bottom oil can. Spread a layer of old newspapers over the body and spray the mixture over them. Put on from four to six layers of paper in this way, spraying each. Then set fire at one corner and follow up with a wide knife. This method will remove the paint in less than an hour where the old way would take a day. More-

over, it will leave the scratch coats intact and never injure the body like burning with a lamp.—Contributed by J. C. Blake, Harvard, Ill.

How to Protect Rubber Gaskets

To keep rubber gaskets in shape and also to keep them from blowing out of boiler-feed pumps when pumping against high pressure, cut out two pieces of ordinary wire netting the same size as the gasket, and place one on each side of it and bolt in place. Gaskets protected in this way can be removed and put back again several times without injury, says Power, and have proven satisfactory even on manhole covers.

Cost of Excavation by Hand

The cost of excavating earth with pick and shovel and loading it is about 40c per cubic yard for hardpan; 20c for tough clay; 15c for ordinary clay, gravel or loam; and 12c per cubic yard for light, sandy soil—wages being reckoned at 15c per hour in each case.

Cutting Oil Grooves in Babbitt

If oil grooves are cut with a hammer and chisel in thin babbitt, the blows are apt to loosen the babbitt so that the pound in the bearing cannot be stopped. To avoid blows take a round file, draw out the end to a U

For Cutting Babbitt

section, put a crook in it, as illustrated, and use it like a carver's gouge. Leave the file handle on the tool.—Contributed by Wm. E. Jackson, 18 N. Washington St., Tarrytown, N. Y.

How to Make Bronze Ink

A good bronze ink for show cards or similar purposes may be made of the following ingredients:

Honey	dr. 1
Alcohol	dr. 1
Mucilage	oz. 1
Water	oz. 8
Bronze	oz. 1

The bronze may be any one of the colored powders found on the market. Rub the honey, spirit and mucilage together in a mortar, then add the water. Shake before using.

Wetting Ashes in Furnace

For a long time I was bothered by fine ash dust floating about the furnace room in the basement of my residence until I hit upon the following plan. I bent a piece of small pipe to fit the shape of my ash box under the grate, and drilled about 20 pinholes. This was then connected to city water supply, a valve being placed conveniently near the furnace. While shaking I turn on the water which sprays the falling ashes and absolutely prevents any dust either then or while they are being removed.—Contributed by W. K. J., Chicago.

Unsoldered Ground Connection

A fairly reliable wrapped joint made without soldering is shown in the illustration herewith, from Telephony. The pipe is first scraped and then covered with a layer of tin foil as shown at A. The ground wire, with its insulation removed for a length of several feet,

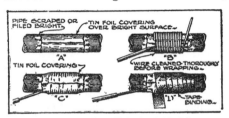

Wrapped Joint Without Soldering

is now tightly bound around this prepared surface as at B, its free end being drawn under the turns of wire by means of a loop formed as illustrated. This keeps the turns of wire from loosening and does away with the necessity of soldering. To insure a good connection and prevent corrosion, another layer of tin foil is applied and the whole is covered with a binding of adhesive tape.

Device for Cleaning Hardwood Floors

People who have hardwood floors in their homes are, as a rule, continually bothered with the dust that accumulates. I have had a good deal of experience with them, and I find that the dust can be very simply removed by this little device: Take a piece of wood, A, about 2 ft. long and tack a

Wiping up Hardwood Floors

piece of flannel, B, along one edge. Then bore a hole in the middle and insert an old broom handle.—Contributed by Clifford B. Brainerd, Chevy Chase, Md.

To Gild on Granite

Apply a coat of size and let it dry; then apply several coats of size and very fine bolted whiting mixed together to form a paint. Let each coat dry, then rub each with very fine sandpaper, says the Master Painter. Then apply the gold size, evenly and thinly, and after that the gold leaf as usual. The same instructions apply for marble.

Template for Drawing Machine Handles

A celluloid template is of great help in drawing machine handles, says Machinery. Make two templates, one containing profiles of the four smaller sizes and the other containing the three

THIS EDGE RESTS AGAINST TEE SQUARE OR ANGLE.

larger sizes. If there is a forming tool for each size it is an easy matter to make the templates and thereby have the drawings the same outline as the formers. They not only facilitate drawing, but also allow of a proper section for each requirement. The outline, A, of the lower half of the handles is scratched on the templates and is filled in with black wax.

Emergency Repair for Broken Wheel

The accompanying illustration shows how repairs are sometimes made when a wagon wheel breaks down in the mountains. A correspondent of the Blacksmith and Wheelwright, who wit-nessed the operation, describes it as follows: This wheel went all to pieces and buckled over the opposite way from which it was dished, bringing things to a standstill instantly. Some lava blocks were collected from the mountain side, the wheel raised clear of the ground, removed from the axle and straightened up. Then four poles were cut, each equal in length to the diameter of the wheel. The poles were then each hewed flat on one side, almost one-half of each being cut away.

Two of the flatted sticks were then placed on opposite sides of the hub, and fastened there, parallel to each other, by tightly wound hay wires,

placed around the flatted sticks and the spokes, close to the felloes. In this repair the poles were used only to resist the lateral strains as the spokes were still strong enough to support the load.

So well did the wheel stand up to its work after "first aid" had been administered that the driver not only made his way with his load to Boise, 20 miles away, but he also made another entire trip into the mountains and return, loading both ways, 65 miles in both directions, while the wheelwright was getting a new wheel ready for him.

How to Make a Glue Spreader

Narrow strips of leather tacked or tied into a cleft stick make excellent glue spreaders that can be thrown away when their purpose has been served. In order to get into a narrow crevice or other inaccessible part of the object being glued, it is well to sharpen the

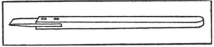

Glue Spreader

leather in the form of a wedge, as shown in the sketch.

This device will be found much better than a brush, as it scrapes off the superfluous glue and does not leave a gob on the work.—Contributed by Dr. C. E. Warren, North Easton, Mass.

Why Wooden Tanks Taper

In the manufacture of tight barrel staves, of oak, for example, one of the greatest problems is that of trying to keep a barrel from drying out and falling to pieces, or at least springing leaks as the wood warps. That is the reason why the barrel has to have a bilge so that steel hoops can be tightened from time to time as the wood shrinks. It is the reason why tanks are made larger at the bottom, it is the reason why flooring is made in such narrow widths.

Quick Repair for Enamel Ware

To stop a hole in enamel ware, bore the hole out large enough to allow a

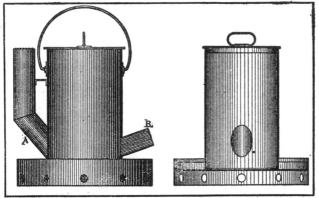

Outside and Sectional Views of Furnace

copper rivet to be inserted and rivet it down tight, being careful not to crack the enamel. An ordinary harness rivet will answer the purpose about as well as anything.—Contributed by G. A. Dale, Virginia, Ill.

How to Test a Square

There are several methods of testing a square, but probably the simplest and 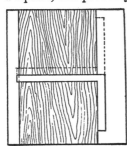 most accurate one is shown in the accompanying sketch. Place the square against the straight edge of a plank as shown and draw a line along the edge of the square. Reverse the position as shown by the dotted lines and redraw the line. The two lines should coincide.—Contributed by Carson Birkhead, Indianola, Miss.

If the air had been as good a conductor of electricity as copper, says Prof. Alfred Daniell, we would probably never have known anything about electricity, for our attention would never have been directed to it.

Charcoal Soldering Furnace

The accompanying illustration shows a very economical soldering furnace that I constructed out of sheet iron. While the general design is similar to other furnaces of the kind, there are certain details in the construction which have a marked effect in the efficiency and convenience of operating. The chimney connection, A, instead of being horizontal as in many furnaces, is inclined as shown, in order to prevent its being filled up with ashes and the hearth, B, is inclined so that the ashes will not come out. The chimney should be provided with a piece of wire gauze to keep sparks from coming out when the furnace is being used on roofs or where there is danger of fire. If a piece of tin or sheet iron is placed on top of the chimney the fire will keep over night. The furnace I made is 15 in. high.—Contributed by Horace Cubberly, 1509 Central Ave., Kansas City, Mo.

Tribute to the Stationary Engineer

In an address to an association of stationary engineers, the Hon. H. V. McChesney said:

"I know something of the character of the work of a stationary engineer, and that it is not in the limelight of the public gaze like that of the man who runs a locomotive. Usually great walls hide you from the public gaze. Your work is not spectacular, yet who shall say that because of that it contributes any the less to the world's progress, or the comfort and happiness of the race? There is a quiet dignity about the stroke of a powerful stationary engine and the noiseless revolution of the great fly-wheel that commands respect. To me it somehow seems to be typical of the great moral and patriotic strength of the republic that we all love so well. In the mills, the factories, the foundries and machine shops of this country these great engines responding to your trained touch, turn the raw material of the field and mines into the finished product of commerce. Thus your work commands the admiration of all."

A Portable Dark-Room

Many amateur photographers who cannot have a regular dark-room will find the device here illustrated very useful and convenient. If desired it may be constructed so as to allow folding up when not in use, by using hinges at A and B and making the sides flexible.

The bottom and frame are made of wood and the walls are constructed of light-proof cloth, formed by gluing black paper between two pieces of black cloth. The back should be full enough to allow plenty of room for the operator and the cloth should be tied securely around his waist to exclude every possible ray of light.

It is well to paint the whole interior a dull black, so that any small leakage of light will not be reflected. The ventilating tube and drain pipe should be bent as shown, to exclude the light, and the ruby glass should be carefully fitted for the same purpose. It is also

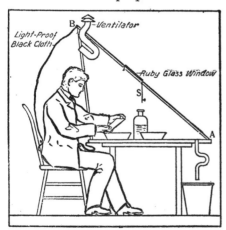

Developing Plates in Portable Dark-Room

desirable to have a hinged shutter, S, to cover the ruby glass while waiting for the plate to develop. This is to prevent any unnecessary exposure to the ruby light, as any light, no matter how colored or subdued, has some effect on the sensitive plate or film. The drain pipe shown on this outfit may be omitted if desired, although it is convenient at times and gives a better circulation of air.—Contributed by Stewart H. Leland, Box 526, Lexington, Ill.

Handy Blacksmith Tongs

A pair of tongs for handling all kinds of stock, round, square, octagonal and flat, is made, as shown in the accompanying engraving. The lower

Handy for All Kinds of Stock

jaw is divided or forked, as shown, while the upper jaw is V-shaped. These tongs are made the same as the ordinary style tongs, except that the lower jaw is flattened and then split. It will probably require more stock for this than in the ordinary jaw, and will need to be allowed for when cutting the stock. It is understood, says a correspondent of the American Blacksmith, that these tongs must fit the work the same as ordinary tongs.

Device for Hanging a Door

A very useful device for lifting heavy articles, setting up or leveling furniture and especially for hanging or unhanging a door is made from a 1-in. strip of hard wood about 3 in. wide. Nail a 1-in. cleat across it about 3 in. from one end and bevel this end from the cleat side across the end. The strip should be at least 18 in. long. An oak barrel stave, by the way, is good for the purpose. In using put the beveled end under the door or whatever is to be raised. Then step on the other end of the lever, the fulcrum being the cleat, which is of course on the under side. Do not use your whole weight if the hinge sticks, but give it a number of light jerks, teetering the lever up and down. The lever should be placed as near the hinge edge of door as possible. This leaves both hands free to manage the door. In hanging a door let it rest on the beveled end of the lifter and raise it with the foot on the lever end until it is high enough to clear the pins guiding it to place with the hands and then letting up on the lever.—Contributed by Dr. Chas. Everett Warren, North Easton, Mass.

To Increase the Area of a Rectangle

In the January number I noticed an article describing a method of covering a 12-in. square hole with a 9-in. by 16-in. board. The following diagram

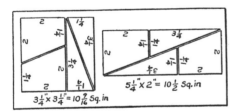

not only shows how to saw a rectangular board so as to form a square, but also shows how to increase the area.

On a piece of heavy drawing paper, lay out accurately a perfect rectangle, $5\frac{1}{4}$ in. long and 2 in. wide, having an area of $10\frac{1}{2}$ sq. in. Cut the rectangle in four pieces, according to the diagram, and mark the dimensions on each piece as shown. Then match the pieces together to form a $3\frac{1}{4}$-in. square, thus producing $10\frac{9}{16}$ sq. in. from $10\frac{1}{2}$ sq. in.

This operation may perhaps suggest great possibilities to the minds of many readers.—Contributed by G. D. Woodruff, Chicago.

Flames and currents of very hot air are conductors of electricity and will discharge an electrified body.

A Sheet Metal Carrier

The shop which is equipped with small conveniences for facilitating work and reducing the labor is apt to cheapen substantially the cost of production, says a correspondent of the Metal Worker. Those who have had occasion to work on large sheets, either

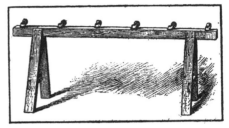

Sheet Metal Carrier

to punch them for riveting or to cut them to shape with shears where the assistance of a helper is required, know what a tiresome task this sometimes becomes. Tiresome alike to the helper who is holding the weight of the sheet and to the workman who must manipulate it under a punch, shear or some other tool. For this kind of work a carrier, such as the one illustrated, has many advantages. It consists of a long trestle like the carpenters use, in the top of which at close intervals are large, easy running turning casters. These trestles are made of a suitable height to carry work in punching, shearing or along the bench on which the workman is engaged, and the sheets are held rigidly at the proper height and level, but can be moved with little exertion.

How to Sharpen a Lawn Mower

Since nearly all lawn mowers are constructed on similar principles, remove the outer drive wheels, change the pinions and replace the wheels. This causes the cutter to rotate backwards when the drive wheels revolve. Then raise the stationary cutter by tightening the front bolts. Form a thick paste of powdered emery and oil, and apply to the revolving cutter. To sharpen, simply turn one of the drive wheels, and in a short time the cutters will have perfect edges.—Contributed by Clifford R. Wolf, 127 W. Nixon St., Cincinnati, O.

Table of Contrasting Colors

The following table is familiar to painters, but for beginners or those having occasion to select colors for their house it will be found useful:

Table of Contrast.

Yellow contrasts—
    Purple, Russet and Auburn.
Red contrasts—
    Green, Olive and Drab.
Blue contrasts—
    Orange, Citrine and Buff.

Table of Harmony.

Yellow harmonizes with—
    Orange, Green, Citrine, Russet, Buff and Drab.
Red harmonizes with—
    Orange, Purple, Russet, Citrine, Auburn and Buff.
Blue harmonizes with—
    Purple, Green, Olive, Citrine, Drab and Auburn.

To Make a Solid Auto Tire

In cases of emergency a very good substitute for the pneumatic inner tube of an auto tire can be made as follows: Take a quantity of ordinary garden hose, not too badly worn, and cut it into lengths just long enough to go once around the rim on the inside of the tire casing. Through each short length of hose draw a piece of rope sufficiently large to fit it snugly.

After these are ready, take four or five (depending on the size of the hose) and bind them together with stout cord from end to end. This bundle must then be wrapped tightly with a strip of old carpet or burlap. Enough of this material is put on to make the entire bundle fit snugly into the outer casing. It is then ready to be applied to the wheel in the usual manner. Be careful to make the ends come together closely, and to have it fit the casing very snug.

After the tire has been used for a short time, take out the filling and add more carpet or burlap. This will keep it up to the size of the casing, and prevent unnecessary wear. I used one of these home-made tires recently while the good one was being repaired, and always carry one in my auto.—Contributed by Dr. N. R. Gordon, Springfield, Ill.

Testing Constructions with a Hydrostatic Level

A Massachusetts man who was having a 60 by 100-ft. shop erected wished to test the accuracy of construction. At each corner of the walls he placed a water pail and also placed one midway of each 100 ft. wall. Then he placed 100 ft. of piping midway between the two rows of pails and ran branch pipes from it crosswise to connect each pair of pails with the main pipe line and, through this, with the other pails. Water was poured into the system and when the liquid assumed its level in the six pails, says the American Machinist, it was found that one corner of the building was one-quarter inch low. The leveling instrument previously used was then tested and found to be slightly defective.

To Make a Ghost Picture

Drape the subject in a sheet and photograph him against a plain background out-of-doors. Give only two-thirds the time necessary for a normal exposure, says the Photographic Times. Remove the subject, and then, without changing the camera, expose the same plate at the background for the remaining third of the time. If the background has some prominent lines in it, such as a fence, a gate, or tree, the effect will be greater. The ghost will appear nearly transparent.

The first distillery for the manufacture of denatured alcohol opened at Peoria, Ill., December 1. The plant's capacity is 8,000 bu. a day, or about 40,000 gal.

Practical Mechanical Movements

PART TWO

The following completes the interesting list of practical mechanical movements as shown in the accompanying illustrations:

47. Link-motion for locomotives. The slotted link is moved up and down over the wrist-pin block by the lever and connecting rod; the lever, locking in the toothed sector, allowing for a close connection to the valve stem by a lever and short connecting rod.

48. Valve-motion and reversing-gear. The slotted link receives a rocking motion from the eccentrics and rods, and is thrown from its center either way for forward or backward motion of the engine by the lever secured thereto.

49. Safety stop for elevators. When the cable breaks, the bow spring will force the plungers secured to the bell-crank levers outward into engagement with the racks.

50. Mangle-rack, guided by rollers and driven by a lantern half pinion. The long teeth in the rack act as guides to insure a tooth mesh at the end of each motion.

51. Breast-wheel. The power of this wheel equals about forty per cent of the value of the waterfall flowing through the gate.

52. Single-acting pumping-beam. Parallel motion is received from a sector beam. The cylinder is open and the piston is lifted by the weight of the pump rods on the other end of the beam. Movement of the piston is reversed by atmospheric pressure.

53. A gyroscope or rotascope. The outer ring is fixed to a stand. The intermediate ring is pivoted vertically therein. The inner ring is fixed in the intermediate ring at right angles thereto, and the globe is pivoted at right angles to the inner ring.

54. Wheel-work used in the base of a capstan. The central gear is fast to the shaft. The intermediate pinions are loosely mounted upon a frame secured to the drum. The gear ratchet ring runs on the shaft.

55. Scroll gears. For increasing or decreasing the speed gradually during one revolution.

56. Pantograph. For reducing or enlarging copies of drawings. The free ends of the arms are provided with drawing instruments which are adjustable. The point of connection between the two intermediate arms is fixed.

57. Diagonal catch and hand gear used in large blowing and pumping engines.

58. Ball and socket tube joint.

59. Toe and lifter working puppet valves in steam engines. The lower arm or toe is secured to a rock shaft operated from the engine shaft and is adapted to raise and lower the lift or upper arm which is secured to the valve rod.

60. A rotary engine. This engine has two abutments and two inlet and exhaust ports.

61. A horse-power tread-wheel. The horse is placed below the shaft and between the spokes which are arranged at the sides of the wheel.

62. A four-way cock.

63. A swape, or New England sweep. The weighted end of the pole overbalances the bucket so as to divide the labor of lifting the water.

64. Ordinary screw-propeller.

65. Chain-pump.

66. Rotary engine, in its simplest form.

67. Hydraulic ram. The "Montgolfier" idea for a fountain supplied by a water ram.

68. Means whereby rectilinear motion of variable velocity is imparted to a vertical bar by turning a shaft having a curved slotted arm thereto.

69. Friction gear. Variable speed is obtained from the pair of cone pulleys, one of which is the driver. The intermediate double-facer friction pinion is moved from one end to the other of the cones.

70. Barker wheel. The reaction of

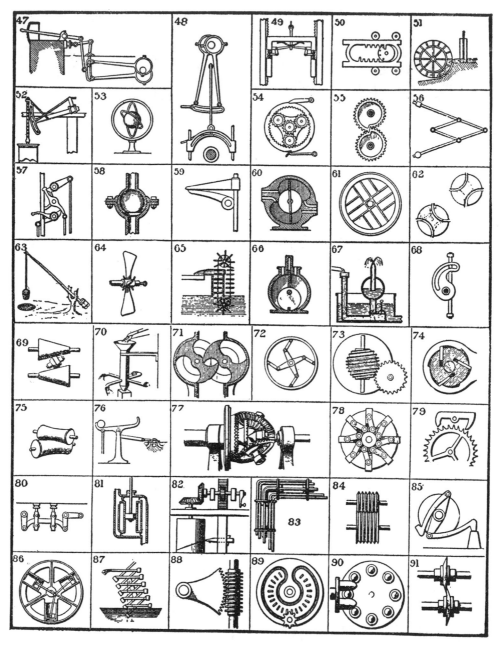

the water escaping from the tangential orifices at the ends of the arms under the pressure of the water-head in the hollow shaft gives impulse to the wheel.

71. "Root" rotary blower. The extended surface of the periphery of the wheels allows them to run loosely in the shell without friction, and with very small loss by air leakage.

72. An elastic wheel having a steel spring tire with jointed spokes.

73. Globoid spiral gear-wheels. The revolution of the globoid gear

gives a variety of differential motions to the spur gear, as it swings between the limits practicable with the globoid teeth.

74. Ratchet head with spring pawls.

75. Means for transmitting rotary motion to an oblique shaft by means of contracting drums having concave faces.

76. A reversing movement for a pump valve. The piston rod trip carries the ball frame beyond the level, when the ball rolls across and completes the valve throw.

77. Multiple speed-gear in line of shaft. The small intermediate gear is secured to the small shaft. The central intermediate gear is secured to the large shaft, while the large intermediate or end gear is fixed to the bearing. The side beveled pinions are revoluble with the large shaft. With this device speed may be increased or decreased on a continuous line of shafting according to the relative number of teeth in the different gears.

78. Toggle joint cam movement, for throwing out a number of grips at once, by the movement of the jointed ring within the disk.

79. Anchor escapement for clocks.

80. Cam-bar valve-movement. The horizontal movement of the cam bar by the bell crank lever alternately moves the two valves.

81. Double acting lift and force pump.

82. Rack and pinion movement for tracing spiral grooves on a cylinder.

83. Right angle shaft coupling. A number of right-angle steel rods move freely in perforated guide flanges on the ends of shafts that are arranged at right angles. In this manner motion may be imparted from one shaft to the other.

84. Grooved friction-gearing.

85. Revolving rapid blow-hammer.

86. Rotary multi-cylinder engine. The cylinders revolve with the fly-wheel and the crank to which the pistons are secured is eccentric thereto.

87. Pendulum water-lift.

88. Means whereby a rectilinear vibrating motion may be imparted to a spindle having an endless worm gear, by a spur-gear sector.

89. Mangle-wheel with equal motion forward and return. The end of the shaft of the pinion is slidably mounted within the groove and retains said pinion in mesh.

90. Tin-tooth wheel and pinion.

91. Disk shears.

Fastening Corrugated Sheet=Iron Roofs

Roofs of sheds and other structures requiring lightness of construction combined with fire-resisting qualities are often made of a combination of structural steel shapes with a corrugated iron roof attached directly to the steel, says the Metal Worker. In this way a roof can be obtained which is made entirely of metal that can be easily removed if occasion should require. It often happens, though, that there are no adequate means for fastening sheets to the iron. Of course, if the sheets were riveted directly to the angle irons, the expansion and contraction would tend to make the rivet hole enlarge continually. In the accompanying illustration is shown a type of fastening which has been found to work satisfactorily in many cases where corrugated sheets were fastened to iron angles. A piece of trap iron is riveted at one end to the

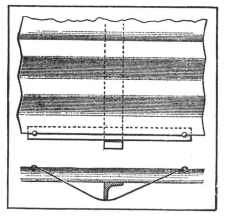

ridge of the corrugation on the under side and passed under the angle iron and then again riveted to the ridge of the corrugation at the other end. In this way expansion of the sheet is allowed for and at the same time there is little or no danger of water passing through the rivet hole. With roofs of this character it is often the practice to make the span between purlins of considerable length, as the corrugations give to the roof a stiffness which will support a fairly heavy weight of snow.

Water Power for Central Generators

Any telephone exchange using hand generators for ringing up subscribers, will find a water motor much more

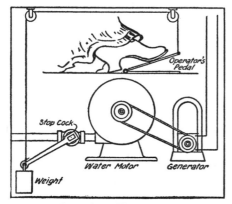

Operating a Water Motor

convenient, as the operator only needs to press the foot lever to ring up and the bell will continue ringing as long as the lever is held down. Another advantage is that the motor and generator may be placed at some distance from the switchboard, thus doing away with all noise.—Contributed by Ora S. Harmas, Fennimore, Wis.

How to Paint a Buggy in a Small Shop

Many a painter is sometimes at his wits' ends just how to handle certain

work in his rather small shop, says the Canadian Implement and Vehicle Trade. If he takes time to study out the right plan he will have no trouble. Say, for instance, the job is a buggy —first take off the shafts, then block the front and rear axle up in the part of the shop where they can have the best light. Then dust out the lining of the top and sponge off the rubber or leather and clean the bows and the shifting rail. The cushion, carpet, side curtains and storm aprons should be removed to the platform and cleaned. Then, wash out the inside of the body. The wheels having been removed, wipe off the axle arms with strips of burlap. Clean all the grease spots, using a piece of cloth saturated with turpentine, dipped in a little pumice stone to quicken the work. Rub the body over lightly with pumice and felt. This removes the grease spots, dirt, etc., and makes the surface ready for the varnish. One mistake some painters make is to touch up too many and too unnecessary places. Touch up only where required and in doing so touch the right spot without smearing the surrounding surface. Mix the match color to dry with a gloss sufficient to reflect more light than it absorbs. When dry color will not have changed from its appearance, when first applied.

Handy Small Screwdriver

A handy small screwdriver with a good "grip" is made as shown in the sketch from 3/32-in. steel wire, about 4 in. long, says Machinery. Part A is

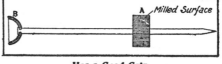

Has a Good Grip

made of brass $\frac{1}{2}$ in. in diameter and $\frac{3}{16}$ in. thick, knurled on the edge. The cup piece, B, is of brass, also, dished as shown.

SHOP NOTES

Self-Oiling Lathe Center

A small oil cup attached to a lathe center in the manner here illustrated will prove a great convenience and will prevent the center running hot. A $\frac{1}{16}$-in. hole is drilled in the point of the center and carried back about $1\frac{1}{4}$ in., or far enough to meet the vertical hole, which is tapped to receive the oil cup as shown. It is obvious that the point of the center will have to be removed before drilling the $\frac{1}{16}$-in. hole, but this will not decrease the bearing surface of

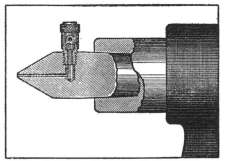

Oil Cup for Lathe Center

the center, as the extreme point never touches the work if the center hole in the same has been properly made.—Contributed by Alfred S. Cromer, 466 E. Buchtel Ave., Akron, O.

Saving Exhaust from Pump

The accompanying illustration, from the Engineers' Review, shows an arrangement for returning the exhaust steam from a steam pump back to the boiler. In case the pump is used as a boiler feed, a feedwater heater is not required. It works satisfactorily on medium high temperatures and can be applied to either duplex or simplex pumps.

As all modern steam pumps are

tapped for suction and exhaust pipes on both sides, all that is necessary is

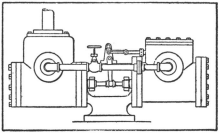

Exhaust Returned to Pump

to pipe up the plugged exhaust and suction openings, and a boiler feeder is obtained which cannot be excelled.

Strap Wrench

A good strap wrench suitable for unscrewing lubricator bodies, glass oil cups and other polished articles, can be made from a piece of hard wood, A, 1 in. square and a foot or more long, a leather strap, B, a metal dog, C, and a piece of sheet brass, D, which acts as a bearing for the dog and as a clamp to hold the strap against the wood. To use the device, pass the strap around

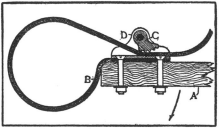

For Removing Lubricator Bodies

the object to be turned and pull the end through the dog as far as it will go. Then turn in the direction indicated by the arrow.—Contributed by Harry Hall, Brooklyn, Iowa.

Cracked Seams on Tin Roof

Should the seams of a tin roof crack it is probably due to the fact that proper allowance for expansion and contraction was not made in laying the roof.

Metal laid under cold weather conditions is contracted to nearly its smallest size. Every tinner knows that

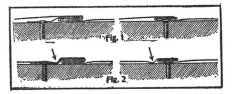

Old and New Method of Making Seams

when a seam is flattened down with a mallet it is about level, so that when expansion and contraction takes place the strain is directly on the solder. The main thing, then, is to overcome and take this strain off the solder and place it somewhere else, says a correspondent of the Metal Worker. I have done this by placing the strain on the tin plate itself. The best way to do it, I have found, is to take the hand groover and go over every seam before soldering it and drawing it down behind the seam as shown on the drawings herewith. Fig. 1 shows the tin as laid for flat seam roofing, fastened down with both the cleat and the nail driven through the sheet. Fig. 2 shows my method of bending the tin down back of the seam with the groover. By going over every seam in this manner before the soldering is done there is an excess of metal back of the seam or an extra length to the sheet, which gives material to draw upon when contraction takes place and entirely avoids any strain on the soldered seam. When the metal expands under heat this groove also relieves the strain that would otherwise be placed upon the solder.

Now that it is again possible to purchase a really first-class quality of tin for roofing purposes, the tin roof is rapidly coming into great favor again.

To Make a Blind Man's Watch

An ordinary hunting case watch may easily be fixed so that a blind person can tell time by it, says a writer in the Keystone. Take out the crystal and file away the "cut" in the bezel which served to hold the crystal. Burnish smooth and then file across the bezel at each five-minute point on the dial. Above the XII make a distinguishing mark of some kind from which the owner may take his bearings.

Simple Home=Made Oil Burner

By the following directions an efficient oil burner may be made at home: Into a 1-in. tee, A, place a $\frac{3}{8}$-in. elbow and run babbitt around it to hold it in place, and also to keep the steam from leaking into the oil. Screw a $\frac{3}{8}$-in. pipe, long enough to reach through the boiler front into the furnace, into the elbow. Over the $\frac{3}{8}$-in. pipe screw a 1-in. pipe, B, 3 in. longer than the other, into the tee, so that the smaller pipe is exactly in the center of the larger one.

Pipe C runs from the tee to the oil tank; pipe D to a steam main or air

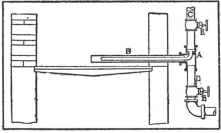

Construction of Oil Burner

tank, and EE are valves to regulate the amount of oil and steam or air. Partly cover the grates, so too much air cannot come through, says the Engineers' Review, and build the bridgewall open, as illustrated. Compressed air is all right to use on getting up steam, but steam is better after it is raised to force the oil into the furnace.

Handy Cleats for Sawing

Wooden cleats like the one shown in the sketch, Fig. 1, are often much more convenient than a vice for holding the work when sawing, chiseling,

Cleats Handy in Sawing

etc., and can be made at very little expense. Two of these cleats are necessary for sawing and are used in the manner shown in Fig. 2. I have several of these and find them very handy. They can be made any size and any length, as needed.—Contributed by F. B. Emig, Santa Clara, Cal.

Paint for Muslin Signs

Use colors ground in japan and thin them with turpentine, says the Modern Painter. Prepared muslin should be used to procure the best results.

Draught in Pipes

A good draught is just as important in a pipe as in a stove. If the draught is from the center it will cause the tobacco to burn evenly, while if it is from the side, as is the case in many pipes, including high-priced ones of

Correct and Incorrect Designs

fancy design, the tobacco will burn down one side and smoulder on the other. This produces more or less distillation, causing a very disagreeable taste and a strong pipe.

Thawing Pipes With Lime

To thaw out frozen water pipes pack them with unslaked lime and wrap up in old rags or carpet. Pour water over the portions thus covered and the heat generated will melt the ice in the pipes.

Emergency Lubricator

When the lubricator on a steam engine becomes broken or out of order, the home-made device here shown will be found very useful. Connect two

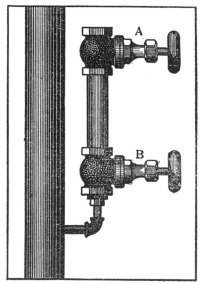

Emergency Lubricator

globe valves, A and B, with a short piece of pipe. Bush the open end of valve B to receive the lubricator connection and connect as shown. To operate, close valve B and open valve A and fill with oil. Then close valve A and partly open valve B from time to time, thus allowing a small amount of oil to run into the cylinder.—Contributed by Fred Eckley, Tekamah, Nebraska.

Device for Opening Shop Windows

It is almost impossible to open and close a window over a wide bench by using a pole, and as it is very trouble- 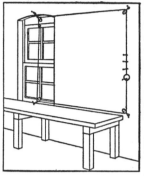 some to climb up on the bench every time one wants to open the window, a device like the one shown in the sketch will prove a great convenience. Simply fasten a screw - eye in the upper sash and carry a rope over suitable pulleys to a convenient place for operating. If there are no weights on the window, fasten a harness ring on the rope and drive a number of nails in the wall. The window may then be held open in any position desired.—Contributed by Ora S. Harmas, Fennimore, Wis.

Building a Cement Reservoir

The placing of a big cement reservoir 38 ft. high and 10 ft. in diameter for the purpose of holding the supply of water for the town of Evans, Col., was done in a novel way.

Two years ago the town put down several 125-ft. deep wells to furnish its water supply. The wells filled with seepage water and were considered unsanitary. Recently four wells each 230 ft. deep were driven to bed rock and a flow of artesian water obtained. The wells were piped and around them was built the cement reservoir.

The reservoir was constructed by outlining its dimensions with meshed wire—the ordinary chicken wire fencing—which formed the center of the circular wall, 1 ft. thick and 38 ft. high. When the cement circle was thoroughly dry, workmen entered the enclosure and dug away the earth to a depth of 38 ft., the structure sinking by its own weight, gradually, into place. Seepage water was encountered toward the last but this was pumped out and a cement floor laid in the bottom of the reservoir. Into this big tank the artesian water is let at will and the result of the construction is most satisfactory.

Washing Glass Negatives

A great deal has been written regarding the handling of glass negatives through the developing and fixing solutions, says a correspondent of the Photographic Times, but not much is being done towards improving the washing methods, which is the only part of the work that is really tiresome. My method for the last four years has been as follows: Procure an ordinary stoneware milk pan which can be found in nearly every kitchen, the round bottom kind are the best and most common, a one-gallon size fits a 5 by 7 plate and a half-gallon size fits the 4 by 5 plates to perfection. Fill the pan nearly full of water, and after rinsing the negative a minute or two in a basin of water, place it face

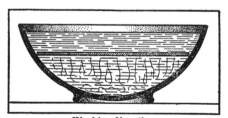

Washing Negatives

or film side down in the pan (it will find its seat about one-third the distance from the top), being careful not to allow any air bubbles on the under side. Should any bubbles have formed by letting the plate down too fast they can be ejected by tilting the plate slightly and then allowing it to settle back in a horizontal position again. After the negative has soaked in this way for thirty minutes, it is ready for the drying rack. Please note that there was no change of water in the operation of this method of washing.

When the negative is placed film side down in water, the hypo, being heavier, releases itself and drops to the bottom of the vessel. In the four years that I have practiced this method I have not lost a negative through carelessness in washing.

Auxiliary Friction Pulley

When power is to be transmitted a very short distance, as from A to C in the accompanying sketch, the necessary high tension on the belt usually results in excess journal friction and consequent wear. To prevent this a correspondent of the American Miller has used a friction pulley as shown at B.

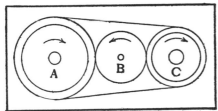

Friction Pulley Used With Belt

This not only relieves the strain on the journals but also helps to drive.

Stains for Oak

There are many ways in which oak may be stained, says the Master Painter, and any of the following will give fine results:

I. Apply ammonia with a sponge or brush. When dry give it a coat of turpentine, then fill with varnish. Or you may omit the filler and give a coat of shellac, then wax and rub to a polish; or simply shellac it, or omit the shellac and use wax only, according to the style of finish desired.

II. Use bichromate of potash dissolved in hot water instead of ammonia, as given in No. I, and you will get a still richer effect.

III. Apply a coat of freshly slaked lime; let this dry on; then brush off clean and apply a coat of boiled oil.

IV. A strong solution of sal soda will darken oak, but it will be necessary to apply two coats. Sandpaper lightly, then finish with oil rubbing.

Electrician's Boring Machine

In electrical work holes for wires are

Boring Machine for Electricians

frequently required in places which are very inaccessible and it was for work of this kind that the machine here illustrated was constructed. The sprockets, crank, and part of the frame from an old bicycle are used for transmitting the power to the auger, which is attached to the rear axle. If the chain has a tendency to run off the sprocket when drilling vertical holes, a small piece of wood may be lashed to the frame as shown.—Contributed by A. J. Swift, Novelty Electric Works, Ocean Park, Cal.

Transferring Dimensions

When it is impossible to transfer a dimension with ordinary calipers, owing to the form of the casting or other article that is being measured, 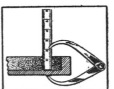 the dimension may be obtained by moving one leg of the calipers to one of the inch marks on a steel rule, as shown in the sketch. The calipers are then withdrawn and applied to the rule. The number of inches originally taken is then deducted from the total amount, thus giving the dimension as accurately as may be obtained by using one of the many intricate calipers designed especially for this purpose.—Contributed by W. F. S.

Forming Tool for the Lathe

A good forming cutter for duplicate work is shown in the accompanying illustration. The holder, A, is made of a piece of cold-rolled steel, slotted out to receive the cutter, which can be any desired shape, and turned down to fit the tail stock of the lathe. To use the cutter, simply turn the handle on the tail stock, thus forcing the cutter against the work. If the work is to have a hole in the center, this can be done in the same operation by making a hole in A to receive the drill, as shown.—Contributed by W. F. S.

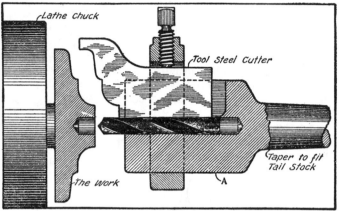

Useful for Duplicate Work

Knot for Cat Gut

Many of the knots commonly used for rope are unsuitable for cat gut, as the structure of gut is such that the fibers are generally weakened or cut when tied in ordinary knots. The accompanying drawing shows a form

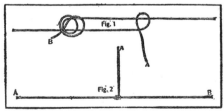

Attaching a Dropper Fly

of knot that is recommended by a correspondent of the Sporting Goods Dealer for attaching a dropper fly.

The points A and B are the two ends made by joining the cast where the dropper fly is required. Take end B and tie an ordinary double fisherman's knot round A, pull up tight; then pass A round B and turn back once through itself (a half hitch) taking care to leave the end sufficiently long to tie the fly on and gently pull tight onto knot at B as Fig. 2. The advantages of this method are (1) that the knot is smaller and neater than any other; (2) there being only one short end where B is cut off close, air bubbles are reduced to a minimum as the end points downward toward the tail fly; (3) it cannot catch in fine weeds, such as flannel weed.

Estimating the Power of a Screw and Lever

Problem :—What pressure will be obtained from a screw having three threads to the inch if acted on by a force of 1,000 lb. applied to the end of a lever 8 ft. long?—C. P. H.

As the end of the lever will travel 604 in. (the circumference of a circle of 8 ft. radius) in one revolution and thereby advance the screw only $\frac{1}{3}$ in., the force produced by the screw will be $604 \times 3 = 1812$ times that applied to the lever. It therefore follows that a force of 1,000 lb. on the lever will produce a pressure of 1,812,000 lb. or 906 tons on the screw. This calculation does not allow for friction.

Electric Light Pole Made from Pipes and Fittings

The sketch shows a home-made electric light pole, several of which were made by a correspondent of the Practical Engineer, from old steam pipe and fittings. The top or upper pipe is 2½ in. in diameter and about 15 ft. long; the middle length is 3 in. in diameter, 15 ft. long; the bottom pipe is 8 in. in diameter and 10 ft. long. This bottom pipe is sunk in the ground a distance of 6 ft. The rest of the construction can be understood by a glance at the sketch.

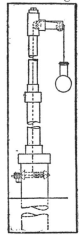

Thread Gauge Used for Spacing

An ordinary thread gauge with the teeth blackened, by rubbing over a lead pencil, makes a very useful and convenient spacing instrument and is far preferable to the bow dividers as no trials are necessary and the paper is not pricked all full of holes. By holding the blade as shown in the illustration and moving sideways about ⅟₁₆ in. each tooth makes a fine hair line, thus dividing the line into equal parts, which may be made fine or coarse by using different blades of the thread gauge.

If the teeth are rubbed on a pencil each time after being applied to the

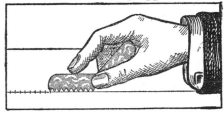

Spacing with a Thread Gauge

paper, the resulting divisions will be very distinct. Every draughtsman who has frequent occasion to draw threads or other work requiring spacing, would find the purchase of a thread gauge a good investment. — Contributed by draughtsman, Chicago.

Pressure Gauge Contact

An easily made electrical contact for a pressure gauge consists of an ordinary binding-post passed through a hole in the glass, as shown in the accompanying sketch. A contact fastened in this way is sure to be insulated from the other metal parts of the gauge and the hole in the glass can be easily made with a file or a drill by keeping it moistened with turpentine. In any gauge where the indicator hand makes electrical contact there is a possibility of the hand be-

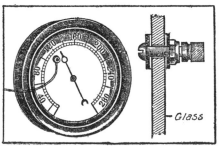

Gauge with Electric Contact Applied

coming stuck and for this reason it is well to use a separate gauge for the contacts. — Contributed by Robert Glaubke, Malott Park, Ind.

To Frost an Incandescent Lamp

A small piece of good emery cloth is all the material necessary to frost an incandescent lamp quickly, but effectually.

Rub the cloth over the entire lamp with a circular motion. Rubbing up and down will not produce the best results. About fifteen minutes' work will produce a very good frosting on an ordinary globe.—Contributed by D. P. Hein, Cherokee, Col.

Tile Furnace Roof for Boilers

In a paper read before the American Society of Engineers on December 3, Mr. A. Bement, of Chicago, discussed the advantages of tile roofs for water-tube boilers, from which the following has been condensed:

The objects sought are perfect and smokeless combustion and the full utilization of the boiler heating surface. The first requirement is secured by the employment of a tile furnace roof

third tiers of tubes is left vacant for the purpose of accumulating dust. The contracted passages among the tube surfaces produce a high resistance, and therefore a strong draft is required. The author considers that a combination of forced and induced draft secures the best combustion.

In the tests that were made with this boiler a very good efficiency was shown and the combustion was nearly perfect and without smoke, while similar boilers without the tile roof emit-

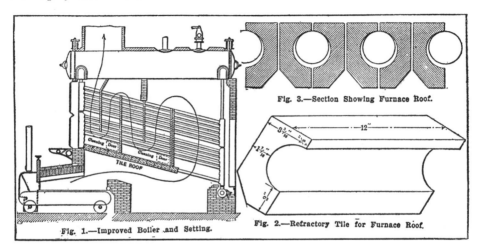

Fig. 3.—Section Showing Furnace Roof.

Fig. 1.—Improved Boiler and Setting.

Fig. 2.—Refractory Tile for Furnace Roof.

supported by the boiler tubes of the lower row. Fig. 1 shows an elevation and section of a boiler equipped with a chain grate stoker and using the tile roof. The individual refractory tiles used in the formation of this roof are illustrated in detail in Fig. 2 and by vertical cross section in Fig. 3. The tile roof prevents the flow of unburned gases among the tube surfaces of the boiler and causes them to travel a considerable distance before the heating surface is reached. Thus the gases and air become sufficiently mixed to insure complete combustion.

To insure the useful employment of all the boiler surface the gases are led over the whole of it by means of passages of less area than are commonly used. A space at the bottom of the boiler above the tile roof equal to that ordinarily required by the second and

ted heavy smoke under the same conditions of operation.

Gasket for Auto Pump

A packing which will make a tight and very durable joint for a water pump is made by coating a sheet of thick paper or cardboard with shellac, in which a little red lead has been mixed. The paper is first cut out to the proper size, and is then painted with the shellac or red lead and allowed to dry till it is almost hard. If one expects to have to break the joint at all frequently, however, some other kind of packing might be preferable, since the shellac will adhere so strongly to both surfaces that it can never be used a second time. In such a case it might be better to use paper painted with white lead, says Motor Talk, since it is possible to hold the slight pressure in a circulating pump with such a packing after the joint has been broken several times.

Recipes for Blue Stains

1. Dissolve copper filings in aquafortis and brush it over the work. Treat with a hot solution of 2 oz. pearlash to 1 pt. water, until a blue color is produced.

2. Boil 1 lb. indigo, 2 lb. wood and 3 oz. alum in 1 gal. water, says the Master Painter, and coat the work until thoroughly stained.

To Fasten Linoleum to Concrete

In order to make linoleum stick to a concrete surface a glue is used which has been boiled down till it is like carpenter's glue and into which wood ashes have been put. This glue is then stirred and makes a mass, somewhat like varnish. After applying it, the linoleum must be held firmly against the floor for some time.

Fillet for Pattern Making

Heat and thoroughly stir together equal parts of beeswax, rosin and venetian red until thoroughly mixed. Apply while hot with a strip of sheet brass formed to a half circle having the radius of the required fillet. Then finish with a common cabinet scraper. —Contributed by Frank L. Smith, Peru, Ill.

Cement for Iron and Marble

Iron may be securely cemented to marble by the use of the following preparation: Plaster of paris, 30 parts; iron filings, 10 parts; sal ammoniac, 1 part; mix to a fluid state with vinegar and use immediately as it hardens rapidly.

Home=Made Adjustable Drawing Table

A very handy and useful drawing table for draughtsmen and others who do mechanical work at home, can be easily made at very little expense. In the table here illustrated the adjustment is accomplished by means of sheet iron strips, cut out in the center as shown and fastened with thumb screws in any desired position. An arrangement of this kind provides for adjustments of both height and incli-

Adjustable Height and Inclination

nation and will be found much more rigid than many of the expensive ready-made tables. A small shelf, S, fastened to the right end of the table will provide a convenient place for laying tools when not in use and will be especially useful when the board is inclined at a steep angle. When not in use a drawing table of this kind may be folded into a very small space and put away.—Contributed by Geo. C. Murphy, Owensboro, Ky.

Good Filler for Woodwork

Corn starch, ½ lb.; fine pumice-stone dust, ½ lb.; white polish or liquid shellac, ¼ gill; boiled oil, ¼ pt. Thin for use with turpentine.

Scales for Duplicate Weighing

Ordinary platform scales may be made useful for duplicate weighing, such as measuring sacks of flour in a mill, or any other duplicate weighing, by drilling a $\frac{1}{8}$-in. hole in the traveling

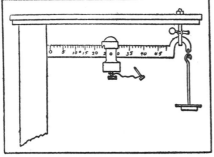

Device for a Duplicate Weigh

weight and saving the shavings. A steel pin is then made and fastened to the weight by a short piece of string or wire. The combined weights of the string and pin should just equal that of the shavings, which explains the reason for saving them. The weight is then moved along the beam to the positions commonly used in weighing and the beam drilled through with a $\frac{1}{8}$-in. drill. Scales treated in this way, says a correspondent of the American Miller, will prevent many mistakes which are likely to occur when no means are provided for holding the weight in position.

Moisture in Gas Engine

The "bucking and snorting refusal to start" of the gas engine is often due to moisture in the cylinder, preventing regular ignition till dried by the heat of several explosions. The difficulty may be obviated by shutting off the cooling water for a few minutes before stopping the engine, and not turning it on again until after the engine begins to explode regularly when again started, says Power and Transmission.

Paint for Invalid's Room

It is sometimes inadvisable to use ordinary paint on apartments occupied by invalids. In such cases, milk paint can be used.

Take 2 qt. skim milk, 6 oz. fresh slaked lime, 4 oz. linseed oil and 3 lb. fine bolted whiting or Spanish white. Place the lime in an earthen vessel, or a clean bucket, says the Master Painter, and add to it enough skim milk to make it like thick cream, then add the oil, a little at a time, stirring with a wooden paddle; then add the remainder of the milk, and after this add the white. This paint will dry in about an hour. The lime and oil unite to form a sort of soap, and the oil loses its smell thereby. One coat may be enough. Coloring may be added. The formula given will do about 25 sq. yd.

Hanger Nuts for Concrete

Appreciating the difficulties that many manufacturers have experienced in concrete buildings by insufficient or imperfect preparations for hanging to the ceiling, shafting, piping, shelving, etc, etc. I

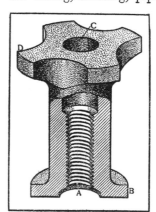

discarded all appliances and contrivances that I had ever seen used, and for a reinforced concrete building I am erecting for my factory purposes I designed and had made a ceiling support similar to the sketch herewith.

When a floor of one story is completed, the opening A shows in the ceiling of the floor beneath, the casting being imbedded in the cement.

These castings weigh 1½ lb. and are 3½ in. in height, drilled and threaded, into which machine bolts or supporting rods with threaded ends can be fastened. Having a sharp collar, B, they can be readily fastened with lath nails to the temporary wood floors on which the concrete is poured. In opening C a cork is placed to prevent clogging. The wing D prevents this casting from ever turning.

As they are inexpensive, they can be set at 3- or 4-ft. centers in any ceiling where there is a possibility of supports being necessary.

They are such a success that in return for the many valuable suggestions I have received from Shop Notes, I pass this on, hoping it will prove of interest and benefit to other readers.— Contributed by Augustus D. Curtis, President Curtis Ledger Co., Chicago.

Apparently Increases the Area of a Square

The sketch herewith shows how to cut a square of 64 sq. in. to form a rectangle of 65 sq. in. The area of any square may be increased in the same way by dividing it into 64 small squares like a checker board

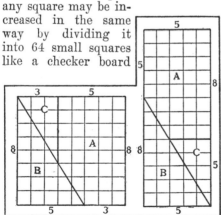

64 Sq. In. Cut and Arranged to Make 65 Sq. In.

and cutting as shown by the heavy lines in the sketch. The result is 65 squares from 64 squares. Where does the extra square come from?—Contributed by J. Peundorf, Lanesboro, Pa.

Why Stone Balls on Monuments Revolve

Why stone balls mounted as shown in Fig. 1 should revolve has always been a puzzle to monument builders. The rate of movement is very slow, probably less than one revolution in two or three years, but is always in

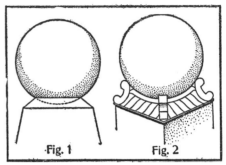

Revolving Ball and Remedy

the same direction—from northwest to southeast. A very plausible explanation of this phenomenon is given by a correspondent of the Monumental News, who recommends the construction shown in Fig. 2 as a remedy for this trouble.

The explanation is based on the fact that a small amount of water leaks in between the ball and spherical cavity in which it rests, thus causing expansion and contraction, due to alternate melting and freezing, sufficient to lift the ball. In melting, the southeast side, which receives the morning sun, melts first and drops back on the die, losing a small fraction of an inch every time it freezes. When the side away from the sun melts it drops back, but does not get back as far as it was before freezing. This, it seems, is the best explanation, because a ball mounted as shown in Fig. 2 will not revolve, as it does not come in contact with the water.

The tensile strength of copper wire is diminished and that of iron wire increased by carrying a current of electricity.

VISIBLE WATER HAMMER

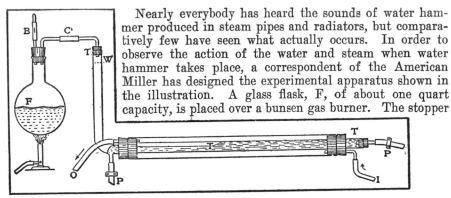

Nearly everybody has heard the sounds of water hammer produced in steam pipes and radiators, but comparatively few have seen what actually occurs. In order to observe the action of the water and steam when water hammer takes place, a correspondent of the American Miller has designed the experimental apparatus shown in the illustration. A glass flask, F, of about one quart capacity, is placed over a bunsen gas burner. The stopper

Showing Action of Water Hammer in Steam Pipes

To Clean a Gauge Glass

Drill and tap the upper valve (see illustration) for a ⅜-in. bilb cock, and by means of a short piece of rubber hose attach the small funnel. Close both valves, also lower bilb cock, and pour either a solution of hydrochloric acid or strong potash into the funnel. For accumulations of lime or similar sediment use the acid and if the dirt in the glass is of a greasy nature use the potash. After cleaning in this way blow water through in the usual manner. This is especially important after using the acid, as a small amount left in the valves will cause corrosion.—Contributed by Chas. Hurt, Milwaukee, Wis.

To Cement Brass Work to Glass

Mix together 2 parts litharge, 1 part white lead, 3 parts linseed oil and 1 part gum copal. Use immediately.

of the flask is provided with a safety valve, B, which is merely a short piece of india-rubber tubing plugged at one end and slitted for about one-half an inch of its length. The flask is connected by the tube C with an L-shaped glass tube of about ¾-in. bore, marked T T T. The vertical leg is about 1 ft. high, and the horizontal leg about twice this length. A small glass tube with a pinch-cock, P, is fitted at the bend, and another at the right-hand end, as shown. Both pinch-cocks should be connected with a fair length of tubing to a water reservoir, from which the tube T T T can be filled up to the level, W.

As soon as steam is issuing freely from the slit B, one of the pinch-cocks is opened and the water level allowed to fall below the top of the horizontal arm of the tube T. The condensation of steam, which now takes place over a considerable water surface, raises a wave near the bend, and as the imprisoned steam is still being condensed, a vacuum bubble is formed which collapses with a sharp blow, sufficient frequently to drive out the plug at the right-hand end of the tube. After a few blows, the water becomes so warm that the rapid condensation is no longer possible, and the action gradually ceases. For continued demonstration, therefore, it is necessary to have the horizontal length of the tube T water jacketed, as is shown in the engraving, with the water entering at I and leaving at O.

Design for Trolley Wheel

There seems to be some difference of opinion about the design of wheels for trolleys for carrying loads, to be used on I-beams, says a correspondent of the American Machinist. Among others I recently noticed an illustration of one in which conical wheels were used upon the beveled flanges of an I-beam, after the manner of the wheel A in the illustration.

I had always supposed that conical wheels were only adapted to circular pathways, which would preferably have a beveled face, corresponding to the angle of the conical wheel.

Referring to the illustration again, a number of lines have been drawn on the wheel A to represent circles on the periphery, and assuming that there is a load on the trolley, it is evident that

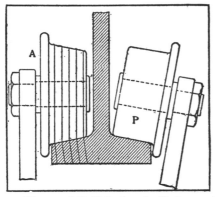

Wrong and Right Designs for Trolley

pressure is brought to bear equally at each of the points of intersection.

Now, when the trolley is moved it is evident that the linear speed of the largest circle is greater than that of any of the other circles, so that the wheel is bound to slip.

The wheel P is made cylindrical, and will run upon a beveled flange without the slippage incident to the

wheel A, and therefore seems preferable to it.

Testing Hemispherical Cavities

To test a hemispherical cavity or a semicircular groove, place a steel square in the cavity in several different positions. If the work is true the square will touch at three points in all positions.

—Contributed by W. F. S.

Trisecting an Angle

Problem.—What is the geometrical construction for trisecting any given angle?—F. L. G.

The solution of this problem has been declared impossible by some of the ablest mathematicians. Of course an angle may be approximately trisected by making numerous trials, and the results obtained in this way may be sufficiently accurate for all practical purposes, but as yet there is no direct method which can be demonstrated along geometrical lines.

Painting Cement

The following method of painting a cement wall was described at a recent convention of master painters. The building had become discolored in places and the joints were of a different color from the surface of the blocks. Two parts of Portland cement were mixed with one part of marble dust and mixed with water to the consistency of thin paint or a thick whitewash. The wall must be well wetted before the application of this paint and kept constantly wet while the material is applied, and then must be kept wet for a day longer, in order to make the cement wash adhere to the cement surface. The wash was applied with ordinary whitewash brushes, and a man was kept busy playing a hose on it while the work was being done.

Locating a Leak in Submerged Pipe

In a system where a brick-lined well, E, was supplied at all times with clean, pure water through a pipe, D, running out into Lake Ontario a distance of 500 or 600 ft., a leak developed in the submerged pipe, so that after a windstorm muddy water found its way into the well. Divers tightened up the joints, but could not cure nor locate the trouble, says Power.

In the system F is the suction pipe from the pumps and C is a heavy cast-iron valve used to regulate or close off the flow of lake water into

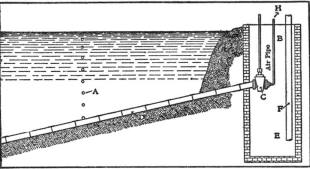

Air Bubbles Show Leak in Pipe

the well. The engineer connected an air pipe, H, to valve C and had air pumped into the pipe. After the pump had been working for some time he went out onto the lake in a canoe and soon discovered a string of bubbles rising to the surface as shown at A, about 200 ft. from shore in about 20 ft. of water. The diver descended at that point, found the break and repaired it.

◆ ◆ ◆

German Silver Knife Castings

Many of the German silver tips on pocket knife handles are castings, being probably the smallest that enter the brass foundry, says the Brass World. In the use of sheet German silver the tips must first be blanked out. This necessitates the production of 40 or 50 per cent of scrap. After the tips have been blanked they must be formed under a drop, with successive annealings, until they are formed into the oval shape ready for use. The cast German silver, however, only requires polishing and is ready for use. The tips are cast with a large number on a gate and with two gates in a flask. They are poured "on end." Scrap

German silver is used, and about 2 oz. of aluminum are added to 100 lb. of metal. The aluminum reduces the oxide in the German silver, and the metal then runs very freely. The color is also much improved and soundness is imparted. In the smallest sizes it takes several hundred cast knife tips to make a pound.

◆ ◆ ◆

Tool Holder for Grindstone

In many shops there are numerous chisels, cutters and plane bits that must be ground from time to time, and if they all must be held by hand the process not only requires much skill, but becomes very tedious long before it is completed. If a clamp is installed like the one here described the work is hastened, the results are better, and the job now can be entrusted

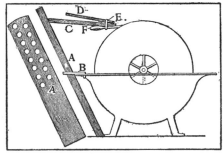

A Grinding Device

to a boy, says a correspondent of Wood Craft.

First, a board must be fashioned similar to A. The lower end of this must be beveled so that it rests flat on the floor when in position. The board is held in position by a hook forged of a light rod of iron with the ends passing down through the holes in the trough that originally were intended for attaching the name-plate. In this board, A, must be bored a number of holes. These afford a number of resting places for the clamp proper, C D.

The clamp is made up of two pieces of inch stock as wide as the widest plane bit and with one end of C rounded to fit the holes in A. Upon strip C is fastened a little rib, F, which serves as a fulcrum for the piece D. At the end of D is fastened by staples an iron rectangle, E, made of welded strap iron which holds the chisel or plane bit against the lower side of C when the hand is pressed down upon the other end of D.

By moving the chisel forward or backward in the clamp, or by raising or lowering the rear end of C, any angle desired may be secured upon the chisel as it is pushed back and forth across the stone.

Planing Large Engine Casting

The accompanying cut shows how we planed a large engine frame which was too large for the largest planer. The length of the cut was greater than the stroke of either of the shapers in our shop which made it necessary to use the planer and in order to support the end not being finished a small planer was moved alongside the large one.

It was found that the reversing of the large planer made it necessary to use diagonal braces to prevent the work from slewing around at the end of the stroke. These braces were fastened from each end of the planer bed to the casting, near the cylinder end, the back brace being so placed as to clear the planer frame in all positions of the work. The entire work of finishing the casting, including bracing and moving the planer, was done in 1½ days.—Contributed by C. R. McGahey.

◆ ◆ ◆

To attach metal letters to glass use 30 parts copal varnish, 10 parts spirits of turpentine, 10 parts glue dissolved in a little warm water, and 20 parts pulverized slaked lime.

Cement for Porcelain

Soak 1 dr. of isinglass in water; pour upon this a sufficient quantity of alcohol to cover the isinglass, and allow

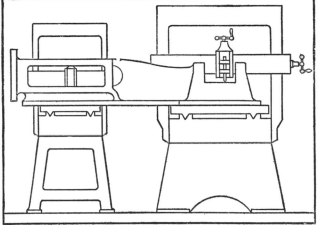

Planing with Two Planers

it to dissolve, placing it in a warm room. Next dissolve ½ dr. of mastic in 1 fl. dr. of rectified spirit of wine; mix both solutions together, add ½ dr. of powdered gum ammoniac, and evaporate the mixture in a water-bath until it has acquired the requisite consistency. Keep the cement in a glass bottle, and when it is to be used place the bottle in hot water, when the cement will become soft so that it can be conveniently applied to the fragments of porcelain to be cemented, which should be previously heated.

Rate of Evaporation of Alcohol, Turpentine, Benzine, Etc.

In an address before the National Painters' Association, W. G. Scott said:

From the result of many experiments it has been found that the "rate of evaporation" per hour, per square inch, for a given volume of water, alcohol, turpentine, and benzine is as follows:

	Per cent (by weight).
Water	0.61
Grain Alcohol	5.10
Wood alcohol	9.74
Turpentine	1.10
Wood Spirit	1.58
Benzine	4.70
Gasoline, 87 deg.	55.11

When paint works "short" or varnish refuses to "level out," the trouble is generally due to the amount and kind of vehicle present. A varnish with the proper amount of turpentine will flow and level out much better than one containing the same amount of benzine, the more volatile thinner causing it to set quicker. This also explains the difference so often noticed in shellac varnishes where wood in place of grain alcohol is used as a thinner.

Benzine has the highest rate of evaporation of all the paint thinners, even higher than the very inflammable coal tar product known as "solvent naphtha," which is 2.23 per cent. The study of evaporation is a complex problem, of which little is known, but it is to blame for many of the troubles incident to paint and varnish.

Slow evaporation generally means slow drying; rapid evaporation should mean quick drying, but more often signifies quick setting.

A very peculiar feature in regard to evaporation and the drying of paint and varnish is, that the rate of evaporation at a high temperature in a closed room is not nearly so great as at a lower temperature with a free circulation of air.

Water is compressed 1/326100 of its volume for each pound of pressure.

Shrinkage of Metal Castings

The following table gives the rate of shrinkage in castings made from various metals:

Bismuth	5-32 in. per foot
Pipes	1-8 " " "
Tin	1-4 " " "
Copper	3-16 " " "
Lead	5-16 " " "
Zinc	5-16 " " "
Thin brass	1-8 " in 9 in.
Thick brass	1-8 " " 10 "

Extracting Pump Pipes

It is often necessary to pull the pump pipe from an old well either for renewing the strainer or for making other repairs, and as this is usually a

A Good Pipe Puller

difficult undertaking, the scheme here illustrated may possibly be beneficial to some readers. A small excavation is made and a chain is wrapped around the pipe, which, being usually somewhat rusty, prevents the chain slipping.

The timbers and jackscrews are then placed as shown and the jackscrews turned up to their full height. They are then lowered; the chain is moved down on the pipe and the jackscrews turned up again, this operation being repeated as many times as is necessary to remove the pipe.

How to Make a Home=Made Band=Saw

The frame of this machine is made of 2-in. by 4-in. lumber bolted together with ½-in. bolts and reinforced with iron rods. The band-wheels are each made from a single piece of oak 2 in. thick. They were first sawed out in 18-in. circles and then mounted on the shafts and turned up perfectly true. A groove ⅛ in. deep and 1¼ in. wide was then turned on the face of each pulley and a piece of rubber belting 1¼ in. wide was then fastened in the groove by means of small nails driven along both edges.

The guides were made by bending 2-in. band iron into L-shaped pieces, as shown in Figs. 3 and 4. The top guide is fastened to a ⅝-in. rod, which works in a clamp fastened to the frame. A cavity is made in the guide to receive the steel ball, B, which may be taken from an old bicycle. On each side of the ball are placed blocks of wood, fastened by means of small bolts passed through slots. This allows the blocks to be moved up on the saw as they wear. The lower guide is the same as the upper except that it is bolted fast to the under side of the table. The saw runs through these guides, which prevent it bending and the ball-bearing at the back keeps the saw from running off the pulleys. The saw blade is 10 ft. long and will cut

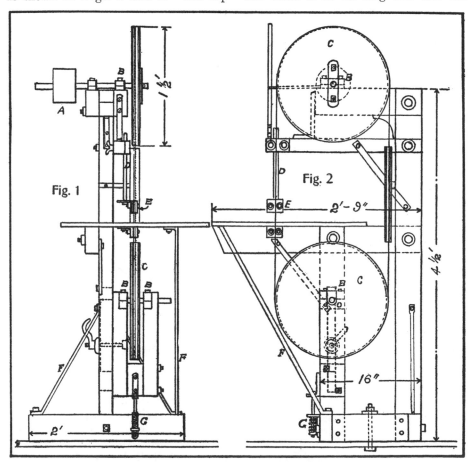

Front and Side Elevation of Band-Saw Machine

to the center of a 3-ft. circle. The general dimensions of this band-saw

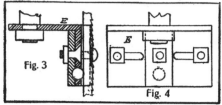

Details of Guides

are given in the elevation drawings, Figs. 1 and 2.—Contributed by Frank W. Rumsey, New London, O.

How to Hang Japanese Leather

Japanese leather, like ordinary pressed or embossed paper, can't be satisfactorily laid on hard walls without they are first lined with brown paper, which gives the paste an absorbent surface and a surface to stick to. Use ordinary wheat flour for the lining paper, but for the Japanese leather paper, as well as for all the heavy papers, use a stiffer paste, which sets quicker, and lessens the risk of soaking into and softening the relief work and injuring the colors. Carefully trim each piece of Japanese paper with the knife and by the straightedge, says the Master Painter. Apply the paste quickly, and get the paper onto the wall as soon as you can. When you have the paper in its place on the wall, go over it with a very soft brush, though some think that even the soft brush is wrong, and that the fingers only should be used. When the paper has become very nearly dry, go over the seams with the seam roller, very carefully. Be very careful not to stretch the paper while it is wet. Remove at once any paste that may press out from the seams.

A good cement for such articles as shells, fossils, etc., consists of beeswax, 1 oz.; resin, 4 oz.; powdered plaster-of-paris, 5 oz., melted together. Warm edges of specimen and apply cement warm.

Temperatures of Flames

According to the results of recent experiments the flame of acetylene is perhaps the hottest known except that of the electric arc. The following figures have been given by Mr. Maffi: Bunsen burner, 1871°; acetylene flame, 2548°; alcohol flame, 1705°; Denayrouze burner, half alcohol, half petroleum, 2053°; hydrogen flame, in air, 1900°; gas jet flame, with oxygen, 2200°; oxyhydrogen flame, 2420°. These are all Centigrade degrees.

To Repair Dent in Musical Instrument

Cornets, trumpets and similar instruments frequently become dented, as shown in the sketch. When this happens bend a wire to the form shown at A and soft solder to the dent at B. Then simply pull on the wire, thus

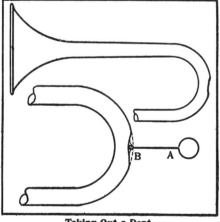

Taking Out a Dent

bringing the dent out to its original position, as indicated by the dotted line. Then apply sufficient heat to melt the solder; wipe off clean with a rag and polish.—Contributed by C. R. McGahey, Atlanta, Ga.

A tight belt is a power-consumer and a slipping belt is a speed-loser, but between the two there is a good point where you don't lose any speed and don't consume too much power.

SHOP NOTES

Coloring Metals

Dissolve 4 oz. hyposulphite of soda in $1\frac{1}{2}$ pt. water and then add a solution of 1 oz. acetate of lead in 1 oz. water. Place articles to be colored in the mixture and heat gradually to the boiling point. Iron is given the color of blue steel, zinc becomes bronze and copper or brass becomes, successively, yellowish, red, scarlet, deep blue, blue, light blue. By substituting sulphate of copper for the acetate of lead in preparing the solution, brass becomes first of a fine rosy tint, then green and lastly of an iridescent brown color.— Contributed by A. G. Wareham, Waterloo, Ind.

How to Make a Dike

In placing a dike or dam on the side of a hill or on a level surface it is well to prepare the surface before building by ploughing furrows on the surface to receive the bank and throwing the dirt so it will not fill the adjacent furrow

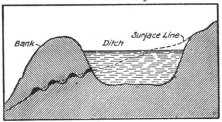

Correct Construction of Dike

but lie on top as indicated by the black portions in the accompanying sketch. This will usually prevent the water seeping through unless the earth is very porous or sandy, when it will be necessary to apply a layer of clay on the bottom and sides of the ditch.— Contributed by Geo. G. McVicker, North Bend, Neb.

Repairing Broken Hammers

In many cases hammers which have been broken can be repaired and made to give good service. When cracked diagonally, as shown at Fig. 1, the re-

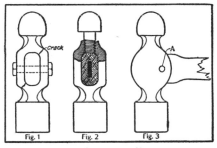

Repairs for Broken Hammer

pair can easily be made by drilling for a small bolt, as indicated by the dotted lines. When the pene becomes broken, as shown in Fig. 2, a quick repair can be made by drilling and tapping to receive a steel screw, which should be ground rounded, as shown. When the head of a hammer comes off and nothing else will hold it on, the scheme shown in Fig. 3 is a good one. Drill a hole at A and drive in a steel pin.— Contributed by W. E. J., Walden, N. Y.

Safe Flash Powder

A safe flash powder which cannot be ignited either through friction or a blow consists of 10 parts magnesium and 10 parts anhydrous chrome alum. Two parts of aluminum can be substituted for the same amount of the magnesium, if desired. The powder will burn more slowly if silicic acid or powdered glass is added.—From Photographische Rundschau, Vol. 20.

A green color may be given woodwork by dissolving verdigris in vinegar and applying hot.

Heating Water by Gas

Gas heaters for heating domestic water supplies are very convenient and the cost of operating is not very large, especially when natural gas is used. The illustration, from the Metal-

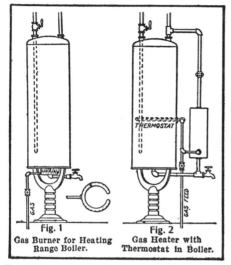

Fig. 1
Gas Burner for Heating Range Boiler.

Fig. 2
Gas Heater with Thermostat in Boiler.

Two Methods for Heating Domestic Water Supply

Worker, shows the two types commonly used. The horseshoe burner, Fig. 1, so called on account of its shape, is a simple gas burner placed about 5 in. below the bottom of the boiler.

It heats the water by burning directly up against the bottom of the boiler, but is objectionable because it will in time burn out the boiler bottom, is very slow in heating the water and is wasteful of gas. Nevertheless this burner has a considerable popularity because of the convenience with which it can be connected without interfering with the regular boiler connections.

Then there is the coil, or the round cast heater, made to connect up, as shown in Fig. 2. The return pipe from the bottom of the boiler is connected to the bottom of the heater, and the circulation pipe from the top of the heater is connected to a tee in the hot water supply pipe in top of the boiler. This can be run as a non-automatic heater, or it can be made automatic by the use of a thermostat, as

indicated. This thermostat, which is made expressly for this work, consists of a brass tube inside of which is a porcelain tube, arranged so that it can be set to operate at any desired temperature. This tube expands upon being heated and closes off the supply of gas to the burner. As soon as the water falls below a certain temperature this tube contracts and opens the gas valve, which allows gas to flow to the heater, where it is ignited by the pilot light.

Hiding Fine Cracks in a Wall

To hide fine cracks in a wall use plaster and whiting, mixed with glue size, says the Master Painter. Brush the mixture well into the wall so that the cracks are filled full, and when dry, smooth off lightly with sandpaper.

Coupling Converted Into Pulley

Some time ago in a shop where I was employed they had a large room filled with various machines run by a single line shaft. The countershaft of one machine was in line with a flange coupling on the main shaft and as the other machines prevented its being moved to one side, the belt was put on the coupling. The machine was driven

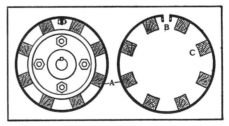

Coupling Converted Into Pulley

successfully in this way except that the speed was too low, which made it necessary to lag up the coupling as shown in the drawing. A piece of band iron, A, $\frac{1}{4}$ in. thick was bent in a circle as shown and drilled at B to allow fastening with bolts. A number of hardwood blocks, C, were screwed to the band, the screws being counter-sunk flush with the band, which was then placed on the coupling and tightened up.—Contributed by Alfred S. Cromer, 466 E. Buchtell Ave., Akron, Ohio.

Repairing Brasses

An engineer recently observed that one of the brasses on the crank of his engine was cracked as shown at A. No new brasses were at hand, and as the plant operated day and night it was absolutely necessary that something be done so that the engine could be put into operation. It was finally decided that the best method of procedure was to drill three holes in each side of the crack and tap the same. A piece of steel plate was then cut out and fitted to the brasses as shown at B. Holes were drilled in this plate to line up with those already in the brass, says the Engineers' Review, but purposely drilled nearer to the center in order to bring the two parts of the brass close together. Screws were then threaded in place and headed over to prevent their working loose.

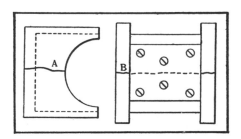

Emergency Repair for Brasses

Babbitt metal was next melted and poured into the brass, the old babbitt having been removed, a piece of shaft slightly smaller than the crank-pin being used to run the babbitt against on the inside. The babbitt was then turned out in a lathe to fit the pin. These brasses were used until new ones could be secured, and are now being kept in case of an emergency.

Electric Rotation Indicator

This device will give an alarm when the machine to which it is attached stops running. In the illustration A is the end of a shaft on the machine, B is the bearing and C is a piece of brass fastened to the bearing by means of a piece of hard rubber or other insulating material. The end of the shaft is threaded to receive a $\frac{3}{8}$-in. steel rod, D,

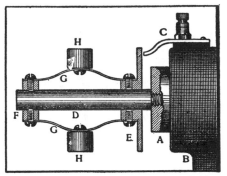

Rotation Indicator Applied to End of a Shaft

which should be run true with the shaft. The brass flange, E, is loose on the rod and the brass collar, F, is attached by means of set-screws.

The steel springs, G G, which may be made from an old clock spring, are attached to both collar and flange and support the brass weights, H H, which revolve with the shaft. The centrifugal force thus produced will draw the flange, E, away from the contact, C, while the machine is running, but as soon as it stops the springs will force the flange against the contact and ring an electric bell. One wire from the bell should be attached to the binding-post and the other should be grounded to the machine. If desired the electric bell may be replaced with small gal-vanometers or other indicating devices running to each machine.—Contributed by W. M. Brown, Philadelphia, Pa.

It is reported the Southern Pacific will electrify 250 miles across the desert from Reno, Nev., to Carlin. Four water power plants on the Truckee river will supply the current.

Low Fuel Alarm for Gasoline Engine

This device is applicable to either motor boats or stationary gasoline engines and is designed to give an alarm when the fuel becomes nearly exhausted. The alarm is given by means

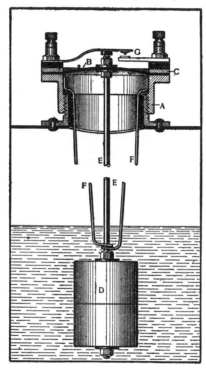

Low-Level Alarm for Gasoline Tank

of a float in the gasoline tank, which holds an electrical contact open so long as there is plenty of fuel in the tank, but allows it to close when the level becomes too low, thus ringing a bell and notifying the operator before the gasoline is entirely exhausted.

The threaded cap of the gasoline tank is removed and an internally threaded brass flange, A, is screwed in its place. The open end of the flange is then covered with a sheet rubber diaphragm, B, held to the flange by a brass ring, C, fastened on with screws. The float, D, is made of cork or other light material and is fastened to a steel rod, E, which is held in a vertical

position by the guide, F, constructed of heavy wire and soldered to the flange. The rod, E, is attached to the center of the diaphragm by means of two nuts and washers, as shown, and the end is adjusted to hold open the contacts, G, thus preventing the bell ringing except when the gasoline becomes too low.—Contributed by Geo. G. McVicker, North Bend, Neb.

Hanging Shelves Made From Gas Pipe

Shelves constructed of gas pipe, as shown in the accompanying sketch, are very useful for storing away books, files and other small articles and possess many advantages over ordinary shelves and cabinets. Shelves constructed in this manner are fireproof, neat in appearance and very strong, besides utilizing considerable room without taking up any floor space. The horizontal pipes, B, may be $\frac{1}{2}$ in. and the vertical pipes, A, $\frac{3}{4}$ in. These should be fastened to the ceiling either with ordinary flanges or floor fittings as shown at C, $\frac{3}{4}$ in. by $\frac{1}{2}$ in. Tees are used at D and may also be used at E if it is desired to allow for adding a lower shelf in the future; otherwise $\frac{3}{4}$ in. by $\frac{1}{2}$ in. ells should be substituted. If the articles to be stored are of such a nature that there is danger of their falling through the spaces be-

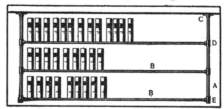

Suspended Shelves of Gas Pipe

tween the horizontal pipes, boards or wire netting may be fastened across the openings.—Contributed by W. H., Chicago.

When varnishing a kalsomined surface, treat it first with light gelatine size.

How to Make Soldering Paste

Soldering paste, says the Brass World, has now come into extensive use in electrical work as a flux for soldering. This has been brought about by the requirements of the electrical trade that in certain forms of soldering no acid shall be used. For soldering copper wires for electrical conductors, soldering paste is almost exclusively used. It has also entered other fields of soldering, particularly in instances where spattering and corrosion are objectionable.

Soldering paste which is now used in the electrical trades consists of a mixture of a grease and chloride of zinc. The grease which is commonly used is a petroleum residue, such as vaseline or petrolatum. Such a material is about right in consistency. The proportions which are used are as follows:

Petrolatum ....r lb.
Saturated solution chloride of zinc
    ....1 oz. (fluid).

The use of petrolatum instead of vaseline is recommended. While they are identical in composition, the name "vaseline" is registered as a trademark and commands a higher price on this account. Petrolatum is much cheaper.

The chloride of zinc solution is made by dissolving as much zinc in strong muriatic acid as it will take up. An excess of zinc should be present and all the acid neutralized. This will form a thick, oily solution. The petrolatum and chloride of zinc are mixed and thoroughly incorporated by means of a mortar and pestle or by vigorous stirring.

The advantage of this soldering paste lies in the fact that it does not spatter and is not corrosive. It will be found excellent and is now extensively used.

In the transmission of compressed air a loss of from 2 to 10 per cent results from pumping the air from the engine room instead of air from a cooler place.

To Remedy Poor Draft in Large Chimney

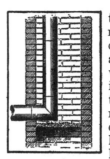

Gives Good Draft

It is an advantage to have a little too much draft in a stove or furnace, as it can always be reduced when necessary, but it is not always good to have a large chimney. A correspondent of the Metal-Worker has found that a large chimney gives a good draft with a large fire but a very poor draft with a small fire and recommends the construction shown in the sketch to overcome difficulties of this kind.

A Wabble Saw Kink

The wabble saw is an old device, but the following application is one that is not generally known. In this case the work was to be notched out, as shown in the illustration, which made

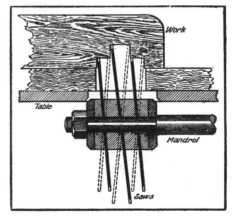

Wabble Saw Kink

it necessary to use three saws instead of one. The washers between the saws were made of babbitt metal and were beveled as shown. The bottoms of the notches were not perfectly straight but slightly curved, as is the case in all wabble saw work, but the curvature in this case was so small as to be almost unnoticeable. In order to hold the work in position while using the saw a bolt was pushed up through the board on the table and into a vertical hole in the work.—Contributed by Experimenter.

Finishing Brasswork

Many readers have doubtless admired the very pretty effect of mottling seen on shop-made brass instruments, some-

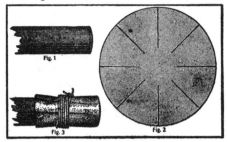

For Mottling the Surface of Brasswork

thing like the veins in marble running over the surface of the brasswork. A smooth finished brass surface readily shows up scratches, and is difficult to lacquer perfectly, evenly and free from brush marks. On the mottled surface lack of skill is not so noticeable.

The "mottling" is really a series of very fine circles running into one another scratched on the surface of the brass, says a correspondent of the Model Engineer, who has done work of this kind in the following manner:

Take a small round piece of wood, Fig. 1 (a piece of a penholder or pencil will do), put it in a drill chuck or self-centering chuck, leaving an inch or so projecting. Start the lathe and with a smooth file make the end very slightly convex. From a piece of the very finest emery paper cut a circle about an inch or so in diameter, as shown at Fig. 2, and fasten to the piece of wood with good stout string, as shown in Fig. 3.

Now, holding the piece of brasswork in the right hand (it is necessary to have a piece of paper between the brass and the fingers, the grease from the fingers prevents lacquering afterwards),

the work being finished to a good surface, run the lathe as fast as possible, press the work lightly against the emery-covered wood, moving it steadily forward at right angles, and a sort of shaded vein will be seen where the rotating emery has cut lightly into the brass. You may follow any pattern you please at first, but the worker will soon be able to obtain some very nice results, and designs will suggest themselves to him.

If two or three diameters of wood are used, the veining may be of different widths. Different grades of emery may also be used, but anything like a coarse grain is useless. Do not use emery cloth, use only the finest emery paper, such as is used for polishing.

To Keep Hot Lead From Sticking

Prepare a mixture of 1 qt. powdered charcoal, $\frac{1}{2}$ pt. salt, 1 gill yellow prussiate of potash and a lump of cyanide of potassium the size of a walnut, says Machinery. Apply this to the surface of the pot or to tools to be heated in the molten metal.

Eraser Holder

Draughtsmen will find this device very handy and well worth the trouble of making, especially if there is much rubbing out to be done. It is made from an ordinary clothes pin cut down

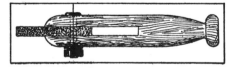

Eraser Holder

as shown and drilled to receive an old binding-post, which is used to hold the eraser from turning. I have used this device for some time and find that it makes the work of rubbing out much easier and prevents the fingers from cramping.—Contributed by Wm. E. Jehn, 195 Fifth Ave., Paterson, N. J.

Surface Finish For Concrete

In considering concrete as a substitute for brick and stone, perhaps the most serious problem confronting the architect is to obtain a satisfactory surface or finish.

composed of 1 part cement, 2 parts sand and 3 parts ⅜-in. screened stone; Fig 2 consists of 1 part cement, 2 parts sand and 3 parts ⅛-in. pebbles; Fig. 3, 1 part cement and 3 parts yellow bar sand. Each example is shown at its actual size.

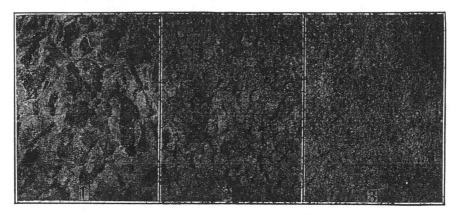

Examples of Surface Finishing for Concrete--Actual Size

The concrete surfaces shown in the accompanying photographs are easily obtained by a method known as the Quimby process, which is described in the Cement Age as follows:

The process consists in completely flushing the face against the form, removing the form after the material has set but while it is still friable, and then immediately washing and rinsing the surface with water.

The washing removes the film of cement which has formed against the mold and exposes the particles of sand and stone. The appearance then depends, of course, upon the character of the aggregate in the concrete and the uniformity of its distribution in the mixtures. As in well mixed concrete the cement merely fills the voids between the grains of sand, and the sand fills the voids between the pebbles or particles of crushed stone, the cement visible in this finished surface is so small a percentage that it has very little influence on the color of the work.

In the illustration the surface shown in Fig. 1 was obtained with a concrete

To Produce Extreme Hardness in Steel

Heat the steel slightly, then immerse in a mixture of 4 parts water, 2 parts salt and 1 part flour, till it is thoroughly coated. Then heat the metal to a cherry red, says Machinery, and plunge in soft water.

Tongs For Pulverizer Discs

A very useful pair of tongs for holding pulverizer discs when sharpening same can be made as shown in the sketch. If an old pair of tongs can be spared for the purpose the labor of altering them for work of 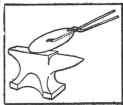 this kind will be very little, as it is only necessary to weld a piece of round stock on one of the jaws and turn up the end as shown.—Contributed by Geo. G. McVicker, North Bend, Neb.

Forging a Rocker Arm

To forge a rocker arm take round stock that is large enough to give, when flattened, the dimension shown at A, Fig. 1. Draw it to the form shown in Fig. 2. This will require great care, says a correspondent of the Blacksmith and Wheelwright, for there is danger that the dimensions C may be too great or too small. Flatten enough of one end to form the arm and draw to the form shown by two views in Fig. 3. Make the dimension D of this view to correspond to D in Fig. 1. In flattening this part the work is done with the hammer, the side toward which the stock is drawn being made as true and flat as possible from the shoulder to the end, forming the recess at D by the use of the fuller. This leaves the projection at F on the end, from which to form the boss. Next clamp the piece firmly near one shoulder and bend the flattened portion down, making the whole piece of the form shown in Fig. 4. This may be done by clamping the piece between the hammer dies and driving the arm down with the sledge hammer. Round the boss to the shape shown at G in Fig. 1. This rocker arm is strong and durable.

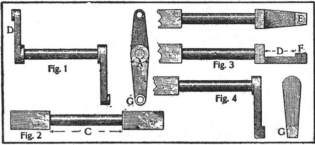

Forging a Rocker Arm

To Recharge Motorcycle Batteries

When a motorcyclist finds himself in the country with his batteries run down they may be revived sufficiently for the return trip, or till new cells can be procured, by the following treatment: On each side of the carbon pole drill a small hole with a pocket knife or screw driver, drilling deep enough to go entirely through the black composition on the top. Then pour water in the holes and allow batteries to stand about 5 minutes.—Contributed by Eugene J. Friedlander, 2803 Second Ave. So., Minneapolis, Minn.

Loading Stern=Wheel Boat

In loading a stern-wheel paddle boat for all ordinary conditions, it is usually best to stow the cargo so that the boat will trim a trifle down at the head, and therefore draw a trifle more water at the bow than at the stern. This not only assists towards higher speed and easy running, but is also a precaution against grounding, as the boat, if running on to a shoal place, touches forward, and is then easily backed off without damage to the paddle-wheel.

Talking Through Your Chest

Persons not familiar with the action of the vocal organs derive considerable amusement from carrying on a telephone conversation with the transmitter placed against their chests. With the instrument in this position the sound transmitted is reproduced with a loudness .almost equal to that heard when the mouthpiece is immediately in front of the lips of the speaker. The voice of the speaker may be readily recognized, says the American Telephone Journal, but there is sufficient alteration in the quality of tones to make it possible for a change from this position to the customary one to be readily detected.

Desk set users will do well not to attempt to muffle a transmitter by pressing it against their coats, as is sometimes done by persons who use the telephone while standing, if they wish to say things which should not be heard at the other end of the line.

How to Mix Plaster of Paris

In mixing plaster of paris do not pour the water on the plaster, but turn the plaster gradually into the water, says Machinery, spreading it about in shaking it in and not stirring until all the plaster has been added. If mixed in this manner a smooth cream or thin dough without lumps will result. The proper quantity of gypsum is usually enough to peep out over the surface of the water over the greater part of the area; that is, about equal volumes of each ingredient. The addition of glue water to the mixture retards setting.

Life of Wooden Poles

The German Postal and Telegraph Department has recently published statistics collected during the period of 52 years on the life of wooden posts impregnated with different preservative substances. The number of posts under observation amounts to nearly 3,000,000 and the following are the average results obtained:

Poles Impregnated with—	Length of Life.
Sulphate of copper	11.7 years
Corrosive sublimate	13.7 years
Creosote	20.6 years
Unimpregnated	7.7 years

The manner of preparing the poles has been improved from time to time, and this is clearly shown in a further table giving the average length of life of the poles under different methods of treatment with each preservative at different periods. For example, in 1883, with sulphate of copper the average life was 9.4 years, while in 1903 the method of treatment had been improved so that an average life of 13.3 years could be obtained.

For common brass for castings use 20 parts copper, $2\frac{1}{2}$ tin, $1\frac{1}{4}$ zinc.

Remedy for Stiff Working Springs

It frequently happens that wagon repairers are called upon to reduce the stiffness in the springs of new vehicles in which the springs are far too stiff for comfort. This is sometimes done by removing a plate; but a better way is to take spring apart, place each leaf, one at a time, in the vise and drawfile until all the scale has been removed. Then mix tallow and plumbago and paint the leaves and reassemble, wiping off all the tallow from the edge. The idea of using tallow is that even in warm weather it will never run out and disfigure the springs.—Contributed by J. C. Blake, Harvard, Ill.

Heating a Radiator from a Range Boiler

Unsuccessful attempts to heat radiators from hot water boilers are usually

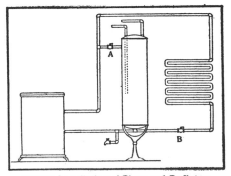

Correct Installation of Pipes and Radiators

due to faulty installation. The sketch herewith shows the correct way to make the connections. Instead of using valves the stop cocks A and B are used, as they offer less resistance to circulation than ordinary globe valves. Cock A must be so arranged that it cannot be closed more than two-thirds, says a correspondent of Domestic Engineering, else if cock B and cock A were inadvertently closed tight at same time there would be danger of the waterback exploding. The operation would be as follows: By partly closing cock A any desired amount of the hot water could be forced through radiator, and by this means radiator could be kept up to the boiling point if desired, while boiler was anywhere from 100 to 120 or at any desired heat. By placing the sediment cock, as shown, the return can be kept clear of sediment. When it is desired to put the radiator out of commission it can be done by closing cock B.

The hot water supply from boiler and from heater to radiator should be run entirely separate, as shown in the sketch.

Cutting in a Boiler

If the following precautions are observed many of the accidents which occur from cutting in boilers will be prevented. Let A and B represent two boilers; B is supplying steam to the line, L; A is about to be cut in, and the pressure in it is nearly up to the required amount.

Now it is possible that some water, W, may have collected in the pipe leading from boiler A. If there is enough of it, the engine might be wrecked when the stop-valve is opened. The secret of preventing trouble consists in opening the valve when the steam is about 5 lb. lower in boiler A than it is in the main line; then any water that may have collected in the pipe will be forced back into boiler A; but be sure and open the stop-valve very slowly, and be sure that you know how nearly correct the steam gauges are.

Also, in cutting in a boiler where there is a condensing engine, be careful that all the air is blown out of the boiler first, says a correspondent of Power, otherwise it would plug up the condenser and the vacuum would be lost.

Anybody can publish a Webster's Dictionary now: Copyright expired.

Cinder Roads Bad for Planing Mills

It is poor economy to make cinder roads around a planing mill, says a correspondent of Wood Craft, who has found that some of the cinders are sure to work their way into the ends and surface of the lumber and make it necessary to keep one man busy filing the nicks out of the planer blades.

Ink for Rubber Stamps

A very good rubber stamp ink which will not rot the rubber, dry on the pad or give bronzed colors can be made by mixing the following: 16 fl. oz. alcohol; 12 fl. oz. glycerine; 1 oz. aniline violet. Dissolve the aniline in the alcohol first and then add the glycerine.

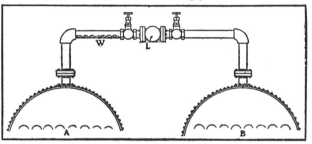

Danger of Wrecking the Engine

To Remove Wheel Stuck on Shaft

Many times a wheel which has been machined for a running fit on a shaft runs dry of oil and begins cutting. This usually results in the formation of one or more small balls which roll up the material in the same manner that boys roll snow balls, until they become wedged in so tightly that the wheel is locked to the shaft. To remove the wheel apply kerosene, allowing it to soak in thoroughly. If this fails, try heating the hub with a gasoline blow-torch, and if this fails, too, it will probably be necessary to use jackscrews and chains.—Contributed by G. G. M.

A cube of air 31 ft. on each side weighs over a ton.

To Color Brass Black

Boil the brass to be blackened in a strong potash solution to remove all grease and oil, then rinse well. Dissolve 1 lb. plastic carbonate of copper in 2 gal. strong ammonia and dip the brass in this solution, which should be heated to 150° to 175° F., until the desired degree of blackness is acquired. This process, says Compressed Air, works best on brass containing much copper. The color is uniform and has little tendency to peel off.

The plastic carbonate of copper can be made as follows: Dissolve blue vitriol in hot water and add a strong solution of common washing soda so long as any precipitate forms. Allow the precipitate to settle and then pour off the clear liquid. Add hot water and allow to settle again. Pour off the clear water again, add hot water, let settle and pour off as before, repeating this process until everything has been washed out of the green carbonate of copper that remains at the bottom of the vessel and which is the plastic carbonate of copper referred to.

A Good Copying Ink

Into two gallons of clear rainwater put ¼ lb. gum arabic, ¼ lb. clean copperas (ferrous sulphate), ¾ lb. powdered nutgalls, ¼ lb. brown sugar. Mix well, shake occasionally for ten days, and strain. If it is needed before ten days steep it in an iron kettle until the desired strength is obtained.

Liquid Glues

Take three parts (by weight) of gum shellac and one part India rubber. Dissolve in separate vessels in ether (free from alcohol), applying a gentle heat. When both are entirely dissolved mix them and put them in a tightly corked bottle. This variety of glue is known as marine glue. It resists the action of hot and cold water and the majority of the alkalis and acids.

Repair for Caster Sockets

When the caster socket in an article of furniture becomes worn or weakened, drill out the socket large enough to receive a piece of ½-in. pipe and after driving the pipe in as far as it will go cut it off with a hacksaw. If the caster has a large shank, it may be necessary to use a ¼-in. pipe. A piece of pipe fitted in this way makes an excellent bushing and is much more durable than the original socket.—Contributed by Axsul Everson, Penn Yan, New York.

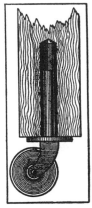

Stake Puller

The device illustrated is used for pulling iron stakes or rods out of paved and other streets and was designed by R. S. Miller, manager of the Gas Co., Muncie, Ind. In this case the handle is made of iron, about ⅜x2 in., which also answers for the stand or rest. It may be noticed that the stand has two sharpened studbolts to prevent same from slipping when setting the device preparatory to pulling a rod. The

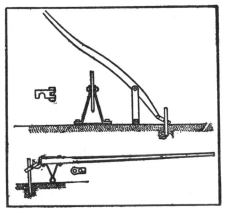

Stake Puller in Operation

toggle is made of forged steel and the opening will take any sized rod by simply varying the angle at which it is applied. This device pulls rods from ½ in. to 1¼ in. with ease, even in well macadamised streets, without in any way disturbing the pavement.

Metal Polish

A good polish for silver, gold or other fine metals is made by mixing a little vaseline with the ashes of burned out or broken gas mantles. Apply with a rag or finger and polish with a clean rag. The result is a superb luster, the best finish being obtained by using a soft rag.—Contributed by Herman Pardeck, 102 Rees St., Chicago.

Keeping a Circular Saw Cool

To keep a saw from heating, the saw teeth and gauge should be suitable to the wood, and the saw should be well sharpened and run at the proper speed. The saw blade should be carefully packed, the feed not crowded and the cut opened out immediately it passes the saw. The saw guide is sometimes continued too far along the face of the saw, and thus crowds and heats the plate through not allowing sufficient room for the wood to open out as it is cut. If the fence extends say 3 in. beyond the roots of the teeth, it is usually enough. Heat is often communicated to a saw through the saw spindle, through the bearings being out of order or screwed up too tight, says Timber Trade Journal. The saw should not fit too tightly on the saw spindle or bind the steady pin. A saw when hung properly should in the horizontal line incline very slightly toward the timber, so that the teeth at the back of the saw may rise without scoring the wood. If the driving pulleys are too small or run at too short centers the bearings will heat.

Average Weight of Telephone Poles

A committee of pole experts reported at a recent convention of dealers the following average weight of poles:

		Pounds.
6 in. 20 ft		190
7 in. 40 ft		850
6 in. 45 ft		900
7 in. 45 ft		1,100
6 in. 50 ft		1,150
7 in. 50 ft		1,350
7 in. 55 ft		1,700
7 in. 60 ft		2,200
7 in. 65 ft		2,500
7 in. 70 ft		3,000

Strength of Grindstones—Wet and Dry

Tests seem to indicate that the strength of a grindstone is considerably reduced when it is wet, says Iron Age. The wetting not only decreases the tensile strength of the material, but it adds weight and thus augments the centrifugal pull at a given peripheral speed. The reduction of strength appears to be as much as 40 or 50 per cent. A dry section of stone broke under a stress of 146 lb. per square inch. Another section of the same stone, soaked over night in water, broke at 80 lb. A better stone, under the same conditions, broke under stresses of 186 lb. per square inch when dry and 116 lb. when wet. Much difference of opinion prevails as to the maximum safe allowable speed at which to operate the stones. Some grinders use a peripheral speed as high as 4,500 ft. per minute, while others limit it to 2,500 ft. Little difference is observed in the liability to breakage, this leading to the conclusion that a frequent cause of breakage must be hidden in flaws or cracks, which would permit the disruption of the stones at the lower speeds.

An Excellent Tracing Paper

Make a mixture of turpentine and mastic varnish in equal parts and apply to separate sheets of double crown tissue paper.

Taking Copies of Medals and Casts

Medals and casts of rare and interesting objects are easily copied and anyone who cares for these things may possess them if he like. The following directions carefully observed will give excellent results:

The material of which the cast is made depends in a measure on the delicacy of the work in hand and whether the impression is in high relief or not. The most delicate impressions are obtained in wax, gutta percha and sulphur, any one of which substances can be used for making moulds.

Suppose a copper medal is to be copied. Smear the face of the medal with a little sweet-oil (olive-oil), applied with the tip of a feather; then rub it over with a piece of cotton-wool, so that the oil covers every minute depression, but collects nowhere. Surround the medal with a slip of cardboard about ½ in. wide, laying the medal flat on a board and wrapping the cardboard tightly around it. Lap the ends of the cardboard and fasten with sealing-wax.

Procure some plaster of paris of the finest quality and freshly prepared. It is sold by the pound and costs very little. For mixing the plaster take a smooth, medium-sized hardwood spoon (never an iron spoon), a small basin and a jug of clean water. To avoid making a mess, lay a board or spread a piece of brown paper on the table. Put some water into the basin and also a small quantity of the plaster, which will soon sink to the bottom. Pour off the water and mix the plaster well, till it is of the consistency of cream. Put a little of this mixture on to the medal, and with a small, stiff brush, held upright, work the plaster into all the hollows of the medal. Then pour in plaster to a depth of ⅜ in. Lift the whole thing, having care not to slip off the cardboard, and rap it sharply on the board once or twice, to set free any air-

bubbles that may exist in the plaster, then allow it to stand for 10 or 15 minutes. By that time the upper surface will be hard. Remove the cardboard, but if the plaster is not fully set, do not lift it off the medal for a few minutes. Freshly made plaster sets quickly, while the older it is the more time it takes to set. The mixed plaster not used may be washed out or thrown away, for it cannot be used a second time. Having made your mould successfully you now have the exact reverse impression of the medal.

In order to take a plaster cast from a plaster mould, the mould must be prepared, so the two will not stick together when one is cast into the other, by oiling. The mould should be almost soaked with the oil, yet oil must not be allowed to collect in the depressions. A mould so prepared hardens, and may be kept for a long time, and have a large number of castings taken from it. When the mould is prepared proceed exactly as before, using the cardboard and plaster.

When taking a mould from a plaster copy of a medal or medallion, where to oil the original would ruin it, sulphur may be used for the mould. Place the original plaster medal in a saucer of water, so that the water does not come above half way up the thickness of the medal. The plaster will absorb the water, therefore watch the face of the medal and immediately it assumes a shiny appearance, remove the medal so no water can percolate through it and collect on the upper surface. In the meantime have some roll sulphur slowly melting by the fire; it must melt very slowly, else it will not become a thin fluid, nor retain its nice yellow color. When this is ready, surround the medal to be copied by the cardboard as before, and pour the sulphur on the face of the medal, allowing no air bubbles to collect between the two. This is not likely to happen if the sulphur has been properly melted and the medal is rapped on the board once or twice. Cover the medal to a depth of ¼ in.; let stand and cool till solid, then lift the casting off the medal. To preserve the sulphur mould against chance of breaking, back it with a ½-in. thickness of plaster of paris, prepared and applied as described. To take a casting from a sulphur mould oil it carefully and then take the plaster cast from it in the usual manner.

From copper, bronze, or other metals, gutta-percha moulds may be taken. They are durable, elastic, and easily managed. The gutta-percha must be boiled, when it is so soft that it can be moulded into any shape, and can be pressed and worked onto the face of a medal so as to secure the minutest impression; but it must be allowed to get quite cold and hard before it is removed.

For low relief and medals of delicate tracery, wax (or paraffin) is a good substance to take impressions in. Ordinary white wax, or paraffin (the ends of candles will do) must be melted carefully, and must be kept very clean, and when melted the process to be followed is exactly the same as that for using sulphur. Remember that wax is very slow in cooling.

To take copies of solid objects, like the cast of a head, or of an animal, or a vase, the mould must be taken in pieces, so that when tied together the inside mould is an exact counterpart of the object. This requires a little more skill than taking the flat medal, and in attempting it it is best to look at such a mould in the workshop of a professional, where one will at once be able to see how the parts are cast and held together.

A polish on the surface of medals can be secured by the following method: Cut some white curd soap into fine shavings with a clean, sharp knife; then make it into a strong solution. Immerse the face of the medal, or whatever it is to be polished, in it several times, but let it dry between each dip. It will then take a good polish on being rubbed briskly and lightly with a piece of cotton-wool.

It will also have the smoothness and whiteness of marble.

The copies may be painted if liked, or may be bronzed by covering with a thin coat of gold size, then sprinkling bronze powder over them.

Bas-reliefs can be cast in the manner described and may be put together so as to form pedestals for ornaments. Brackets may also be made in plaster, taking castings from real fruit and leaves. In taking a cast of fruit or solid object, it must be partially buried in fine white sand just sufficiently moistened to hold it together; then a frame of cardboard can be put round the projecting part, and a cast taken. When the plaster is set, the portion of the fruit that was buried can be cast in the same manner. Oil well the edge of the mould first taken, so that the second portion may easily separate from it.

Pickling Castings

Hydrofluoric acid as a cleaning agent for castings has been in general use but a short time, being treated a few years ago as a secret process by those who understood its value and made use of it in removing the clinging sand. Formulas for the acid containing superfluous and innocuous ingredients to mystify the purchaser have been sold for considerable sums, says the Iron Age.

Anything used in connection with this "pickle" aside from the hydrofluoric acid and water, is wholly unnecessary, the usual formula being 1 part of acid to 10 of water. In adding water, however, care should be taken to know the strength of the raw acid, as this is by no means uniform. The idea is to get a dip that will remove the sand perfectly and quickly, the operation requiring 10 to 15 minutes, depending upon both the amount of sand to be removed and the condition of the pickle. The most practical tanks for performing this operation are those constructed of wood and lined with lead.

SHOP NOTES

Emergency Pipe Wrench

A file, cold chisel and monkey wrench make a very efficient pipe wrench, except when the pipe is too large such as a 5- or 6-in. pipe. In such emergencies the device here illustrated will be found very effective, says

Emergency Pipe Wrench

the American Miller. Take 3 or 4 ft. of new rope. Fray out both ends thin and put them together. Commence with tip ends and wrap tightly around the pipe until you have a loop. Then with a piece of pipe or a round bar for a lever, turn the pipe as you would with a pipe wrench.

Repair for a Jack-Screw

To repair a broken jack-screw, which has been cracked at the base, cut off the lower part, as indicated by the dotted line and insert in a piece of extra heavy pipe flared out at the bottom. If desired a set-screw

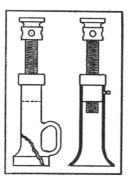

or steel pin may be used to hold the pipe to the remaining portion of the base and if an old flange the same size as the pipe is available it may be used instead of flaring.—Contributed by G. A. B., Chicago.

Device for Removing Underground Pipe

The removal of bored well castings, vertical pipes and other underground objects is often a difficult task but can be accomplished in many cases by using the device here illustrated. Two pieces of spring steel, S, are welded to the end of an iron rod, R, and formed in the shape of a catch at the ends. The device is pushed down through the pipe, P, until the catches engage with the lower end as shown.—Contributed by C. R. M.

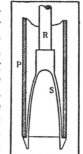

Chimney Top to Improve Draft

The illustration shows a device for increasing the draft of a chimney and for preventing a reverse draft, which usually occurs when a chimney is located near a high building. In making this device, says a correspondent of the Metal Worker, it is necessary to run a joint of pipe above the top of the chimney. Near the top of this pipe run two horizontal braces, one above the other, for the purpose of fastening a vertical rod, extending about 6 in. above the top of the pipe and terminating in an eye at the top. A conical cap is then made of sheet iron and fastened to the end of the rod by means of a second eye, which passes through the eye at the end of the rod. This allows the wind to tilt the cap in any direction, thus

preventing the wind from blowing down the flue of the chimney. The wind in passing then causes the cap to act like an inspirator and draws air up through the flue.

The "Old Man" and Ratchet Drill

Just why this device is called the "Old Man" is an obscure bit of machine shop mythology beyond the knowledge of the writer, says a correspondent of the Blacksmith and Wheelwright.

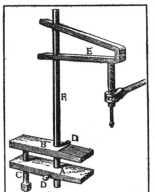

It is easily made in the shop and can be applied to a wide range of work. The device consists of the clamp pieces, A and B, which can be made of bar iron, or of malleable iron castings. The size of these clamp pieces depends entirely upon the work to be done. For the smith shop, a bit of 1x4 in. bar steel (Bessemer) will answer, but for large work the clamps are sometimes made 3 in. thick by 8 in. wide. The set screw, C, may be 1x6 in. The bar, or shaft, F, should be about $1\frac{1}{2}$ in. in diameter for a length of 3 ft., or 2 in. for 4 ft. in length and for small drills. The set screws, D D, may be $\frac{1}{2}$ in. or $\frac{5}{8}$ in. or they may be placed in collars and slipped upon the shaft above and below the clamp pieces, A and B.

The drill-piece, E, may be made of $\frac{3}{4}$x3 in. bar iron or steel, or a heavy knee casting may be provided for this piece, as desired. The ratchet is one of the familiar type on sale at any hardware store, and it should be fitted with square shank drills. Do not try to make a ratchet drill; that tool can be purchased much cheaper than made, and five or six dollars will procure a good one.

Cement to Render Cisterns and Casks Watertight

An excellent cement for resisting moisture is made by incorporating thoroughly 8 parts melted glue, of the consistence used by carpenters, with 4 parts linseed oil boiled into varnish with litharge. This cement hardens in about 48 hours and renders the joints of wooden cisterns and casks air and watertight.—Contributed by Frank Pavlik, Jr., Winnetka, Ill.

Waterproof Glue

Dissolve gum shellac, 3 parts, and India rubber, 1 part, by weight, in separate vessels in ether, free from alcohol, subject to a gentle heat. When thoroughly dissolved, mix the two solutions and keep in a tightly sealed vessel. This glue resists the action of hot and cold water, and most acids and alkalies. If thinned with ether and applied to leather along sewn seams it gives a strong watertight joint.

Jack Cart

The accompanying illustration from Railway and Locomotive Engineering shows a jack cart which is very convenient, being simple in construction, light and inexpensive.

It sets low on the floor, thus doing away with the necessity of two men handling a jack of any size; it also permits running the jack right up to the spot where it is to be set. The material necessary to make this cart consists of a few pieces of gas pipe, boiler iron, two small wheels and material enough for a small axle.

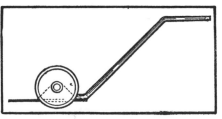

Simple Jack Cart

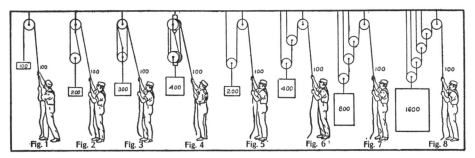

Various Arrangements of Pulley Blocks Showing Lifting Power

Lifting Power with Pulley Blocks

A man pulling with a force of 100 lb. can lift only that amount with a single block, as shown in Fig. 1, but by using two single blocks he can lift double the amount, as indicated in Fig. 2. By using a double block above and a single block below, as shown in Fig. 3, 100 lb. pull on the rope will lift 300 lb. and by using two double blocks, as indicated in Fig. 4, 100 lb. will lift 400 lb.

In Fig. 1 the load is supported directly by one rope; in Fig. 2 by two ropes; in Fig. 3 by three and in Fig. 4 by four ropes; the weight being 100, 200, 300 and 400 lb. respectively. Thus with pulley blocks arranged in this way the weight that can be raised is in direct proportion to the number of ropes that support it. In these calculations the portion of rope which the man holds is ignored, as he pulls in a direction opposite to the movement of the weight, but should he take his position above the pulleys and pull up, then the rope which he holds should be counted also.

Another system of arranging pulleys is shown in Figs. 5, 6, 7 and 8, the pulley blocks being all single. In an arrangement of this kind the power is just doubled by the addition of each pulley as indicated by the figures. In all these calculations no allowance has been made for friction so that the actual force required to lift the given weights will be somewhat greater, the exact amount depending on the flexibility of the rope, diameter of pulleys, smoothness of the bearings and other conditions.

To Recover Lost Drill Points

When drill points are lost, even at considerable depth, they can be recovered by means of an electro-magnet. A heavy drill point stuck in a well at a depth of 250 ft. was loosened and brought to the surface in this way.

Keeping an Engine Cylinder Warm

A plan for keeping an engine cylinder warmed up in case it is standing idle part of the time, especially in cold weather, is to tap a pipe into the main steam pipe above the throttle valve, the same size as the bleeder drain pipe, as shown in the illustration. To operate, open valves B and B, and slightly open

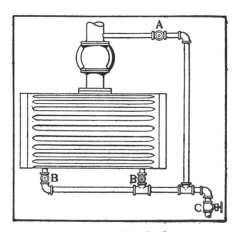

Arrangement of the By-Pass

the valve C, and then open wide the valve A, says a correspondent of the Engineers' Review. The steam will find its way all through the cylinder and steam chest and the condensation will pass away through the valve C.

Pipe Hangers

The accompanying illustration from the Practical Machinist shows a few practical suggestions for supporting pipes from I-beams. The most common form is shown at A and is used

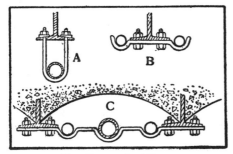

Pipe Hangers for I-Beams

for supporting a pipe directly under the beam. When pipes are to be run on each side of a beam the form of hanger shown at B may be used, unless the pipes are some distance from the beam, when it will be necessary to use the form shown at C.

Home-Made Bromide Paper

When the photographer receives a rush order for a bromide enlargement from a negative and has no bromide paper on hand, nor can procure any as soon as required, the following expedient will help him out of his difficulty: Prepare a 2½ per cent solution of potassium bromide and place a sheet of ordinary printing-out paper in it, allowing it to float for two or three minutes. Then remove the paper and hang it up to dry in such position that warm air circulates freely about it. Paper thus prepared requires about double the exposure of the regular kind, and the results are satisfactory,

says Camera Craft, for the coarse screen effects of newspaper reproductions.

Hardening Drills

Hardening an ordinary drill in sulphuric acid makes an edge that will cut tempered steel or facilitate cutting hard rock, says Compressed Air. The acid should be poured into a flat-bottomed vessel to a depth of about ⅛ in. The point of the drill is heated to a dull cherry red, and dipped in the acid to that depth. This makes the point extremely hard, while the remainder remains soft. If the point breaks, reharden but with a little less acid in the vessel. After hardening a drill in this manner, wipe off the acid, if any remains on the point of the drill, before it attacks the metal and destroys the cutting edge.

Red Copper Bronze on Tin

Dissolve 9 dr. copper sulphate in pure water to saturation; then add 40 to 80 drops sulphuric acid. Brush the tin, previously cleansed with onion juice, with the liquid. When dry, rub the article with chalk.

To Drill Glass

Use a drill like the one shown and temper by heating to a cherry red and plunging in mercury. Drill part way through from one side and then finish from the opposite side. This will make a good clean cut and prevent chipping the edges of the hole. Apply sufficient pressure to make the drill "bite" at all times, and keep the drill point moistened with 2 parts turpentine to 1 part sweet oil.—Contributed by H. W. Snook, Prof. Optics, Scottsbluff, Neb.

To Fasten Celluloid to Wood or Tin

Celluloid can be fastened to wood, tin, etc., by the use of the following compound: Shellac, 2 parts; spirits of camphor, 3 parts; strong alcohol, 4 parts.

A Large Vertical Drawing Board

The accompanying illustration from the Metal-Worker shows a large vertical drawing board that is very useful for making large drawings.

For Making Large Drawings

A pair of bearings are screwed to the top edge of the board, through which passes a rod or piece of small shafting, running the entire length of the board and extending sufficiently beyond at each end to receive a pair of sprocket wheels. Chain belts are attached to each end of the movable straight edge and are passed over the sprocket wheels and attached to a pair of counter weights sufficiently heavy to balance the weight of the straight edge when at the position most used. As both sprockets are firmly keyed to the shaft, any movement at one end of the straight edge insures an equal amount of motion at the other. Sprocket wheels and chains of the type used on bicycles will be satisfactory for the purpose, though chains of lighter weight, such as those used for hanging pictures, if constructed without play, will perhaps be more desirable. A small clip or slide fixed to the projecting ends of the straight edge at the back and

passing behind or under the edges of the board will prevent the straight edge from lifting away from the face of the board.

Monel=Metal

An alloy called "Monel-Metal," says Brass World, consists of:

	Per cent.
Nickel	75.0
Copper	23.5
Iron	1.5

The alloy possesses a high tensile strength and elastic limit. It is also non-corrosive and takes a high polish. The color is practically that of nickel.

Home=Made Steam Separator

There are numerous plants where a steam separator would prove a paying investment, but the purchasing power refuses to buy one. Although this be so the engineer need not be discouraged, because he can make one on the premises, says the National Engineer. Take for example an engine with a 5-in. steam supply, with the main supply from the boiler 6 in. As near as possible to the engine use a 6x5x6 long

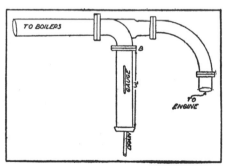

Home-Made Separator

sweep flanged tee. To the opening, B (see illustration), connect a 6-in. pipe, with a cap on it, and a 1-in. outlet.

As the steam from the boiler passes through the 6-in. pipe its velocity is somewhat slower than that which will occur in the 5-in. pipe, especially when the engine load is heavy. The water in the steam pipe is carried along the lower end of the pipe, and as it comes to the long sweep tee it will naturally seek the pipe B, from which it can be drained.

For sizes less than 4 in. screwed fittings will answer. For piping with a vertical riser close to the engine a double sweep is recommended as herewith shown. With the home-made separator, or in fact any make of separator, the engineer should insist on having a first class trap, one that will care for a large volume of water instantaneously and without possibility of failure.

Hand Knurling Tool

The advantages of a tool like this are obvious: stock can be knurled to the full capacity, and to less than $\frac{1}{8}$ in. diameter; lengths can also be fin-

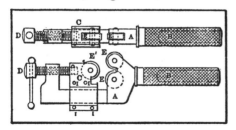

Used Without a Tool Post

ished, which is not possible with the ordinary style. It is not dependent on a tool post, says the American Machinist, as it is held in the hand and a speed lathe or any other will answer.

The body, A, is one piece with the handle, B. The sliding part, C, is made in two parts and riveted over A. This is adjusted to accommodate the stock by the screw, D. EEE are the knurling rolls. II are rivets. A hole is drilled in the handle to lighten it. The tool is held in the hand, by the handle, B. The stock is placed between the rolls at H. Then the part C is adjusted until the three rolls come in contact with the piece to be knurled. By working the tool back and forth, and by applying pressure with the screw D the piece is soon knurled.

Easily Made Pipe Vise

The sketch shows how I made a pipe vise from an old carpenter's vise. Take an old coarse rasp; break it in half and draw the temper at the ends to allow drilling and countersinking for screws, which should be used to fasten the two halves to the jaws of the vise as

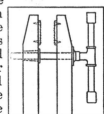

shown. Fasten one with the teeth pointing up and the other with the teeth down.—Contributed by C. J. Barton, Big Rapids, Mich.

Double Belts

There are many who think that a long belt drives better than a short one, and under certain conditions it may, but under other conditions the advantages are very doubtful. Take the case where the drive is nearly horizontal, says a correspondent of the Wood-Worker, and the pull is on the top side; you have the slack side of the belt dropping away from the driven pulley, and, of course, less gripping surface—and with a long belt there is a lot of slack to drop away—so that I fancy it is a disadvantage rather than an advantage to have a long belt. In cases where it is necessary to drive under these conditions it would be an improvement to use compound belts—that is, one on top of the other. The action

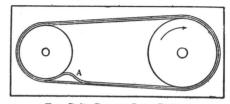

Two Belts Run on Same Pulley

is peculiar, for the belt next the pulley rises and clings to the driven pulley, as shown at A, when the strain comes on, giving more gripping surface. I have watched that action frequently, and feel certain that the grip is increased very much.

Blueprint Drying Frame

When blueprints are required in a hurry the drying frame shown in the accompanying illustration from the Railway Review will prove very useful. A white pine latticed frame was constructed on which a large piece of blotting paper is placed to receive the wet print.

The wet prints on the upper side of the frame and the intense heat of the radiator about $2\frac{1}{4}$ in. beneath the lower side made a specially strong construction necessary to resist the warping and buckling strains due to the difference in temperatures.

The frame is 48 in. long by 30 in. wide. It is composed of strips $\frac{3}{4}$ in. wide halved and screwed at all intersections and spaced $2\frac{1}{2}$ in. apart in centers. The recesses cut in each strip are bolted together in a manner so substantial that buckling is impossible. The frame is finished with shellac. The height above the floor is 32 in. when the table is down ready for service. The frame is hinged and equipped with hooks and eyes so that it folds back against the wall when not in use.

Lamp Cement

A useful cement for fastening the tops on kerosene lamps is as follows: One part caustic soda; 5 parts water; mix with one-half the weight of plaster of paris.—Contributed by Frank Pavlik, Winnetka, Ill.

Emergency Boiler Repair

Temporary repairs on a boiler will often save considerable trouble and expense until permanent repairs can be

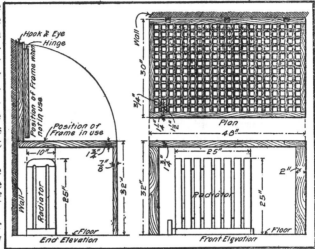

Will Dry Blueprints in a Few Minutes

made. The following is a job of this sort which proved successful:

The leak was in a seam of a butt-strap joint, and two 1-in. holes were drilled through the butt strap with a flat end drill, care being taken not to damage the shell itself. These holes were threaded to the bottom with gas taps, and were spaced twice the distance apart that they were from the extreme end of the leak.

Red lead putty was then prepared smooth as oil, free from grit and not too thick. Round iron rods were threaded to fit the holes already bored and a square end filed to take a wrench, the whole apparatus being termed a "putty pump."

One hole was half filled with putty and the threaded bar screwed down with the wrench; the operation was repeated with the other hole, and then with the holes alternately until no more putty could be squeezed in. Putty could be seen squeezed through around the seams and between the plates, and plugs were then screwed down hard to the taper threads and cut off flush. The boiler was left for a day or two to let the putty harden, and was then put into condition and used for several months. This method is not to be recommended for a permanent repair, says the American Machinist, but for an emergency job it will answer the purpose until a permanent repair can be made.

Non=Rolling Penholder

When working on a drawing table turned up at an angle, considerable annoyance is often caused by penholders and other round tools. They will not stay on the board.

Penholder with End Bent

If you are using a hard rubber holder you can get around the difficulty very easily. Heat the holder over a lamp or in the flame of a match. Then bend the end back slightly as shown in the accompanying illustration. This will overcome the tendency to roll.— Contributed by Wm. E. Jehn, Paterson, N. J.

How to Read a Vernier Scale

A vernier is an instrument used in taking fine measurements, some as fine

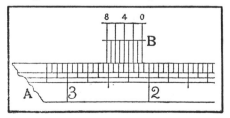

Vernier Scale

as 1/1,000 in. The one shown in the sketch consists of a true scale, indicated at A, and the vernier, shown at B. The vernier is $\frac{7}{8}$ in, divided into eight equal parts; thus when the vernier is used in connection with the true scale, as shown in the sketch, the true scale is subdivided into 128 parts —16 on the true scale $\times$ 8 on the vernier, equals 128.

To read the units and subdivisions of the vernier in the position here illustrated the Wood-Worker gives the following instructions: Beginning with the zero line on the vernier, we find that the line at the end of the third space coincides with a line on the true scale. As each space on the vernier counts 1/128 in. on the true scale, we have 3/128 in. to be added to the reading of the true scale, which will be $2\frac{7}{8}$ in. plus 3/128 in. equals 2 11/128 in., the reading of the vernier, and shows that the zero line of the vernier is 2 11/128 in. from the end of the true scale.

Thoroughly Dried Wood Nearly Fireproof

Many people believe the longer a stick or piece of wood is dried the more inflammable it becomes, but beyond the first thorough drying process this is not true, says Wood Craft.

After wood has been exposed to moderate heat for a long time it becomes partly oxidized and approaches a little nearer the nature of coal, many of the highly inflammable and volatile elements of the new wood having slowly passed away.

The first proof of this fact ever brought to the writer's attention was during the repairing of an old dry kiln. The timbers were very dry and brittle and someone remarked how easily it could be ignited. A piece was tried and to our astonishment it could scarcely be made to blaze at all The fire seemed disposed to hang to it very well though and it burned slowly like punk. The wood, however, seemed to have lost nearly all its elasticity. It appears that those elements in the wood that give to it springiness and elasticity are the very highly inflammable ones and they are also the ones to depart first.

Sustaining Strength of Ice

Two in. thick, a man.
Four in. thick, man on horseback.
Ten in. thick, crowd.
Fifteen in. thick, a railway train.

To Find the Length of Band Iron

To find the length of iron for a band: Take a 2-ft. rule; measure up from the hinged ends 3 13-16 in.; draw a line across as shown in the illustration and open the rule to once

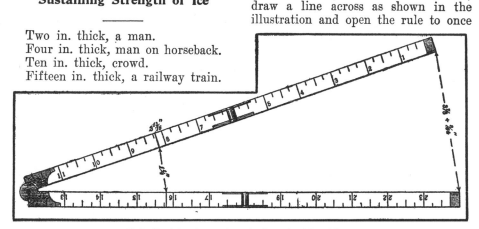

Rule Used for Computing the Length of Band Iron

Universal Soldering Fluid

A soldering fluid which will not rust or corrode the soldered parts is made by dissolving as much zinc in muriatic acid as the acid will take up and then adding water, glycerine and alcohol. To one part glycerine add one part alcohol and one part water; then add two parts of acid with the zinc dissolved. This fluid has been used for all kinds of soldering, says the Street Railway Journal, and has been found especially desirable with greasy or dirty connections as well as for soldering to iron. It is claimed that the glycerine prevents all rust, which plays havoc with many soldering fluids which contain muriatic acid.

Composition of Solders

Fine solder is an alloy of two parts of block tin and one part of lead. Glazing solder is equal parts of block tin and lead. Plumbing solder, one part block tin and two parts lead.

To make a cheap fireproof wash dissolve 1½ lb. salt in 1 gal. whitewash.

the width of the diameter plus once the thickness of the iron, from the inside points, says a correspondent of the American Blacksmith. Then measure the distance between the end of the rule from the inside corners as shown, which will be the length of your iron. If measured right you will find this correct. In case the diameter of the band plus the thickness of the iron is 1¼ in., as shown in the illustration, the length of the piece must be 3⅞+3-64 in., as shown.

Splicing Broken Armature Parts

A method of splicing broken armature shafts which is proving satisfactory has been developed at the Columbus, O., shops of the Indiana, Columbus & Eastern Traction Company. Shafts broken near the gear or on the taper at the pinion end are easily repaired so that the armature may be used until it is necessary to tear down the winding for some other reason.

The method of making this splice is simple, says Electric Railway Review. The broken end of the shaft is turned down in the form of a cone, longitudinal grooves being cut in its surface. After this is done another piece of shaft steel is hollowed out, cup-shape, to fit the taper snugly. One-fourth of an inch of spelter is placed in the bottom of the cup. The two parts are fitted together and placed in a screw jack or wheel press and are then heated by means of a coke air blast flame which is made to circle around the shaft. As the parts to be spliced are heated pressure is applied through the screw jack and the spelter is forced from the bottom of the cup to all parts of the taper. When the shoulders of the two pieces are brought together the weld is complete. The shaft is then placed in the lathe centers and trued. The method described has been used very successfully and in many instances the welded shafts are still in use after several months of severe wear.

Exhaust Muffler and Heater

The accompanying illustration shows how the feed water was heated in a small plant. The exhaust from the pump was brought into a barrel, as shown, and in order to avoid the cracking noise, which usually takes place when steam is condensed in cold water, a wooden box was built around the pipe. This box is about 8 in. square, says a correspondent of the Engineers' Review, and the top is kept below the surface of the water in the barrel about

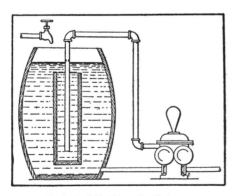

Method of Muffling the Exhaust

1 in. In a few minutes the water in this pipe becomes hot and then all noise ceases. The hot water overflows and cold water enters over the top, thus making a noiseless heater. A small $\frac{1}{16}$ in. hole is drilled in the exhaust pipe close to the water in the barrel to avoid a vacuum in the pipe when the pump is stopped.

Air Cylinder Converted Into Post= Hammer

An old air brake cylinder makes an excellent post-hammer when arranged as shown in the accompanying sketch. The object of the home-made appliance is to straighten brake rods, hangers,

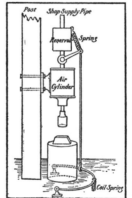

bent bars of iron, or do any kind of work where a few well directed blows of a fairly heavy hammer are needed, says Railway and Locomotive Engineering.

From the upper cylinder head a pipe comes off and supports a 3-way plug cock, which opens and shuts to let air into the cylinder or exhausts it according as it is moved to inlet or exhaust positions. The supply pipe above the plug cock runs up to a reservoir into which the air supply of the shop is piped. The object of the reservoir above is to keep a sufficient quantity of air close at hand to fill the cylinder quickly without making the shop supply pipe gasp for air every time the hammer strikes a blow.

The plug cock is arranged with its handle connected to a long rod which hangs down nearly to the ground, and to this long rod is attached a piece of $\frac{3}{4}$-in. curved pipe hinged at each end to form a treadle.

A good polishing powder consists of 4 lb. magnesium carbonate, 4 lb. chalk and 4 lb. rouge, intimately mixed.

Luminous Ink

Shines in the dark. Phosphorus, 1 dr.; oil cinnamon, ½ oz. Mix in a vial, cork tightly, heat slowly until mixed. A letter written with this ink can only be read in a dark room, when the writing will have the appearance of fire.—Contributed by Frank Pavlik, Winnetka, Ill.

A Ready Wire Stretcher

For stretching barbed or other wire in long lengths the farm wagon is a very handy and efficient tool. One of the rear wheels is raised from the ground and the wire is passed once around the hub and fastened to a spoke of the wheel. The wagon is then braced by any suitable means and the wheel turned in the manner of a mariner's wheel. In this way a pull of 100 lb. on the tire will exert a force of 400 or 500 lb. on the wire.—Contributed by Experimenter.

Iron Brackets for Pumps

The pump foundations in many plants are only high enough to serve the purpose for which they were intended, little thought being given for convenience and accessibility. Therefore, the under portion of the pump is seldom cleaned and in many cases the top is covered with filth.

In the plant where I am employed we have done away with foundations for small pumps, says a correspondent of the Engineers' Review. Instead they are placed on brackets made of a suitable size of iron. The brackets are bolted to the wall of the room where the pumps are located and at a sufficient distance above the floor to permit of an easy access.

The illustration shows the manner in which the pumps are arranged. It will be seen that the floor underneath

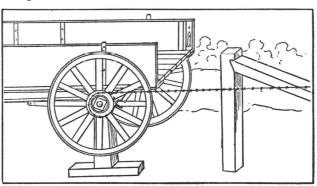

Ready Wire Puller

the pump can be kept clean without any trouble, and that it is an easy matter to thoroughly wipe the entire surface of the pump. I have never seen any arrangement which gives as much satisfaction as this method of placing a pump.

Paper Cambric Screens

Draughtsmen who are obliged to work at south windows find the glare of the sun on clear days a great inconvenience. The light is too dazzling with the shade rolled up and when it is drawn down there is not enough light to work by. This difficulty is sometimes overcome by tacking a piece of muslin over the window frame, but a better way is to use a shade made of white paper cambric. This material is inexpensive, very transparent and, unlike muslin, is not easily soiled, as it has a glazed surface

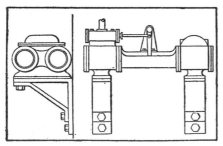

Pump Supported on Bracket Irons

very much like tracing cloth, which is also suitable for this purpose. The price of tracing cloth is, however, about three times as much as that of paper cambric.—Contributed by W. H. G., New York City.

A Shop=Made Trip=Hammer

This machine, which was made at a very small cost, saves much labor and time and is very useful, especially for drawing-out purposes. The manufacture of this machine, which was built

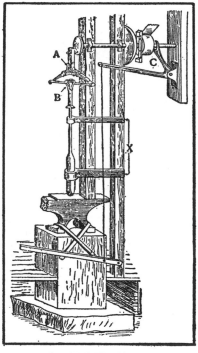

Shop-Made Trip-Hammer

by a correspondent of the American Blacksmith, is described as follows:

"After picking out a place for its location, I dug down about 3 ft. and placed a large stone. Upon this I erected a good, solid anvil-block, and upon the block I fastened an old anvil which was minus the horn. I then took two pieces of 4 by 4-in. timber and placed one stick directly behind the anvil and fastened it solidly to the

floor and roof. The other piece was placed on the anvil, as shown, and run from here to the roof. I now secured a short shaft and, after placing thereon in the order mentioned a flywheel 18 in. in diameter, a good, stout coil spring and a belt pulley, on the end of which was fastened a piece of flat stock bearing on each of its ends a hardwood block, placed it well up on the uprights. I then run a short, stout piece of timber from the roof, to support the pulley end of the shaft. To the other end I now fastened a small flywheel, which would give me a 3-in. stroke. For the hammer I used an old shaft, to one end of which I welded a tool steel face similar in form to the pene end of a sledge. For the spring I used a five-leaf buggy spring, with the long leaf and loops on the outside. I then took two pieces of ¼-in. stock the same width as this spring and bent them, as shown at A in the engraving, fastening them in the center of the spring by means of four clips. The connecting rod then joins the spring to the small flywheel. I placed guides on the uprights, as shown at X, the lower guide being about 10 in. above the anvil. To connect the foot lever with the clutch pulley I forged a Y-rod, as at C, and connected it by means of a lever and a rod, as shown in the engraving."

Waterproof Ink

An ink suitable for inscriptions on stone, tombs, or other place where dampness may attack is made as follows: Pitch, 11 lb.; lampblack, 1 lb.; turpentine sufficient to make soluble. Mix with heat.—Contributed by Frank Pavlik, Jr., Winnetka, Ill.

To Restore Color to Aluminum

To restore gray or unsightly aluminum to its white color, wash with a solution of 30 parts borax in 1,000 parts water, with a few drops of ammonia added.

SUCCESSFUL LONG MAIN HOT WATER SYSTEM

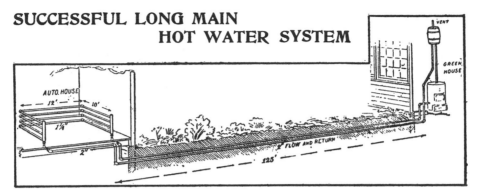

A Successful Long Main Hot Water Heating System

As there are many failures in long-distance heating systems the following successful arrangement may be of value to some readers. In this case the heater is 125 ft. from the radiating coil. The success of the system depends largely on the elevated receptacle. In this case the flow main was carried up from the heater to a barrel. Any other receptacle would serve the same purpose, says a correspondent of the Metal Worker, provided it was located twice the height above the boiler as the drop of the main is below the boiler. The piping must be direct from the boiler to the barrel, then from the barrel to the specially made header coil. This heating system has been working with perfect satisfaction for the past two winters. The header coil is likely to be the cause of trouble if it is not made to form at least one angle, so that the unequal expansion of the hotter pipes at the top and the colder pipes at the bottom may be compensated for in the spring of the piping.

◆ ◆ ◆

File for Maps or Other Drawings

The usual method of suspending maps from the ceiling not only presents a very untidy appearance but causes rapid destruction of the drawing due to rough handling and allows them to become dirty in a very short time. The device here illustrated is recommended by a correspondent of the American Telephone Journal to overcome many of the disadvantages of the method mentioned.

It is nothing more than an ordinary table with a box arrangement mounted on each end, in which is fitted a roller with a handle so that it can be rotated conveniently. A drum made of zinc is fitted onto the roller. A heavy grade of linen cloth attached to both drums moves over the surface of the table as the rollers rotate. On this linen cloth are mounted the cable layout maps or other drawings. The boxes have lids so that access can be had to the rollers in case they need adjusting. As the drawings are mounted on the linen cloth they are numbered consecutively and a list is

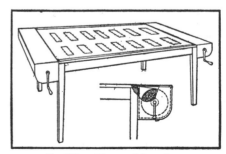

For Filing Maps and Drawings

pasted on one of the lids giving the name and corresponding number of the various drawings so as to facilitate the manipulation of the rollers in locating any particular drawing.

This table can also be used for the purpose of keeping record of the work in hand. Diagrams of the work to be done can be mounted on the linen cloth and as it progresses it can be checked off. When the work has been completed the diagram can be removed from the cloth with the aid of a wet sponge.

To Convert a Gas Engine Into an Air Compressor

Any gas engine of ordinary design can be converted into a fairly efficient air compressor by making a few alterations and additions. If the engine is of the 2-cycle type remove the spark plug and replace with a check valve as shown in the sketch at A. The exhaust may be plugged up with an ordinary pipe plug, B although this is not absolutely necessary.

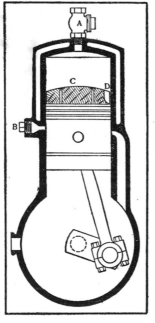

In order to reduce the space of the compression chamber and thereby increase the efficiency of the compressor fasten a block of wood on the end of piston as shown at C. This should be of a shape to conform to the top of the cylinder which it should nearly touch when the engine crank is placed on the dead center. In order to avoid obstructing the passage of the air from the inlet port it will be necessary to cut a small cavity in the block as shown at D.

If a 4-cycle engine is used to make the compressor it will be necessary to remove the exhaust valve. It is also a good plan to disconnect the gear in order to prevent noise and unnecessary operation of moving parts. A check valve should be placed on the exhaust, as near the engine as possible and a block of wood similar to that used in the 2-cycle engine should be fastened to the piston. If there are two cylinders on the engine, one may be converted into a compressor as described above and the other used for furnishing power.—Contributed by J. S. Kemp, Chicago.

How to Hang Canvas and Burlap

Raphael Pedretti, in the Master Painter, gives his method as follows:

Our process of applying muslin, or canvas, as it is sometimes termed, is pure and simple handwork. We do not use a brush to paste nor a paperhanger's brush to smooth out the material on the wall.

Ten quarter heavy unbleached muslin is used which is 7 to $7\frac{1}{2}$ ft. in width. The selvage is ripped off, for if left on will show ridges in your work.

It is then soaked in a wooden tub of paste (with a board with a hole in it nailed to the tub) in strips the length of the width of the room.

The muslin is then drawn up through the knot-hole, which removes all the loose paste. When the muslin, thus soaked, is placed on the ceiling, it is thoroughly scraped and rescraped with broad knives and painters' scrapers until all the superfluous paste is removed.

When dry, all blisters, stains and extraordinary cracking of the plaster and mottling of painted walls often seen, caused by the improper gauging of the plaster, is eliminated forever, and nothing can dislodge or disturb the canvas so treated. Burlap, both the lining and dyed, should be thoroughly worked onto the walls with the hands. After applying the paste first to the walls and then to the burlap, if thoroughly worked out with the hands, not using a brush to smooth it out, it will stay out, you will not be aggravated by seeing the butts pull apart and corners turn up or by receiving a hurry telephone call from some fair client to come out and look at your poorly executed work.

Our method of lining walls is somewhat expensive, but it is thorough and reliable. In preparing the walls I wish to say we invariably use the alum size, for we find that we can use it heavier and stronger; it dries harder and nothing softens or disturbs it.

There is nothing so essential in producing good results, in decorative work, as lining walls, for it not only covers up many defects in the plastering, but gives the coloring a soft and brilliant effect, and is very durable if in the last coat a little beeswax is used with the zinc, making what we call an encaustic finish.

How to Make a Pocket Knife

"A thing of beauty is a joy forever" except when it comes to buying a 25-cent pocket knife that was made to sell. A home-made knife while somewhat crude in appearance is very serviceable if well made.

To make the handle take a piece of $\frac{3}{8}$-in. round iron and flatten out a piece

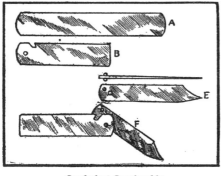

Crude but Serviceable

about 9 in. long and $\frac{3}{4}$ in. wide. Then bend it double, B, till there is just sufficient room for the blade to go in between. Now bore the rivet hole and you are ready to make the blade. Old files make very good blades, says a correspondent of the American Blacksmith, but most of the blades I make

are of old hay-rake teeth. These are about $\frac{3}{8}$ in. thick. I flatten out and shape roughly, then cut off a piece for a blade and anneal it. I do this by heating red and burying it in warm wood ashes till it cools. Then it drills easily and you can grind it down nearly to a finish. You want two holes in the blade, one for the rivet on which the blade turns, the other to receive a rivet which is to act as a stop when the knife is open. After finishing the blade, E, and tempering, assemble in the handle as shown at F.

Balanced Valve Stem for Pump

Pumps often give trouble because of

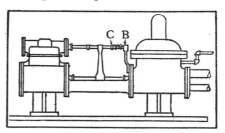

Pump with Spring to Balance Pressure

an unequal pressure within the steam chest acting on the area of the steam valve, or the valve stem. As the valve stem extends through only one side of the steam chest there is a constant tendency to blow it out. To overcome this trouble a correspondent of the Practical Engineer recommends the use of a coil spring between the bracket B and the collar C in the illustration. The spring should be given sufficient tension to counterbalance the action of the steam acting on the area of the valve stem. While the action of the steam is to force the valve stem out of the chest, the spring forces it in again, and, therefore, the forces are neutralized and the valve stem stays where it is left by the tappet arm.

To make can varnish, dissolve 15 parts shellac, 2 parts Venice turpentine and 8 parts sandarac, all by weight, in 75 parts spirit, by weight.

SHOP NOTES

Handy Keg Carrier

The illustration shows a two-wheel truck for picking up and carrying nail kegs or other small heavy objects. The handles and jaws may be made of iron

Easily Made; Very Handy

or the handles may be made of wood and bolted on the jaws. One handle is held in a stationary position by means of a brace, B, shown in the detail sketch. The jaws should be curved up near the axle so as to lie parallel with the floor when the handles are held in the hands.—Contributed by Experimenter.

How to Calk Pipes Under Water

One way is to use "lead wool," a substance consisting of minute fibers of

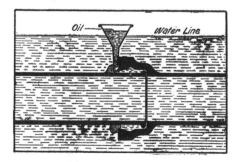

Ready to Pour

lead, which on being compressed form a solid mass. But when this cannot be obtained the apparatus shown in the accompanying sketch will permit pouring melted lead in the usual manner, unless the water level is too high. An ordinary funnel is used for the purpose and is arranged in position as shown in the sketch. Oil is then poured in the funnel, thus displacing the water and preventing the melted lead from touching the water until it has passed through the oil. This gives the melted lead a greasy surface which prevents the water from coming in actual contact with it and allows it to fill the cavity. The lead can then be calked in the usual manner.—Contributed by C. E. Thomas, Chicago.

To Tighten Threads in a Cap

Here is a good way to tighten a screw cap or cover for a bottle, jar, or other article. If the cap does not hold, put it over the end of a round stick and with a nail, or, better, a center punch, make small dents in the thread about $\frac{1}{4}$ in. apart. This makes the thread deeper and will usually hold very well.—Contributed by E. N. Bunce, 1050 Kilbourne Ave., Seattle, Wash., Fremont Station.

To write on celluloid or celluloidin paper, first rub the face of the paper with a chalk crayon and wipe the dust off with a clean cloth.

Cheap Reflector for Incandescent Lamp

A very good reflector for electric light bulbs, lantern globes, lamp chimneys, etc., is made as follows: With pen and ink lay out a circle on the

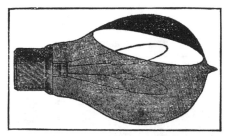

Aluminum Lacquer Reflector

bulb or chimney the size of the reflecting surface desired. Then give this section of the bulb two coats of aluminum lacquer or aluminum enamel. Do the coating while the lamp is lighted, so as to get the coating on evenly. To draw a circle on glass with a pen compass, paste a small piece of cardboard on the glass and push the center point of the compass into the cardboard.—Contributed by Charles E. Frary, Norwalk, O.

Safety Valve Made from Check Valve

The accompanying sketch shows how I made a safety valve from a check valve. The body of the check valve was tapped to receive the stud, A,

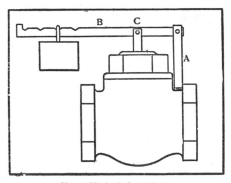

Home-Made Safety Valve

which was slotted out at the unthreaded end to receive the lever, B. A similar stud is screwed into the valve disc and is hinged to the lever at C. This stud passes through a hole in the cap, which should be drilled a little larger than the stud so that it won't bind. In connecting with the steam or other pipe be sure that the pressure comes on the lower side of the disc, otherwise the valve will not operate.—Contributed by C. E. Mayne, Park City, Utah, Box 223.

Reheater for Compressed Air

Engines run by compressed air frequently give trouble on account of the moisture in the air freezing in the cylinder. This is due to the loss of

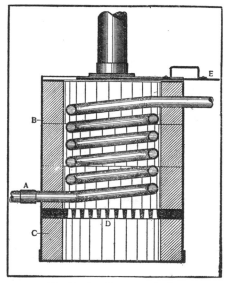

For Heating Compressed Air

heat produced by the expansion of the air in the cylinder. The engine of which I have charge is a long distance from the compressor (3,000 ft.) and thus the heat produced by compression was allowed to escape before the air reached the engine.

When first started the engine would run all right, but after it had been running a few minutes the valve would work stiff and the link would begin to quiver. Then the piston would groan, and after running irregularly for a little while the engine would stop altogether and all the pressure we had wouldn't move her an inch until the cylinder was thawed out.

In order to overcome this difficulty and at the same time to expand the compressed air, I built the reheater here shown, which successfully prevents the engine freezing up and materially reduces the consumption of air.

A piece of 1-in. pipe was coiled as shown at A, and enclosed in a sheet iron casing, B, having lap joints riveted together. This was lined with fire brick as shown at C, and provided with a circular grate, D. The fuel is put in from the top, which is covered by a sliding lid, E, of sheet iron. Another sliding door not shown in the sketch is placed at the bottom to allow the removal of ashes and to regulate the draft.

The operation of this reheater has been so successful that we now run it all the time; even during the warmest weather when there is little danger of freezing, the object being to reduce the amount of air used. The engine develops 12 hp. at 85 lb. air pressure. —Contributed by A. E. Scheetz, Trevorton, Pa.

◆ • ◆

How to Make a Drill Chuck

A very serviceable chuck for holding drills and small work can be made from an old brace. With a hack-saw cut the chuck, A, off the brace, leaving about 2 in. of the rod on the chuck. The rod portion is then

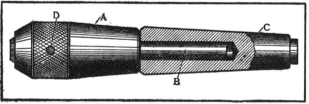

Drill Chuck Made From an Old Brace

to be heated, straightened out and turned up true, as shown at B. An old lathe center, C, is then drilled to receive B and the chuck driven in. Then drill a small hole at D for a spanner wrench and the chuck is complete.—Contributed by A. S. C., 466 E. Buchtel Ave., Akron, Ohio.

Muffler for Gas Engine

The silencing of a large gas engine is often a difficult problem. The ordinary gravel box stuck on the end of the pipe takes only the sharp edge off the noise, says a correspondent of the American Machinist. We used it for some years, but a job came along where an engine of 30-hp. had to run on Sundays and occasionally all night.

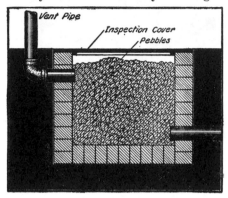

Muffler for Large Gas Engine

As it was located in a quiet residential neighborhood, it was essential that the engine cough should not be heard. We dug a hole about 3 ft. each way and lined it with a single course of brick set in cement. The top of the pit was fitted with an inspection cover to facilitate cleaning. The pit was filled with clean pebbles about the size of a walnut and the exhaust pipe turned into it. In one corner a vent pipe was introduced and carried to a convenient height. This pipe prevented the accumulation of any pressure, and also carried the smell out of reach.

It answers perfectly, and we have many times since adopted the same plan. The pebbles want removing about every six months, washing and replacing. Don't use anything but pebbles (broken bricks won't do), and don't let them be too small.

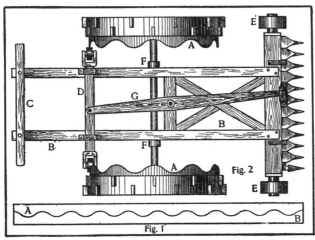

Made from an Old Field Mower

A Simple Lightning Protector

In the protection of telephone cables an idea that may be valuable needs investigation, says Journal of Electricity. It was found from eleven years' experience in the installation of aerial cables that if a single loop 2 ft. in diameter were made in the end of the cable, or even a "goose neck" of 3 or 4 ft. in length, that in case lightning should puncture the cable, one need never look for trouble beyond this loop; that lightning coming into the cable from an overhead line would encounter such impedance at this point that it would jump the conductors and go to the cable sheath every time.

To Glue Asbestos to Iron

Silicate of soda glue is probably the best substance to use for the purpose named. Brush the glue on the back of the fireplace and then stick on the asbestos fiber, using the asbestos freely. This glue will withstand the heat and hold the asbestos firmly in place, says the American Artisan. It can usually be obtained from druggists and always from dealers in asbestos.

Home-Made Lawn or Weed Mower

Anyone having an old field mower and a few metal-working tools can make a good lawn and weed mower. The following parts of the old machine will be needed: The driving wheels and shaft, a portion of the cutter-bar, including knives and fingers, bolts, nuts, and any other part which can be used, depending on the make of the old machine.

Procure a strip of sheet steel, Fig. 1, 6 in. wide, about 1/32 in. thick, and long enough to go around the circumference of the driving wheels. Cut this along the wave line AB and rivet the two pieces to the two driving wheels as shown at AA, Fig. 2. These should be riveted to the wheels in a position such that the crest on one side will be opposite the trough on the other.

The frame B is made of wood, also the handle, C. The piece D can be made of either wood or iron, and is fitted with a roller at each end to reduce the friction against the cams, AA. Two wheels, EE, about 6 in. in diameter and 3-in. face, are fastened to the front of the machine in order to prevent the cutters from striking the ground.

The driving wheels must be in the right position and then made fast to the shaft in order to have the cams work properly and it will be necessary to use two collars, FF, to prevent lateral movement of the shaft. When the machine is pushed along the cams operate the cam bar, which oscillates the lever, G, and thus works the knives.
—Contributed by Geo. G. McVicker, North Bend, Nebr.

An Emergency Pump

Once while freighting on the border lands of the Rocky mountains I indiscreetly attempted a short cut, mis-

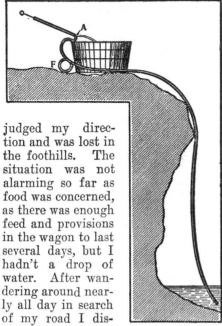

judged my direction and was lost in the foothills. The situation was not alarming so far as food was concerned, as there was enough feed and provisions in the wagon to last several days, but I hadn't a drop of water. After wandering around nearly all day in search of my road I discovered a wide crevice in the rock with water at the bottom, which was some 15 ft. below the surface. A rope and bucket could not be used on account of the rocky slope, so I used a tub and a piece of hose as shown in the accompanying sketch.

Removing the iron rod from the endgate of the wagon I used this for a plunger. On the threaded end of the rod I screwed two nuts and wrapped the portion of the rod between the nuts with string until I had a piston that would fit in one end of the hose. I then cut a hole in the hose at A to let the water run into the tub. To prime my newly-constructed pump I tied a rope to the other end of the hose and lowered a few feet of it into the water below. Then by pulling up the end of the hose with the string I succeeded in getting the plunger wet.

I then began operating my pump as follows: Holding the hole closed with my hand, the plunger was pulled

nearly all the way out. I then put my foot on the hose at F, uncovered the hole and forced the plunger in again. Continuing in this way I soon had a good stream flowing and in a few minutes had a tub of water which was relished greatly by myself and horses.— Contributed by George G. McVicker, North Bend, Neb.

Damp-Proof Coating for Walls

Dissolve 30 parts tin in 40 parts hydrochloric acid and add 30 parts sal ammoniac. Prepare a powder of 50 parts freestone, 20 parts zinc oxide, 15 parts pounded glass, 10 parts powdered marble and 5 parts calcined magnesia. Make the powder into a paste with the liquid first prepared. Add coloring matter if desired. This composition may also be used for repairing stone work or molding statues.

Old varnish may be removed from a metal surface by dipping it in equal parts of ammonia and 95 per cent alcohol.

Tempering a Hammer

Blacksmiths' and machinists' hammers frequently chip around the edges. This is caused by the hammer being too hard, says a correspondent of the

For Drawing the Temper

Blacksmith and Wheelwright, who recommends the following process for drawing the temper:

Make a ring of $\frac{1}{2}$-in. round iron to fit the face of the hammer. Then chill the hammer face. Next, heat the ring red hot and fix it round the hammer and bring the edge of the face down to a blue color; remove the ring and cool the hammer head. The center will be hard and the edges fairly soft and you will have no more bother.

◆ ◆ ◆

Mica Winding Device

We had been having a great deal of trouble with our producer-gas engine due to the short-circuiting of the spark plug. The sparking device, which is of the "make and break" type, is so designed that the mica insulation must

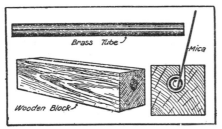

Device for Winding Mica

cover a stem over 6 in. long. After sending the spark plug to several repair shops, with results which were unsatisfactory, I decided to try the method here illustrated, which has proved very successful.

First, I procured a piece of brass tubing 8 in. long, and by means of a hacksaw slit it open from end to end. Then I made a block of wood 7 in. long and drilled through it a longitudinal hole, a little smaller than the hole in the spark plug, but somewhat larger than the diameter of the tube. Then by placing the tube in the hole, with the end projecting, it was an easy matter to twist the tube with one hand while the mica was fed in with the other. By overlapping the edges, I found that scrap mica could be used in this way with excellent results.

When enough mica is wound on the tube, place one end in the spark plug and push it in with a twisting motion. The tube can then be withdrawn by turning it backwards, thus allowing the mica to release itself and cling to the hole in the spark plug. By using this simple device I can insulate a plug in less time than it would take to get

a repair man, and with results that are much more satisfactory.—Contributed by J. A. Manning, Manager of Manning Wood Fibre Co., Owen Sound, Ontario.

◆ ◆ ◆

How to Make a Focusing Glass

Remove the film from an old plate, apply a thin, even coat of shellac and, while it is wet, spread over the coated side a piece of white tissue paper. Or, frost the glass as described in the March number, 1907.—Contributed by F. H. Schubart, 241 Pine St., Elizabeth, N. Y.

◆ ◆ ◆

A Dustless Ash Sifter

To make this device all that is needed is a galvanized iron can, such as is generally used for scraps or ashes; a circular sieve, a wooden cover and some round iron for making the links and handle. The links are hung on screw hooks screwed into the cover and support the sieve by means of hooks fast-

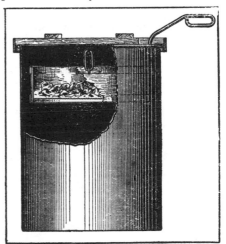

Dustless Ash Sifter

ened to the sides. In operation the sieve may either be moved backward and forward or it may be given a revolving motion. The revolving motion is more effective at first, but soon causes the ashes to pile up around the edge of the sieve.

Tool Holder

Take a piece of steel the right size to fit the tool post. Split about 2 in. back. Spread the under ends and file the notches so as to hold a piece of a three-cornered file. Put a bolt on the machine and screw to clamp the file.

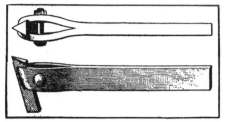

Holder for Threading Tools

In this tool holder old files can be used to make many different shaped tools, says a correspondent of the Blacksmith and Wheelwright, and it is not necessary to temper them. Simply break the file off at a convenient length and grind up on the emery wheel, leaving the teeth on the eyes to bed in the holder.

Cheap Method of Cutting Shaft

The end of a shaft often projects into valuable operating space and in many cases is very annoying or even dangerous. In order to provide a cheap and efficient method of cutting

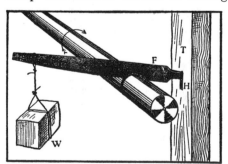

Making a Shaft Cut Itself

off the unnecessary portion, a correspondent of the American Miller recommends the use of an ordinary flat file and a weight, as shown in the accom-

panying sketch. The vertical timber, T, has a hole at H to hold the file, F, which bears down on the shaft and cuts the same by its own rotation.

The weight, W, may be a brick or other heavy object and is fastened to the file by a piece of wire. It may be necessary to guide the file by hand at first, but after the groove is fairly started the file will guide itself.

Boring Tool for Lathe

Round tool steel down to $\frac{1}{4}$ in. can be used to advantage for making boring tools. The steel is to be forged to a cutting point at A and, after being tempered and ground, is clamped between two grooved pieces of machine

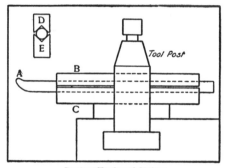

Boring Tool and Holder

steel, B and C, shown in detail at D and E. These are made just wide enough to fit the hole in the tool post, and when the screw is tightened up it makes a very rigid tool. The grooves in the steel clamps are made V-shaped in order to accommodate different sizes. Contributed by E. Viall, Menomonie, Wisc.

To Make Transparent Paper

To make ordinary paper transparent, spread a thin solution of Canada balsam in benzole on the paper to be prepared and allow it to dry. If the paper used for this purpose is not too heavy, the result will be a fine transparent membrane, with a hard, clean surface. This solution can be used to advantage for making blueprints, or photographs of pictures printed on opaque paper.—Contributed by H. Maude, 311 W. Main St., Madison, Wisc.

Knuckle=Guard for Wheel Barrow

The device here illustrated was exhibited at the International Exposition of Safety Devices, and was pronounced

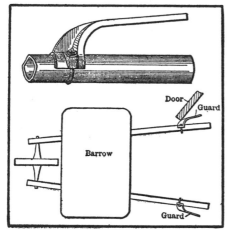

Prevents Injuring Knuckles

by some to be the neatest device on exhibition, says the American Machinist. It was designed and manufactured by a large manufacturing

concern for use in their works, to protect the knuckles of those who push barrows from being barked by doors when passing through doorways.

Clean funnels and measures for varnishes and oils by soaking in strong solution of lye or pearl-ash.

Gate for Wire Fence

In the western states where pasture fences are constructed of barbed wire it is frequently a difficult problem to construct the gates in a good substantial manner so that the wires will not sag and allow the stock to break through. About the cheapest and most practical method of overcoming this difficulty is shown in the accompanying sketch.

A round stick, A, is fastened to one of the fence-posts, B, by means of wire loops, C. Fastened to this stick are a number of wires, D, which are continuations of the fence wires. These wires will be loose when the stick, A, is in the position shown in Fig. 1, but when it is turned by means of the lever or handle E, which also acts as a latch, the wires will be drawn up tight as shown in Fig. 2. — Contributed by G. G. M., North Bend, Neb.

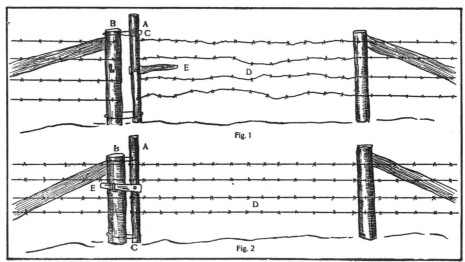

First and Second Operations in Closing Wire Gate

Design for Frieze—London Plumber and Decorator

Using the Handsaw

To cut across the narrowest amount of wood is the most effective, or at least the most rapid way of cutting with a handsaw, says a correspondent of the Wood-Workers' Review. This fact is not generally recognized; or, to be more precise, it is usually ignored.

For instance, let a 6-in. board be sawed flatwise; that is, so the board will be cut across the broad side; then afterward turn the board up on edge and cut it off by sawing the short way through it. It will be found that on an average the board can be cut in two much quicker when the teeth pass the short way through the board.

Therefore the lesson to be thus learned is, that when sawing a large piece of wood, to so use the saw as to avoid the teeth all touching across a broad surface at once, and to contrive to make as short a cut as possible. In order to do this in the most practical manner a piece of timber of very considerable size should be cut by beginning at one corner and sawing to a reasonable depth. (See diagram marked A.) Then change the slant of the saw so the timber will be cut to the line B; then, as the cutting edge of the saw will begin to touch a wide surface, again shift the saw to another position, or slant, and cut inward to C, and so on D, E, F, etc., in their order, as shown. In this way the timber will positively be cut in two one-quarter to one-half quicker than if it were kept at one angle all the way through.

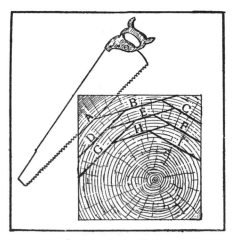

Sawing a Large Timber

Printing from Cracked Negative

Very satisfactory prints may be obtained from cracked negatives, if the film is not injured. Place in the frame carefully and cover with tissue paper or ground glass to diffuse the light as much as possible. Rotating the frame during the printing operation is also beneficial. By making prints in this way the cracks will be hardly perceptible.—Contributed by J. W. Beardmore, 301 13th St., S.E., Washington, D. C.

An easy way to clean painted walls is to dampen a piece of flannel with a few drops of ammonia in tepid water, and wipe the surface gently.

Making Boiled Water Palatable

Typhoid fever is principally transmitted by drinking water. Boiling kills the germs, but such boiling renders the water flat and unpalatable. The following simple means can be applied by any housekeeper to make the family drinking water both safe and palatable. It is highly recommended by Professor Marsden Manson, of San Francisco, Calif., who has thoroughly tried it, says Cooking Club Magazine.

1. Take exactly 2 gal. of water. If the water is not clear, beat up the white of one egg and add it to the water before boiling. This will gather up every particle of foreign matter in the water and carry it to the bottom. The water should be brought to a brisk boil and then stood aside to cool and settle.

2. Pour off the clear water and stir into it a level teaspoonful of bicarbonate of soda. Then stir in two-thirds of a teaspoonful of hydrochloric acid. This will make the water perfectly safe, sparkling and refreshing, without any flat taste.

Adjustable Countersink and Drill

This tool is very useful for making center holes in work to be turned up in the lathe. A piece of tool steel is

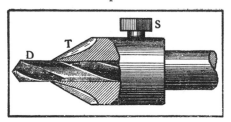

Adjustable Countersink and Drill

drilled to receive a small drill, D, which is held in place by a set screw, S. The cutting teeth, T, are made at an angle of 60°, or the same angle as the lathe center. These teeth may be cut on a milling machine and should be shaped like those of a reamer. The cutting end is to be hardened and tempered in the usual manner. The great advantage of this tool is that the drill may be replaced if broken or it may be adjusted to any desired length.—Contributed by J. W. Beardmore, 301 S. E. 13th St., Washington, D. C.

Thread Chaser for Tool Steel

As tool steel often expands when hardened it is a difficult matter to cut threads which will be the exact size after hardening. Not long ago I had occasion to cut threads in tool steel, and knowing the peculiar properties of this material, allowed three thousandths of an inch for expansion. But

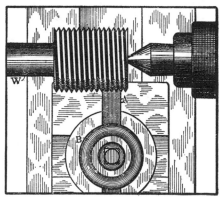

Chaser for Hardened Tool Steel

on trying the thread I found that it was too large.

Not wishing to go to the trouble of annealing and recutting the threads I made a chaser, A, of a piece of brass that would fit the tool post, B. A tap having the required number of threads was placed in the lathe and the brass was fed up against it. The work, W, was then placed in the lathe and flour of emery applied to the threads. The brass chaser was then brought up against the threads, thus reducing the size and giving them a good polish. In this way the threads were cut down much better and quicker than could be done by annealing and recutting.—Contributed by E. V., Menomonie, Wis.

To clean old medals, soak them in lemon juice for 24 hours or longer.

Pump Rod Spring

This device will prevent the jerk in the plunger rod of a windmill pump. An old wagon or seat spring will answer the purpose very well and can be

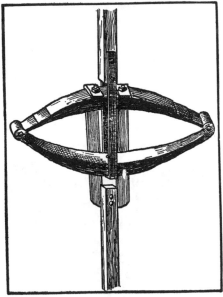

Made from an Old Wagon Spring

fastened to the plunger rod by sawing out a piece of the rod about 2 in. longer than the height of the spring. The spring is fastened to the two ends of the pump rod by means of iron straps, the upper rod being fastened to the lower half of the spring and the under rod fastened to the upper half.—Contributed by H. C. A., Brooklyn, N. Y.

Stock Solution for Preparing Sepia Paper

FORMULA.

A. Carbonate of potash............1 oz.
   Water ....4 oz.
B. Gold chloride ....15 gr.
   Water ....7½ dr.

Mix solution A, stirring well, and allow to stand till clear. Then filter and bottle for stock. When wanted for use add to 10 oz. water 1 dr. of A and 20 drops of B, which amount will tone one sheet and give a warm sepia. The bath will keep.

To Insert a Hose Nipple

When it is found very difficult to insert a nipple in a hose, such as an air brake hose, heat the nipple to a point where it will soften the rubber. The nipple can then be inserted without any difficulty, says a correspondent of the American Machinist, but it is well to have a bucket of water handy to immerse the end in as quickly as possible, so as not to spoil the hose.

Rendering Wall Paper Washable

This may be done either before or after the paper is hung.

Dissolve 2 parts borax and 2 parts shellac in 24 parts water and strain through a fine cloth. Apply to the paper with a brush or a sponge, and when dry polish to a high gloss with a soft brush. Washing will not remove nor smear the colors.

Removing Cinders from the Eye

As a safe and efficient means of removing any foreign substance from the eye, a correspondent of the American Machinist submits a scheme successfully used by the eye doctor in his shop. A piece of letter paper is folded and cut with a sharp knife to an angle of about 30°, as shown by the sketch. The folded paper is then held between

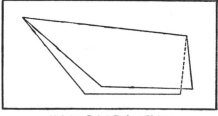

Moisten Point Before Using

the forefinger and the thumb, and the point is slightly moistened on the end of the patient's tongue. Then that part which is cut at an angle is held at right angles to the surface of the eye and brought straight down over the eyeball until it comes in contact with the substance in the eye, which it invariably moves at the first trial. If the point is too sharp, bend it up a little on the thumb nail.

◆ ◆ ◆

Sawdust for Cleaning Hands

Sawdust is not only useful to put under automobiles or other machines to catch and absorb the dripping oil, but is also useful to "wash" greasy hands with, says Gas Power. The clean, porous, angular and finely divided wood makes an excellent absorbent and possesses enough grit to make it just the thing for working into creases and cracks and taking out the oil and dirt both by absorption and friction.

◆ ◆ ◆

Belt Tightener

The accompanying sketch shows an easily constructed belt tightener which was designed by a correspondent of the American Miller. It consists of four pieces of wood which may be anywhere from 2 to 3 in. wide and long enough to extend 4 or 5 in. each side of the belt to be spliced, and $\frac{7}{8}$ in. thick. The ends should have the sharp corners cut off and slightly notched in, so that the rope will not slip off. Use a rope about $\frac{3}{8}$ in. diameter or about the size of clothesline.

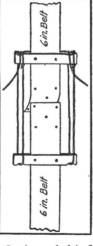

Place one of the wood pieces behind the belt above and below the splice, far enough apart to allow you to draw belt tight and have plenty of room to make the splice. Place the other pieces directly in front of the back ones and drive two 6d. wire nails through each and through the belt. Then take the two ropes; make a loop in each and place loop over the two cleats at top, one on each end. Run the rope down around cleats at bottom, then back around cleats at top. Pull up on bottom cleats and tighten ropes, and when sufficiently tight, wrap rope around upper cleats and throw half hitch over, and it is fast for splicing.

◆ ◆ ◆

Shaper Used as Surface Grinder

Many toolmakers have run up against the proposition of trying to do a smooth and accurate job of surface grinding with an old and worn-out machine, or else the machine is too small to handle the job.

A shaper can be very easily used for this purpose as shown in the above

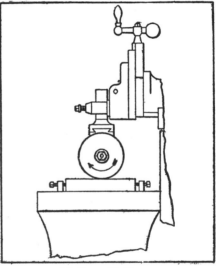

Grinding with Shaper

illustration. This method is far superior to the use of an old surface grinder, both for accuracy and convenience. The emery wheel is electrically driven and should rotate in the direction shown by the arrow. Care should be taken that no emery be allowed to get into the bearings, as this would quickly damage the shaper. Waste can be used to protect the bearings from flying emery.—Contributed by A. J. M., Denver, Colo.

Enlarging Hole for Propeller Tube

The cutting off of rails, bolts or other metal when encountered in an auger hole in wood is always a nasty proposition. Let the length of the hole be something like 4 ft., and the obstructions the ends of some six or

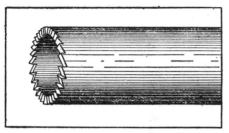

Made of Steel Tubing

eight $\frac{1}{2}$-in. bolts, and the job is all that can be desired in the way of cussedness, says a correspondent of the American Machinist.

We had a launch hull all ready for the engine when the customer suddenly changed his mind and decided that he wanted a reversible wheel instead of a solid one. In this case it was found that the tube of the wheel furnished with this make of engine was extra large, necessitating reboring of the shaft hole.

It was found that if the hole in the log were enlarged to the required diameter for the shaft tube it would be necessary to cut a little from the ends of the bolts, eight in all, and the hole was but 2 in. in diameter. It looked like a new wheel and shaft for Mr. Customer, who was a foreman in a large factory.

He said he would get a large twist drill and have a long shank fitted. When the drill came we started it, the lip of the drill got hold of the first bolt end, and we strained until the log threatened to split, without budging the drill. I wished that I was in the mining country and could run a diamond drill in that hole. However, the diamond drill gave me an idea. Procuring a piece of steel tube about 10 in. long, and the same diameter as the

hole required, I cut a series of teeth on one end, giving them a slight outward set. The teeth I then case-hardened. For turning the bit I attached to it a length of $\frac{3}{4}$-in. pipe.

We bored in with a wood bit until a bolt was reached, and then cut the latter off with the cutter. It was slow business, but did the job. We had to reharden and sharpen the cutter several times during the job.

Threading Pipe With Cold-Chisels

Some 25 years ago the piping went wrong at an important water station of one of the railroads entering Chicago. The Superintendent of Water Service, who is responsible for the following account of the incident, got together such men and tools as he could and hurried to the scene, says the Valve World. Arriving at the station he found the 4-in. wrought-iron pipe broken squarely off, only 2 ft. of water in the tank, and no means of getting a piece of pipe from any shop cut to length and threaded inside of 24 hours.

Unwilling to interrupt the water supply and determined not to acknowledge defeat until the last resource was tried, he cut a piece of pipe to length with cold-chisels, chalked the unthreaded end, placed it in line end to end with a threaded old piece of the same size pipe, and with a two-pointed tram, one point engaging the thread of the old pipe, the other ascribing on the chalked end of the blank pipe, he followed the thread with one point, always keeping the tram parallel with the axis of the pipe.

The path of the right-pitch thread was thus ascribed by the tram point on the chalked surface of the blank end of pipe requiring thread. The spiral scribe mark made by the tram was nicked with chisels, and deepened and made continuous, until at the end of an hour and a half a good thread was cut, the job put up without a drop of leakage and without interruption of the water service.

Air Mains

Pipes supplying air to rock-drills should be of a size to permit the passage of air at a velocity not greater than 25 to 30 ft. per second, while all bends and angles (especially short ones) should be avoided, as they add greatly to the friction of the air, and thus decrease the pressure. The friction of the air is proportional directly to the length of the pipe, and to the square of its velocity, says Compressed Air. For this service, pipes up to 5 in. diameter are provided with couplings; above that, with flanged joints made up with gaskets. Great care must be taken that these joints are perfectly tight, as the loss, even from a pin-hole, is considerable.

Home=Made Chain Pipe Wrench

To make this wrench, procure a piece of old bicycle chain, A, and a steel handle, B, about 1 in. wide and the same thickness as the solid links, LL, of the chain. The handle should be about 15 in. long. Make two steel jaws, C, $\frac{3}{16}$ in. or $\frac{1}{4}$ in. thick, and rivet to the handle by the rivets DD.

An old leaf spring or almost any flat piece of tool steel will furnish the necessary material for the jaws, which

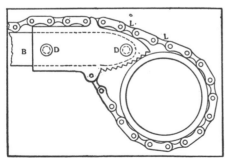

This Works Well

should be cut nearly to size with a hacksaw and then finished by filing. If the steel is too hard to cut, anneal it by heating to a red heat and allowing it to cool very slowly. After shaping and drilling the jaws, harden and

temper to a dark straw color.—Contributed by H. L. G., Milwaukee, Wis.

Vehicle Design from Blacksmith and Wheelwright

Pumping Without Attendance

A gas-engine-driven pumping plant requires very little attention, if one knows just how to manage. In a plant where there are two engines used for pumping water into a storage tank and located more than a mile apart, one being run during the daytime and the other at night, the operator lives about halfway between the two engines. At 6:30 a. m. he passes the reservoir and notes the amount of water and conditions in general, and then stops the engine that has run all night. At about 7 o'clock he starts up the other engine and then goes about his day's work. At 5 in the afternoon he starts up the night engine and then goes to the other and stops it. The engines require some intelligent attention while running, but not constant attention.

At another plant, the oil tank under the engine holds 20 gal. Only 11½ gal., sufficient for 10 hours' run, are put in the tank, however, and when this amount is exhausted the engine stops of itself, and requires no attention until ready to start up next day.

For white solder for silver use: Silver, 1 oz.; tin, 1 oz.

To Remove Fast Nuts

When it is found impossible to remove a nut by any other method, take a hammer, sledge and a dull cold chisel, as per sketch, and strike several blows, then change sides and hit some more, thus causing the nut to swell, when it can be easily removed. This will remove the nut every time, says a correspondent of the Blacksmith and Wheelwright, unless it is a very large one.  It can then be removed by heating to nearly a welding heat and cooling quickly in water.

Locomotive Turned Without Turntable

Several years ago I found it necessary to turn a locomotive around to head in the opposite direction. Having neither turntable nor "Y" available, I selected a place on the railroad where there was practically no cut or grade and a tangent of about 200 ft. Placing the engine at the end of the tangent, I cut the track at the opposite end and swung it about 30 ft. (at the end) in a proper curve—keeping the last 60 ft. straight to hold the engine—and ran the locomotive to the end. Then I had the other end of the tangent cut and swung on the opposite side in the same way, and again ran the engine to the end. After repeating this process five times, I had the engine replaced on the track, headed the right way, the track, of course, being kept in gauge all the time and the curve in proper degree. Where the ground on each side can be utilized and the rail-joints are exactly opposite, the track can be reset in the opposite direction without drawing spikes at the end. The entire operation, including the rail connections, was done in two hours and was performed with lining bars and ordinary trackman's tools.—Contributed by G. H. Crumb, Bloomfield, Mo.

Welding Compound

Borax, 10 parts; sal ammoniac, 1 part; grind or pound roughly together and fuse in a metal pot over a fire. Continue heating until all the froth has disappeared from the surface and then pour the clear liquid into any suitable receptacle to cool and solidify. When cold grind to a powder.—Contributed by Y. Pavlik, Jr.

Correct and Incorrect Designs for Eveners

Many articles are designed for appearance at the expense of strength. This is true of the eveners used on wagons, which are often made with the taper on the side which bears the tension. The evener shown in Fig. 1 is designed for strength while the one shown in Fig. 2 is designed for appearance. The conditions in Fig. 2

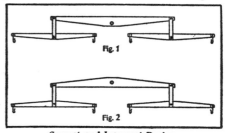

Fig. 1

Fig. 2

Correct and Incorrect Design

are similar to those of a leaf-spring in which the short leaves are on the wrong side, because the grain of the wood intersects the tapered edge in much the same manner as the leaves do in a spring.—Contributed by G. M. L., New York City.

Brass and steel may be cleaned quickly and cheaply by rubbing with vinegar and salt, or with oxalic acid. Wash immediately and polish with Tripoli earth and sweet oil.

SHOP NOTES

Removing Mired Traction Engine

Last fall while moving over the road with a traction engine we encountered a large mud hole which let the drivers sink nearly to the hubs. It would have taken all the horses in the township to move the engine in that condition, so after experimenting for some time we finally hit upon the following plan: First we fastened a piece of chain to each of the driving wheels and laid the chains in a position such that they would wind up on the drivers when

Hub Deep in the Mud

they revolved. Next we drove a strong stake some distance ahead and fastened the chains to the stake. The engine was then started and the drivers wound themselves up in the chain, thus removing the engine from the mud hole.—Contributed by Axsel Everson, Penn Yan, N. Y.

Circular Glass Cutter

For cutting out circles of glass for headlights or other purposes, a correspondent of the Electric Traction Weekly uses a device, the details of which are indicated in the drawing. This consists of a wooden base near one end of which is pivoted a circular rest for holding the glass. The rest is 14 in. in diameter and is made of cast steel covered with leather. The diamond cutter is carried on the end of an arm which slides on the base piece as shown. The scale permits the arm

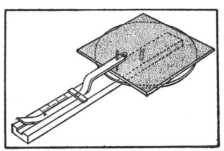

Circular Glass Cutter

to be set at any point to give the desired diameter of glass disc.

Corner Design for Mosaic

In laying ceramic floors the tile setter or mosaic worker frequently has occasion to cut and match the different design sheets, especially in laying the border, in making corners, and in filling in recesses in the floor of the room. The manner in which this cutting is done frequently determines whether the finished job is to look good or bad, says Mantle, Tile and Grate. The mitred corner, as shown in Fig. 1, can be executed with little difficulty, by simply cutting the margin along the lines

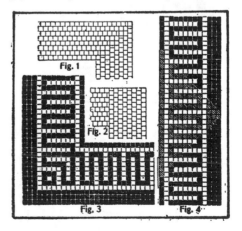

Corner Design for Mosaic

here indicated. This miter is symmetrical, artistic and appropriate to the general design. Every mosaic worker should know how to improvise this margin corner from the ordinary plain sheets of broken joint mosaic. Fig. 2 illustrates a common but undesirable method of applying a broken joint margin. This has an unfinished and unsymmetrical appearance, which is displeasing to the eye.

A very neat corner design for a border is shown in Fig. 3, and the manner of cutting and matching the design sheet is shown in Fig. 4. By making the bevel at 45° and omitting two squares at the outside edge, the design in the border will be made continuous, giving the pretty effect shown in Fig. 3.

- - -

Red aniline ink (except eosine) will be removed promptly by moistening with 95 per cent alcohol, adding acetic acid drop by drop till the stain disappears.

- - -

To Fasten a Bolt in a Brick Wall

When an expansion bolt is not available an ordinary bolt applied in the

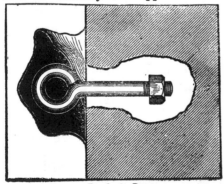

Ready to Pour

manner here illustrated will prove equally as good, if not better. A hole is made in the wall and roughly undercut as shown. A lump of clay is then pressed against the wall in such a manner that the bolt will be held in the hole in the proper position. An opening or gate is made to the cavity, which is then poured full of melted lead or

sulphur.—Contributed by H. G. L., Boston, Mass.

- - -

Measuring the Flow of Gas from Wells

In order to estimate the number of cubic feet of gas per hour that flows from a well, the instrument here illustrated is often used, says the Well

Drillers' News. In its simplest form this instrument consists of a bent glass tube, which can be made in any laboratory, with a wood or cardboard scale fastened between two of the legs as shown. Water is then poured in the tube until the level reaches the zero mark, or if the pressure of the gas is unusually high, mercury is used in the tube in place of water.

The long leg of the tube is then held in the pipe, as near the center as possible, and the difference in the levels noted. The discharge in cubic feet per hour can then be obtained by consulting suitable tables, which give the rate of discharge from various sized pipes with gas under different pressures.

- - -

Non=Corrosive Soldering Paste

The following is now used extensively in electrical work as a flux for soldering, especially of copper wires, and wherever no acid should be used. It is a mixture of zinc chloride and some grease, such as petrolatum (practically the same as vaseline, but cheaper). Make the zinc chloride by dissolving zinc in strong muriatic acid, with excess of zinc to neutralize all acid. The solution will be thick and oily and is to be mixed thoroughly with the petrolatum in the ratio 1 fl. oz. to 1 lb. This makes an excellent soldering paste which neither spatters nor corrodes.

Original Frieze Design--London Decorator

Oil to Preserve Ties

The experts have decided that heat and moisture when present at the same time are the forces which cause railroad ties to decay. Results of an experiment begun in 1902 have just been announced. Pine ties, thoroughly seasoned, were immersed in crude California oil heated to 180° and subjected to a pressure of 150 lb. per square inch. The ties absorbed from four to eight gallons each. A large number of these ties are found in sound condition after five years where the same quality of ties, untreated, lasted only two years.

Device for Forming the Ends of Springs

Having occasion to make 300 small helical springs I consulted Shop Notes and found a method of winding them by means of a brace, which proved very satisfactory. As an exchange for this valuable idea I send the following sketch and description of a device for forming the ends, after the springs are wound and cut. A piece of iron or machine steel is bent to the shape shown in Fig. 1 and drilled at A with a drill having the same diameter as the outside diameter of the spring. A cold chisel is then driven in the crack at the end

until the jaws are spread about 1/32 in. The device is then placed in a vise; a spring is inserted in the hole, A, and by means of the forming tool, Fig. 2, the end of the spring is bent up as shown in Fig. 3. The operation is thus easily and accurately performed and my 300 springs were quickly finished.

The forming tool, Fig. 2, is made from a piece of ¾-in. drill rod, A, slotted at B by means of a hacksaw and driven into a file handle, C. The lower jaw, D, which is slightly longer and sharper than the other, is inserted in the last coil of the spring and the handle is then lifted up until the tool is in a vertical position. This forms the end successfully without spoiling the other coils of the spring. The springs I made were so short that I found it better to cut away a portion of the die or clamp shown at B, Fig. 1, in order to get hold of the spring, but this would be unnecessary when forming the ends of long springs.—Contributed by A. W. Griggs, 955 Market St., Kenosha, Wis.

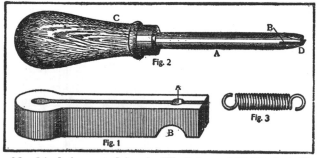

Fig. 2
Fig. 1
Fig. 3

Pipe Wrench for Soft Pipes and Hose

To make a wrench for gripping soft pipes or rubber hose secure a piece of heavy clock spring, punch a hole in each end and rivet to

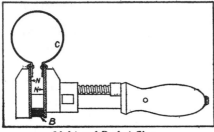

Light and Pocket Size

two pieces of iron, N N, about 4 in. long. To use when it can not be gripped tight enough by hand, place any solid object between ends of handles and apply monkey wrench, as shown. It is light and small and may be carried in pocket. For gripping small pipes or hose, wind a leather strap about the pipe and grip the strap.—Experimenter.

Drying Electric Plant After Flood

The power house of a large Eastern manufacturing concern was recently flooded with water to a height sufficient to cover the two turbo-generators, two-thirds of the switch-board and a large part of the auxiliary apparatus, including the exciter units and the condenser pump motors. S. L. Sinclair and E. D. Tyree, who were called upon to get the plant in operation with the least possible delay, tell how they did so, in the Electric Journal.

Upon arriving at the power house it was found that the employes of the local company were attempting to dry out the generators by the use of a steam coil enclosed in an air flue. A blower was connected at one end of the flue and the other end opened at the generators so that hot air could be blown through the generator windings. This method would have taken an indefinite time to dry out the generators. It was therefore abandoned and an enclosure of sheet iron and tin, that was found around the works, was built up around the generators. Inside of this enclosure were placed a number of charcoal furnaces made of powder kegs. Thermometers were suspended near the generators and the temperature inside the enclosure was maintained at 85° C.

While the generators were being dried by this process a small hoisting engine was belted to a 20-hp. motor for use as an exciter. Arrangements were also made with the local railway company to furnish 500-volt direct current for making tests of insulation resistance. Insulation tests were made with a 600-volt direct-current meter having an internal resistance of 85,000 ohms.

After the generator had been drying for 36 hours the insulation resistance was about half the normal value. The generator was then started on a short-circuit heat run, and at the expiration of 30 hours, making 66 hours in all, the readings showed that the insulation was thoroughly dry and the generator was ready to go into service.

The second generator was dried in the same manner, with the same results. The motors, exciters and switch-board were dried by the use of charcoal furnaces.

Cure for Hot Handle on Furnace Door

Usually there is nothing to assist the fireman to open the doors of the

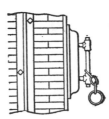

furnace, except a knob which is always too hot to handle, writes a correspondent of the Engineers' Review. In my plant the furnace doors have a wooden handle, but they become so hot that it is unpleasant to use them. To assist in opening the doors I have attached one end of a chain of four links to the handles, and to the other end attached a ring, as shown. When a door is to be opened, pull on the ring and that is all there is to it.

◆ ◆ ◆

Table of Machine Screw Taps

The following table gives the sizes, in fractions of an inch, of ordinary machine taps. The taps are all designated by the numbers in the first two columns. Thus a No. 2 tap is called 2—56; a No. 4, 4—36, etc., except when the number of threads is not standard, when it will then be called by the number in the first column, followed by the number of threads. Thus a No. 4 tap with 42 threads to the inch would be called 4—42, etc.

The last column gives the size of drill to use with any standard tap to cut perfect threads. In practice a drill one size larger is often used to avoid breaking the taps:

No.	Standard Threads to the inch	Diameter About	Size of Drill to Drill for Tapping
2	56	3/32—	No. 53
3	48	7/64—	48
4	36	7/64+	43
5	36	1/8 +	42
6	32	9/64	33
7	32	5/32	31
8	32	11/64	28
9	30	3/16—	26
10	24	3/16+	24
11	24	13/64	21
12	24	7/32	17
13	22	15/64	12
14	20	1/4 —	6
15	20	1/4 +	5
16	18	17/64	3
17	18	9/32	2
18	18	19/64	15/64″
19	18	5/16	1/4 ″
20	16	21/64+	17/64″
22	16	11/32	9/32″
24	16	3/8	19/64″
26	16	25/64	5/16″
28	14	13/32	21/64″
30	14	7/16	11/32″

Celluloid Drawing Templets for Draughtsmen

Draughtsmen whose work requires duplicate shapes such as gear-tooth curves, switchboard instruments and the like, will find the use of celluloid templets a great convenience. The celluloid used for this purpose should be quite thin ($\frac{1}{16}$ in.  is thick enough) and should be transparent. To make the templets trace off directly from the drawing, using a pair of well-sharpened dividers. By bearing on a little, the celluloid will be scratched deep enough to be readily broken, thus leaving a clean, sharp edge of the required shape.

The accompanying sketch shows a templet that has saved much time and labor in our draughting office. It is used for drawing standard volt meters and ammeters and comes in very handy when making drawings of switchboards.—Contributed by Frederic Schaefer, M. E., American Telegraphone Co., Wheeling, W. Va.

◆ ◆ ◆

Cheap Die Holder

A very cheap, but efficient, die holder can be made by bending the ends of two pieces of iron, AA, a little less than 45° and drilling for the bolts, BB, which should be spaced far enough apart to allow the insertion of the largest size die.—Contributed by F. G. M., San Francisco, Cal.

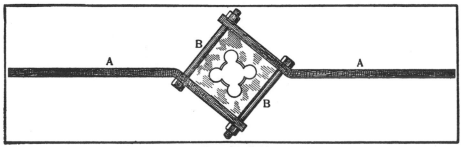

A Cheap Die Holder

A Home=Made Drawing Table

Here is another style of table, adjustable for both height and slant, which presents the advantage of being made easily of wood. The cut needs no

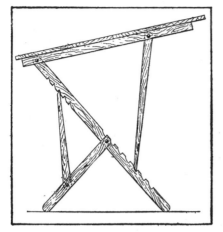

Adjustable Drawing Board

explanation. Any wood may be used, but some hardwood like ash or maple for the supports will combine lightness with strength. If the whole is fastened together with $\frac{1}{4}$ by 2-in. stove bolts, instead of nails, it can be taken apart readily and packed in very small space. —Contributed by Fred Robinson, Chicago.

How to Manufacture Metal Polish

Metal polish is one of the easiest things in the world to manufacture, and, as the cost of materials is little or nothing, the profits are very large. Take any quantity of yellow or blue clay, perfectly free from sand, and allow it to dry. Pulverize by pounding it and run through a flour sieve, or a finer sieve if one is available.

To 5 lb. of this sifted clay add 1 lb. of sifted wood ashes and mix to a very stiff paste with a solution of water and lye, in the proportion of 1 gal. of water to 2 heaping tablespoonfuls of lye. Spread this mixture on a flat, planed board and level off the top until it has a uniform thickness of about 1 in.

When it has become set, mark it off into squares about 2 in. on a side and cut apart.

To use this polish, scrape off a little on a moist cloth and rub the article to be polished, thereby giving it a glittering, lustrous shine. To my own knowledge, one man has made a good living making and selling this polish. If the material is sifted carefully in the making the preparation will not scratch the finest polished surface.—Contributed by James E. Noble, 999 Queen St., West, Toronto, Ontario.

Cementing Iron to Stone

Grind brickdust fine, sift, and stir it into melted rosin to form a putty-like substance, which runs easily while hot. Set the iron into the hole in the stone and pour the hot putty in around it. Push bits of heated brick into the mass, smooth off and let cool. This cement is not affected by the weather and does not injure the iron, but secures it firmly.

Filing Aluminum

Aluminum is hard to finish, but I found by first rubbing the file on an oil stone that it can be brought to a good polish. A common mill file is the best. — Contributed by Claire Bird, Menominee, Wis.

To Show Working of Sight Glass

A convenient device in the engine room is a piece of tin painted white

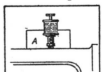

and placed behind the sight glass of the feed cups on the engine. Engineers know how difficult it is to tell just how the oil cup is feeding, especially at night, says the Engineers' Review. With the white showing behind the sight glass the drops of oil can be distinctly seen as they fall. The arrangement is shown in the cut, where the white tin is marked A.

How to Burn Names on Brass

Melt some white wax smoothly and evenly over a brass plate and let it harden. With a point needle trace the inscription on the wax, penetrating through to the brass. Apply strong nitric acid to the design, let stand 60 seconds or less, then wash off the wax. Nitric acid requires care in handling, as it destroys whatever it comes in contact with. It is well to practice the process on old brass first.

Spout Knocker for Mill

In spite of good arrangement and size of spouts they will choke up. A correspondent of the American Miller has had good success with the simple

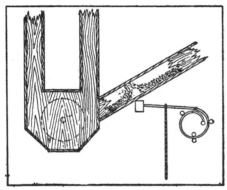

Clearing Choked Spout

device illustrated. The knocker rests against the under side of the spout and is fastened to a strong band spring which, when pulled down by means of a cord and quickly released, strikes a blow on the spout, which releases the contents.

Sandpaper Holder

Workmen who use sandpaper much, especially wood polishers, waste a great deal for want of a good holder for the sandpaper. The cut shows a simple and excellent model for such a holder, which almost explains itself. The edge of the wedge should be slightly rounded so that it will not cut right through the paper, but not so much as to prevent getting into the angles of the woodwork to be polished. Cut your sandpaper so as to fold over both sides

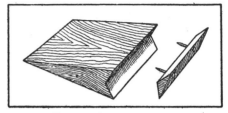

Economical Sandpaper Block

of the wedge and leave sufficient margins to turn back over each edge of the groove. Draw tight and screw the clamp into place.

Sawing Steel

Either drive your saw slowly, 25 ft. a minute, or else rush it up to 2 miles a minute, which will heat the steel so that you can go through it like cheese. The saw may or may not have teeth at that speed; it will cut through large I-beams or heavy shafting with ease.

Device to Prevent Insects in Poultry Houses

Take a piece of wood of suitable length and size for a roost and plane a groove in it as shown in the cut. Fill the ends of the groove with putty and the groove itself fill with any good fluid insecticide. The fumes will rise and penetrate the feathers of the fowls

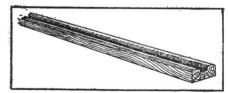

Fill Groove with Insecticide

and kill the vermin. Insects will not remain long on the bar. One filling of the groove will last quite a long time; when refilling first clean out the groove. —Contributed by "A Reader."

Cutting Belt Holes in Floor

When drawing board and instruments are not available it is sometimes a difficult problem to cut a belt hole in a floor so that it will come in exactly the right place.   The problem here

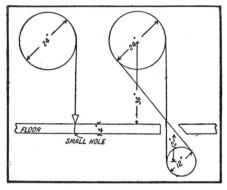

Locating Hole in Floor

illustrated is one that confronted a correspondent of the National Engineer, who describes its solution as follows: The machine had to be located in a place where there was barely sufficient room for it, and the power to drive was to be taken from a shaft in the room below. The rotation of the driving shaft was such that we must use a cross belt for driving the new machine.

After getting the machine in place and line and leveled up, I dropped a plumb-bob from the face of the pulley on the machine to the floor, as shown in the illustration. A hole was then bored in the floor at the point indicated, which gave us the starting point from which to put up the countershaft, which was easily done.

The next question was that of locating the belt holes. I drew a sketch with chalk on the boiler room floor, making all the dimensions full size. First, was the thickness of the floor, 4 in., and then the distance from the floor to the center of the shaft on the machine, 36 in., and next the pulley on the machine, 24 in., and the countershaft pulley of 12 in. diameter.

The common tangents of the circles were then drawn, thus showing the exact position of the belt. Following out this plan I cut the belt holes and found my calculations to be correct.

Magic Polishing Cloths

So-called "magic" polishing cloths are being sold at 25 cents each. The recipe for making them is as follows: Take 1 gal. gasoline, 2 lb. of whiting, and ½ oz. oleic acid. Mix all together and shake up well. Soak pieces of woolen cloths in this mixture, wring them out and hang up to dry. It will be found that this will place a fine gloss on any polished surface or silverware, etc., and no matter how soiled the cloths become, they will not dirty the hands or lose their polishing efficiency. Contributed by James Ellethorn, Toronto, Ont.

Lifting by the Head

A few days ago I saw an engineer trying to lift the cap off his main bearing with a rope and a couple of pulleys which he had rigged up, as shown in Fig. 1. He pulled on the rope at A till he lifted himself clear off the floor, but could not raise the cap. By jerking down with his whole weight he

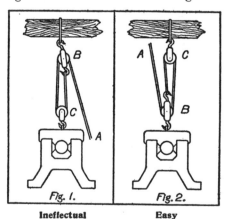

Fig. 1.   **Fig. 2.**
Ineffectual   **Easy**

could just jerk up the cap about ¼ in., and there he was stuck. After he had tugged away in vain for a while I suggested that he make a change in his rig and attach the pulley C to the beam and the pulley B to the cap and then get up on the beam himself and try pulling up; just the reverse of the arrangement which he had. He soon had the change made as shown in Fig. 2, and found that the cap came up easily. After a little study he figured that he could lift half as much again by the arrangement in Fig. 2, as by the arrangement in Fig. 1. That engineer was myself and I am learning that in working about machinery one can sometimes lift more with his head than with his hands.—R. Manley Orr, in Canadian Machinery.

Reamer Holder

One of the best and simplest ways of holding a shell reamer for use in a

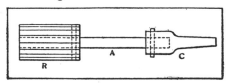

For Accurate Work

lathe is by using a "floating reamer socket," as it is sometimes called. It consists of an arbor, A, one end of which is attached to a socket center, C, and the other to the reamer, R. The arbor is kept from turning by pins which may be either tapered or provided with heads to hold them in place. The arbor should fit loosely in both reamer and center, in order to allow a slight amount of play in the reamer. This style of socket is used in all our general shop work and is the simplest and most accurate that I have ever seen.—Contributed by E. V., Menomonie, Wisc.

A cheap and easy way to clean the clock is to saturate a little cotton, egg-size, with kerosene, and put it on the floor of the clock. Shut tight. In four days the works will be as clean as if new, and the cotton will be black with the particles of dirt which have been loosened by the kerosene fumes.

A Common Defect in Draughts

When a stove doesn't draw properly the trouble can often be found where the pipe enters the flue. The pipe is

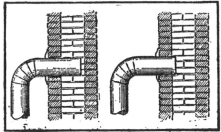

Remedy for Poor Draught

often pushed too far in, thus making the space at the end so small that the smoke cannot rise naturally. To avoid this a correspondent of the Metal Worker bends a piece of sheet iron 1 in. wide and 5 or 6 in. long, so that a $\frac{1}{4}$-in. edge turns over the bottom side of the stove pipe, then when it is pushed into the chimney far enough the other end of this piece of sheet iron is turned down against the side wall to prevent the stove pipe being pushed in too far.

Ventilating a Cold Dry Storage Room

The most effective way of ventilating a room for cool dry storage is to lay a line of 8-in. drain tile, or better, sewer tile, lengthwise and at least 2 ft. below the bottom of the room in the

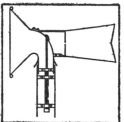

ground, each end provided with an elbow and riser terminating just above the floor level. From one end of this cold dry-air duct carry up above the ridge of the barn an 8-in. galvanized flue provided at the top with a revolving funnel 30 in. in diameter, which is made always to face the wind by means of a vane, the whole constructed as represented in diagram. With such an arrangement as this the wind pressure will force the air down and through the sub-earth duct and up into the storage room, making it dry and cool, says the Rural New-Yorker. At the opposite end of the storage room from that where the air enters an 8-in. outlet in the ceiling should be provided. This need not rise above the roof. The storage room should be provided with a cement floor both to shut off dampness from below and to make it a better conductor of heat, thus more effectively cooling the room, and less favorable to the development of molds.

Insulation Scraper

A good one can be made from thin steel, spring brass, or stiff tin. If the latter, the edges should be turned over, to strengthen it. A good size for the scraper is $2\frac{1}{2}$ by $1\frac{1}{2}$ in. and the notch should be about $\frac{1}{4}$ by $\frac{2}{3}$ in.—Contributed by Geo. W. Fry, San Jose, Cal.

How to Make a Drill Gauge

It will not be necessary to follow any exact dimensions when making this gauge, as the divisions are to be marked by trial with actual drills. Simply measuring the distance between the bars and marking accordingly is a very poor way to make a gauge, because drills are manufactured with diameters slightly less than the nominal size. For instance, the actual diameter of a $\frac{7}{8}$-in. drill is somewhat less than $\frac{7}{8}$ in., so that if the graduations on the gauge were exact dimensions of the nominal

sizes, a $\frac{7}{8}$-in. drill would read 55/64-in.

The accompanying sketch shows a form of gauge which is very accurate, convenient, and easily constructed. By making a more gradual taper, greater accuracy will be obtained at the expense of a reduction in range. It is of the greatest importance that all the pieces be fastened together in such a manner that there will be no movement at the joints, and if necessary, the joints should be soldered in addition to being riveted. The material for this gauge may be either machine steel or tool steel, but as it is very difficult to harden without warping, it would probably be advisable to construct it of machine steel.—Contributed by W. J. S., Emsworth, Pa.

Experience With a Gas Producer Engine Plant

[Extracts from paper read before the American Street Railway Association by Paul Winsor, of the Boston Elevated Railway.]

"As a result of my experience with these plants" [one is a 700-kw., the other a 975-kw. station feeding trolley lines—Editor.] "I am absolutely convinced of the economy and reliability of a gas-engine power station. The fuel consumption will be about one-half as compared with a steam plant, running less than 1.5 lb. to 1.75 lb., according to the load factor and almost regardless of the size of the plant, as against 3 to 4 lb. in similar steam plants.

"The disadvantages of a gas power station as compared with a steam plant are few. The gas-producing portion of such a station is simpler, easier to operate, and holds its efficiency better than a steam plant. The losses from banking fires are extremely small, and

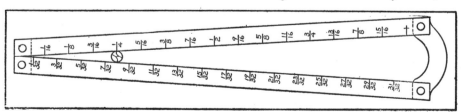

¼-In. Drill in Position for Measuring

the plant can be gotten into service much quicker than can a steam plant. It is our practice to shut down at 11 at night and start at 7 in the morning. Fifteen or 20 minutes are required to get the gas plant into full operation, while of course with a boiler plant it takes from one to one and a half hours to get the fires into first-class shape. The ashes have to be periodically removed from the producer. In our plant this has to be done while the producers are out of commission and takes about 3 hours twice a week, although the plant can be run a couple of days longer without cleaning, if necessary. With some forms of producers the cleaning can be done while the plant is in operation, but I have had no experience on this point as yet, as our second plant, which has this form of producer, has not been in continuous operation. The wet and dry scrubbers have to be cleaned every two weeks, but this work is certainly no more difficult than the work required around a boiler, cleaning soot from the tubes and from the soot chambers.

"An ordinary gas man, such a man as would be considered a first-class fireman, can run at least as many horsepower of gas producers as he can of boilers. He can make a uniform grade of gas and will get regularly very much nearer the possible efficiency from the gas producers than from the boilers."

Cleaning Zinc Articles

Make a paste of rye bran stirred into boiling water and add a handful of silver sand and a little vitriol. Rub the zinc articles with this paste, rinse with water, dry and polish with a cloth.

You can bleach your old straw hat by washing it in clean water and then tying it inside a barrel and turning the barrel down with its open end over a flat stone. On the stone ignite a bit of sulphur and let the hat bleach.

File Sharpening Machine

It would seem that a sand blast directed against a file would take the sharp edges from the teeth, but instead the files are sharpened by the treatment. The machine here illustrated is constructed on this principle. It consists of a sheet-metal hood with an opening in front for inserting the file and a small sand blast apparatus, operated by compressed air or steam.

The sharpening process will be clearly understood from the sectional view of the file teeth shown in Fig. 2 and

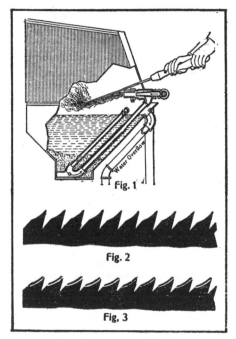

For Resharpening Old Files

Fig. 3, which are drawn to an enlarged scale. The teeth shown in Fig. 2 are those of a new file, and those in Fig. 3 are the worn, rounded teeth of an old one. When the file is held in the sand blast the teeth are cut down, as indicated by the white lines, thus replacing the sharp cutting edges and making the file nearly as good as new. The number of times a file can be re-sharpened depends upon the work for which it is intended and upon the cut and depth of the teeth. In any shop where a large number of files are used the installation of a file sharpening machine will prove a good investment.

◆ ◆ ◆

Shearing Attachment for the Lathe

The accompanying illustration shows a rig for shearing sheets on the lathe.

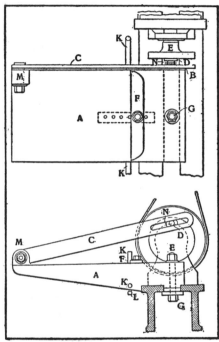

Shearing Attachment for the Lathe

It consists of a casting, A, bolted to the lathe bed and having a boss at the outer end on which is pivoted the knife or shear, C. The shear side of the casting is faced with a plain steel strip about $\frac{1}{4}$ by 2 in. section, held by fillister-head screws, and set at a slight angle from the vertical, says the Practical Engineer, so as to provide clearance without the necessity of grinding to shape. The shear blade, C, $\frac{1}{2}$ by 2 in., is slotted for a crankpin, D. This crankpin is made in the form of a headless shouldered stud having a screw at the face-plate end which is inserted through a slot in the face-plate and held by a nut on the back side.

A coil spring, N, between the shear blade and stud collar keeps the blade in close contact with the opposite cutting edge. The action of the shear is obvious and needs no further explanation.

◆ ◆ ◆

A Magnetizing Kink

This is a little kink which may be convenient for engineers to remember in case they are drilling or tapping out a hole which cannot be readily emptied, says a correspondent of the Engineers' Review. The other day I watched an erecting man who was employed in setting up a new engine. In order that the outer bearing should not bind, he found it necessary to enlarge the hole, A. In chipping out the hole to make it fit easy, the chips of course fell to the bottom, and as the hole had to receive a pin which would fit into the hole its full length, it was necessary that these chips be removed in some manner. To remove the babbitt casing would have made it necessary to block up the end of the shaft and remove the outer pillow block in order that the casing might be turned so that the chips would fall out of the hole.

While I was wondering what process would be employed in removing the chips, the erecting man procured

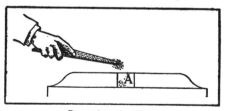

Removing the Chips

a file and, going to one of the generators which was in operation, magnetized it. It was then an easy matter to remove the chips from the hole, as shown in the illustration.

◆ ◆ ◆

The darkest egg-stain may generally be removed from silver by rubbing it with salt on the end of the finger.

Waterproofing Concrete

Treated Blocks Practically Impervious to Water

In an article read before the Detroit Engineering Society by Clarence M. Barber, C. E., the problem of waterproofing concrete was discussed in detail, from which the following has been condensed:

Concrete can be made practically waterproof by making the aggregate as dense as practicable and using about one-half as much cement as sand. It is also claimed that a little thoroughly hydrated lime is an advantage. In the case of blocks, however, the quantity of cement required for a 2 to 1 mixture in the body of the block is generally prohibitive on account of its cost.

The most recent and, we believe, the best, method is to make the body of the block of a good strong concrete with properly graduated sizes of pebbles or broken stone and sand, together with cement enough to make a thoroughly strong concrete and then face the block with a thoroughly dense and waterproof mixture by using 1 to 2 cement and sand and 1 per cent of a good waterproof compound. This protects not only the inside face but the entire block and practically no moisture is absorbed even by the outer face.

A glass of water inverted on the face of such a block will hold the water for weeks with practically no absorption by the block. The writer has a glass of water inverted on a piece of a block that has been standing four weeks. About one-third of the water has escaped in that time. On an ordinary clay brick the water passed wholly out of the glass in an hour.

In a well equipped concrete block factory the freshly made blocks are kept for a time in rooms where the atmosphere is saturated with moisture and generally a sufficient quantity of steam is admitted to hold the moisture above the dew point. This treatment gives sharp, hard corners and edges to the blocks, and together with a little heat, it hastens the setting.

Chimney Brace

One of the simplest and strongest chimney braces consists of two pieces of angle iron, A and B, drilled to receive the steel rods, C and D. These can be fastened to the house in any substantial manner and should be

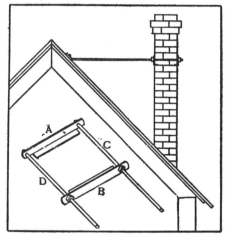

Bracing a Chimney

threaded for nuts to hold the angle irons against the chimney.—Contributed by H. L. M., Philadelphia, Pa.

Easy Way to Temper

Probably the easiest way to temper center punches, cold chisels, etc., is as follows: Heat the tool to a cherry red and dip the point in cold water about ½ in. Hold in this position for about 3 seconds or more, depending on the size of the tool, and then remove. Place a little clean, dry sawdust on the cutting edge and wait until it begins to turn black. Then plunge the entire tool in water and allow it to remain there till cold.

If the sawdust turns black as soon as it touches the steel, it shows that the point was not held in the water long enough, and if it doesn't turn black at all, it was held in too long.—Contributed by Geo. A. Lowell, Chico, Calif.

Speed for Grain Elevator Cups

In order for the cups of a grain elevator to discharge the grain freely in the spouts at their head the wheel which drives the belt at the head should run of following speeds:

Diameter of head pulley	Revolutions per minute
24-in.	40 per min.
30-in.	36 per min.
36-in.	33 per min.
42-in.	32 per min.
48-in.	30 per min.
54-in.	28 per min.
60-in.	25 per min.
72-in.	22 per min.
80-in.	20 per min.

To Mend Bursted Cold Water Pipes

Get five or ten cents' worth of gutta percha chips at your druggist's; scrape bursted place about one inch past either end of burst; burn the gutta percha over the place to be repaired with a hot piece of iron (a stove poker will do); make the gutta percha about ⅛ in. thick and while very hot wrap tight and closely with mason's twine and fasten the ends; let the repaired place cool, and turn on water very slowly, giving the gutta percha time to harden. Do not expect to get good results, if mending pipes larger than ¾ in. or above a pressure of 70 lb. Repairs made as above must not be made where ground will come in contact with the repaired place, as it will cause the twine to rot. I have used the above method with excellent results.—Contributed by A. C. J. Campbell, Altoona, Pa.

Gilding Iron and Steel by Dipping

The dipping process of gilding is not very durable, but may sometimes be found suitable for iron and steel articles. For gilding pin heads, use a solution of gold chloride in potassium cyanide, says the Keystone. Stick the points of the pins into holes in a thick sheet of zinc and hold the heads for a few seconds in the gilding fluid.

A solution of gold in aqua regia to which soda in sufficient quantity to make an excess of this latter constituent has been added, is used for steel pens, which may be dipped entirely, or only the points, as desired.

For coating iron or steel with gold procure crystallized gold-and-sodium chloride by dissolving gold in aqua regia, evaporating the solution to dryness, mixing with an equal quantity of salt, dissolving again and evaporating to the point of crystallization; dissolve the gold-and-sodium chloride so procured in three or four volumes of water, shake the solution with ether, allow the ether to evaporate and then apply the fluid. This coating is susceptible to a high polish. Designs may be drawn on iron or steel with a quill pen dipped into the fluid. Or, coat the article with shellac, make the design with an etching tool, dip the article in dilute sulphuric acid which will etch in the design, and then dip the article into the gilding fluid. Remove the shellac by a treatment with strong alcohol.

How to Draw Pen Lines

As a rule draw pen lines from top to bottom, diagonally across the paper, beginning at the upper right hand corner, especially long sweeping lines where the fore-arm can be used as an axis, the entire hand swinging freely and with a rapid movement. When drawing slow lines, where much care is needed, such as the outlines, etc., says Art Students' Magazine, the lines are drawn more perpendicularly and with the finger movement, that is, the arm and hand remain rigid and only the fingers move. There are no hard and fast rules for holding or using a pen; all artists do not work in the same way, but the above points will help you. Taken altogether, you should acquire an easy swing to your strokes and avoid a slow, cramped movement, but this easy swing must come from practice and confidence gained through knowledge.

In "inking in" a drawing, ordinarily start at the upper left-hand corner and work towards the lower right-hand corner, thus keeping your finished work clean and always before your eye. Keep a sheet of paper or a clean blotter under your hand or fingers; be careful not to allow your hand, when moist or sweaty, to rest on the paper over which you have not worked, as this will make it greasy and it will not take ink readily. In holding and turning your paper with your left hand (as you should in finishing a drawing with pen) it is well to touch it only with the first and fourth fingers, or the thumb and second or third finger, whichever you find most convenient.

Short, Accurate Method for Securing Length for Belt

When it is not convenient, or possible, to measure with line the required amount of belt needed, add the diameter of the two pulleys together, divide the result by 2 and multiply the quotient by $3\frac{1}{8}$. Add your product to twice the distance between the shafts carrying the pulleys and your length for belt is found.

Emergency Repair for Broken Eccentric Rod

Recently a belt run off the flywheel of a small upright engine and jammed between the wheel and the eccentric, breaking the eccentric rod. Repair was made as shown in the illustration, says the Engineers' Review.

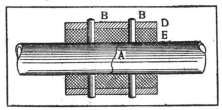

Rod as Repaired

Two $\frac{1}{4}$-in. holes, B and C, were drilled through the rod A and a $1\frac{1}{2}$-in. coupling, D. Pins were then driven through the holes. Babbitt, E, was

then poured into the coupling. This worked well for several weeks, when a new rod was put on.

A Wind Curtain

By using the device here shown an abundance of fresh air may be obtained without the objectionable wintry winds.

Admits Air but Prevents Draughts

It is very simple in construction, of practically no cost and easily put up. A piece of burlap, slightly wider than the window, is sewed at the top and bottom edges to form casings. Two pieces of curtain rod are then pushed through the casings and fastened to the window frame by means of brass hooks. The hooks should be placed far enough apart to hold the burlap taut, the upper hooks being turned up and the lower ones down.—Contributed by a reader.

Files clogged with tin or lead will be cleaned by a few seconds in strong nitric acid. For iron filings use blue vitriol, rinse in water and dip in nitric. For copper or brass, use nitric several times; for zinc, dilute sulphuric acid. After any of these treatments, rinse the files in water, brush vigorously and dry in sawdust or by burning alcohol on the file.

LARGE MARINE GAS ENGINES

It may not be a great many years before battleships and other sea-going craft will be propelled by gas engines instead of reciprocating steam engines or steam turbines. According to statements made by Commander A. B. Willits, of the U. S. Navy, the outlook for

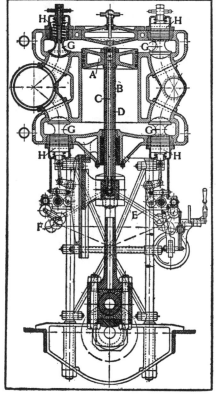

gas engines of high power is very favorable. Gas engines up to 500 hp. have already been installed in many boats with results that have been entirely satisfactory

Aside from increased fuel efficiency the gas engine has other advantages, as follows: Less weight for a given power; no boilers; no pipe lines under pressure; no smoke; no ashes; no coaling-ship distresses; no stoking; no fuel cost or delay in getting up steam; no fuel cost by keeping fires for standing by; and many others.

But the present perfection of the high-power gas engine was not obtained without encountering many difficulties, as it was found that simply increasing the dimensions of an ordinary gas engine resulted in overheating, disordered valves, and decreased reliability. The illustration herewith from the Journal of the American Society of Naval Engineers shows a longitudinal section through one of the cylinders of a modern 500-hp. gas engine. This is a double-acting 4-cycle engine, i. e., explosions occur on each side of the piston, thereby giving the same stroke efficiency as a 2-cycle engine, or one explosion for each revolution.

The cooling of this engine was a serious problem, as the piston and some of the other moving parts required water jackets, which made it necessary to use what might well be called heroic treatment. It is an easy matter to cool the cylinder, but to cool the piston and other moving parts, swinging couplings and expansion joints are required. The piston, A, and piston rod, B, are made hollow as shown, the hollow piston rod containing a pipe, C, which is somewhat smaller than the bore, thus leaving a space, D, for the return of the circulating water. The cooling water can thus be brought into the pipe by a swinging connection, E, at the cross head and carried into the hollow piston, where it absorbs some of the heat and then passes down through the circulating space, D, and out through the cross head into another swinging connection, F. It then passes through a cooler and is returned to the circulating pump to be used over again.

The construction of the valves, G G, is such that they are balanced, i. e., the pressure tending to force them against the seats is opposed by a pressure in the opposite direction acting on the small pistons, H H, thus preventing pounding and wearing of the valves and seats. The valves are all mechanically operated and internally cooled by water brought in through expansion joints.

Compressed air is used for starting this engine, as it would be very difficult to turn the shaft by means of a hand power device.

SHOP NOTES

To Repair a Gasoline Pump

The piston or plunger that becomes worn, where it comes in contact with the packing (Fig. 1) in a gasoline or oil pump on an engine can be repaired by using a piece of brass tubing near the size of the piston cut to a length that will cover over the part that is worn (Fig. 2). Dress the piston with a file until tubing will fit close. The tubing should be soldered to the piston if it does not fit close enough to keep the air from passing between them. The hole through the packing nut and head will then have to be drilled with a drill large enough to admit the brass tubing.

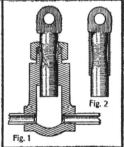

Special Forms for Cutting Blueprint Paper

Anyone using blueprint paper from rolls will know that it is not easy to cut the right size and when cut it has some curl to it. We use different sizes of paper, says a correspondent of Industrial Magazine, and, therefore, we have a form for each size. The smallest is simply a $\frac{1}{2}$-in. board cut true and provided with a knob handle in the center. The larger forms are made of

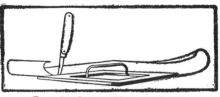

Form for Cutting Blueprint Paper

$\frac{1}{2}$-in. by $1\frac{1}{2}$-in. poplar, braced with brass corner pieces, as shown in sketch.

By using these forms we can cut enough paper to last several days; lay it in a dark drawer, face down, one sheet on top of another, and then place a flat surfaced weight on top of it all. The advantages are: rapid cutting, cutting to size, practically no waste, and flat paper instead of curled paper to put in the printing frame.

Repairing Leaky Valves

Often globe or angle valves used for cold or hot water, or other liquids, start leaking after being in use for some time. Of course, where a set of reseating tools are available they can soon be repaired, but these handy tools are not always on hand. A simple method of overcoming the difficulty is to remove the hood and sandpaper the brass valve disc bright at A where it sets on the seat, then go all around it with a hot soldering iron and place a coating of solder all around it; when it is put back it will be found to be perfectly liquid tight. This scheme is not effectual where high pressure steam is used, as it will not stand long in this case.—Contributed by Jas. Ellethorn, Toronto, Ont.

Screwing Flanges on Large Pipe

The difficulty of screwing flanges on pipe of large size is well known to those who have tried it, as these flanges are made so short that it is difficult to grip them in any way. An expedient which has been resorted to and found amply satisfactory in many cases is to place bolts loosely in the bolt holes in such a manner that a large stick of timber

Screwing a Flange on a Large Pipe

will be held between them, says The Metal Worker, the stick acting as a lever by which the flange can be turned. This method is shown in the accompanying illustration, and will commend itself not only on account of its simplicity but the rapidity with which the work can be done.

A Handy Reamer

Forge the shank A to go in the brace or bit stock, then draw the end down to the taper you want the reamer to be and make a little short, say ¾ in. If the reamer is to be ½ in. at the large and ¼ in. at the small end, draw it down to that size and flatten down to ¼ in. at both ends. In making the twist, care should be taken that it is done properly and not given too many turns, says a correspondent of The Blacksmith and Wheelwright. After the twist is given, hammer lightly at a low heat until proper size is obtained, then let it cool. File with a round file, using care not to touch cutting edges. One thing to remember is

Handy Reamer

the twist should be just the opposite from a twist drill. To temper, heat it all except the shank at a low heat, plunge in water and cool entirely, after which polish with emery stick and draw temper over the fire, using care not to heat small end too fast. Let color run to a purple and cool.

To Stop Gas Tube from Leaking

The ordinary woven tubing for connecting lights, stoves and heaters to the gas jet almost invariably leaks. The salesman will claim that the gas soaks through the webbing and that the odor cannot be avoided except by buying expensive tubing—10 to 15 cents a foot. The fact is that the leak is at the junction of the rubber tips with the webbing, as you can prove easily by wrapping the joints carefully with bicycle tape. Examine your tubing closely before buying to make sure that it is not defective or broken at any point, and then wind the joints spirally and tightly with the tape, going over it twice in opposite directions and continuing it at least 1½ in. each way from the junction. It will be still better, if you have any rim or tire cement, to smear joint freely before wrapping. In this way a 5-cent tubing is made odorless.

Removing Paint from Iron Tank

To remove paint from an iron tank, take lime and mix with common lye into a thick paste by the addition of water, says Engineering Review, and apply over the surface of the metal with a mason's trowel to a thickness of about ⅛ in. After allowing the mixture to remain a short time, wash off with a hose and most of the old paint will be entirely removed, the remainder being easily scraped off with a scraper. If the tank contains several coats of dried paint, two or three applications will be necessary before the entire surface is clean.

Cleaning Porcelain Bath Tubs

To clean a porcelain-lined bath tub, use hot water and a rag saturated with gasoline. If the gasoline is objectionable, smear a little vaseline on the dirtiest parts and remove dirt and vaseline at once with rag and hot water. Never scour porcelain tub, nor nick or scratch its surface in any way.

Home-Made Turning Lathe and Emery Grinder

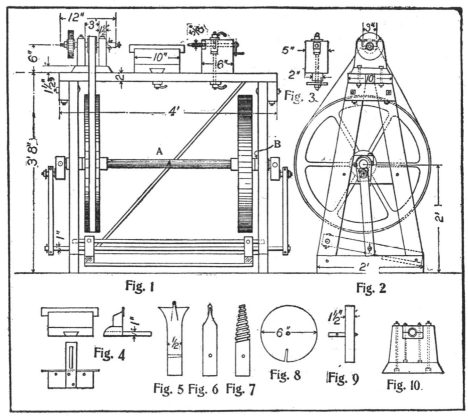

Fig. 1   Fig. 2

Fig. 4

Fig. 5 Fig. 6 Fig. 7   Fig. 8   Fig. 9   Fig. 10

Details of Home-Made Turning Lathe and Emery Grinder

The frame is made of 2 by 4-in. timbers framed and bolted together. The driving power consists of a pair of old mowing-machine wheels and their axle, A, mounted in brass boxes, B, also taken from old mower. The lathe head is made of $1\frac{1}{2}$-in. lumber, and held together with $\frac{3}{8}$-in. bolts. The spindle is a piece of 1-in. bright turned shafting turned down to $\frac{3}{4}$ in. at bearings and to $\frac{5}{8}$ in. for emery wheel. In end of shaft opposite emery wheel a $\frac{1}{2}$-in. hole is drilled in center of shaft 2 in. deep. Into this hole is fitted the different attachments. A spur center is made by flattening the end of a piece of $\frac{1}{2}$-in. shafting and filing a point on it, Fig. 5, and the screw center, Fig. 7, is made out of a wood screw with head re-

moved, while the face-plate, Figs. 8 and 9, is made of another piece of $\frac{1}{2}$-in. shafting fastened in a round disc of wood. A $\frac{1}{2}$-in. bolt with head removed makes the arbor. The spindle bearings are held in separate wooden boxes fastened in head standards and are babbitted, which allows adjustment of bearings without loosening standards.

The tail screw is made of a $\frac{5}{8}$-in. bolt screwed in its own nut which is countersunk in the face of tail block and is held from turning by an eye bolt, with hand nut. A piece of rat-tail file ground to a point is inserted in a hole drilled in the tail screw.

The lugs were removed from mower wheels by striking them on the side with a hammer and dressing down with a file and cold chisel.—Contributed by Frank W. Rumsey, New London, O.

Home-Made Arc Lamp for Blue-printing

An arc lamp that will save time and trouble for those having large quantities of blueprinting or photographic work may be built as follows:

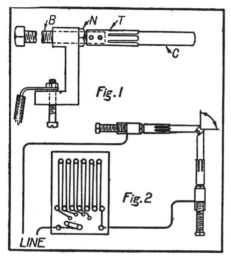

Blueprint Arc Lamp

In a plaster mold, cast two lead uprights as per sketch. If you want a fancy job make them of brass. Drill and tap the shoulder for a $\frac{3}{8}$-in. bolt and the base for a 10-24 machine screw. Thread two $\frac{3}{8}$-in. bolts 4 in. long up to the head (B, Fig 1), pass on a lock nut, N, and then screw one through each of the uprights. Bush the ends of the bolts to fit tightly inside of a piece of thin wall brass tube 2 in. long by $\frac{1}{2}$ in. inside diameter, the other end of the tube being double slotted (T, Fig. 1). Two pieces of $\frac{1}{2}$-in. carbon, such as is used for trimming ordinary arc lamps, should be forced into the tube, the slotted ends gripping them firmly (C, Fig. 1).

The two uprights should then be mounted on a board, over which has been pasted a piece of asbestos $\frac{1}{8}$ in. thick, at right angles, so that when the bolts are screwed clear back the carbons will be about $\frac{1}{2}$ in. apart.

As the lamp will probably have to operate on a 110-volt circuit it will be necessary to have some sort of a resistance to hold down the current to the required 50 volts at the arc and 5 amperes also for regulation.

For this resistance we will need about 100 ft. of bare German silver wire No. 18 which may be wound on porcelain insulators on the face of a board which has been lined with asbestos. A 4-point switch should be connected in to cut out the required resistance for regulation. Small prints from linen tracings may be done in from 8 to 15 seconds, while those from co-ordinate paper will take from 40 to 80 seconds. With this piece of apparatus you can do as good work as can be done with a lamp that would cost in the open market from $10 to $25.

With suitable lenses this lamp may also be used in connection with a stereopticon.—Contributed by A. D.

Adjustable Drop Light

Cut a spring shade roller to any convenient length for attaching, by the usual sockets at each end, to rafters or other supports over the spot where you wish an electric light to be suspended. Attach a cord to the roller

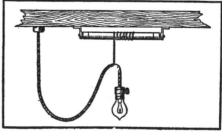

Adjustable Drop Light

and wind it so as to coil the spring when it is pulled down, just as a shade would do. Tie the other end of the cord to the insulated wire of your electric light. Of course, the latter can now be made to hang at any desired elevation.—Contributed by Joseph M. Campbell, Altoona, Pa.

Home-Made Jib Crane

A small jib crane can be made out of material gathered up around the scrap heap. The standard, R, as

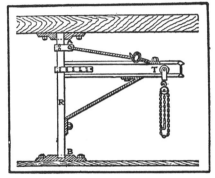

Home-Made Jib Crane

shown in sketch, may be cut from an old piece of 3-in. shafting, says American Machinist, while bearings for top and bottom ends, A and B, may be made from reinforced blank-pipe flanges. Suitable grooves should be cut around bottom of the shaft for lubrication. A one-ton chain block hung on trolley, T, travels on the I-beam. It can be made to cover a circle 20 ft. in diameter.

How to Make a Portable Table

A table for outdoor use that can be taken apart, stored or changed from place to place may be made at small expense. Fasten cleats with screws, as shown in Fig. 1, to the bottom of a board of suitable size. The legs are built with a crosspiece, A, Fig. 4, at the top which fits into slot formed by the cleats, CC, and a crosspiece, B, that has two cleats, D, making a place to receive the bot-

tom end of the brace, E, Fig. 2. The upper ends of the braces, EE, fit in between two pieces, F, fastened in the middle of the board. The three pins fitted loosely in DD and F, Fig. 2, is all that holds table together. The end view is shown in Fig. 3.—Contributed by F. B. Ewing, Santa Clara, Cal.

Snap Flask Weights

After using weights as shown in end views, Fig. 2, for snap flasks, I devised ones as shown in Fig. 1. Weight

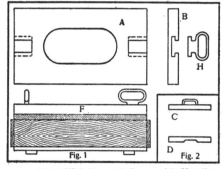

Snap Flask Weights with Removable Handles

C, Fig. 2, is cast with a wrought-iron handle in it, which makes it very inconvenient for stacking. The cutout for the fingers in weight D, Fig. 2, brings the hand in contact with the hot gases. In Fig 1, A shows top plan and B end view of the flask weight I constructed. The handle H is removable and allows weights to stack well

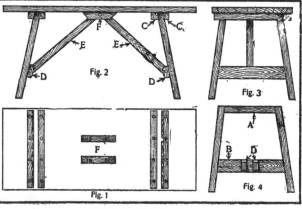

Table for Outdoor Use

when not in use, and also remains cool for the hands. A flask is shown at F with the weight in use.—Contributed by C. R. McGahey.

Device for Long-Distance Tape Reading

A little device used for the purpose of taking ordinates is illustrated in the accompanying sketch. The device fits over the tape and slides along it, and when properly set is clamped by the thumb and the distance read, says Engineering News. This device enables one to take right-angle ordinates from

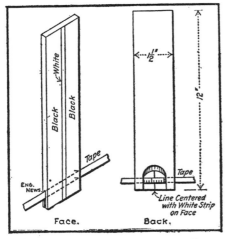

"Fits Over Tape and Slides Along It"

the transit line at a distance of five or six hundred feet with great accuracy and convenience.

Pointer for Turning Tapers on a Lathe

A point which should be remembered but is often neglected is that in turning tapers of any kind on a lathe be sure to have the cutting edge of the tool exactly the same height as your centers. If you don't the taper will vary with each cut, no matter whether you are using a taper attachment or a set-over tail stock. The variation may be slight, but on fine work it tells.—Contributed by E. V.

Saves Belt Wear

It is poor policy to let an idle belt hang loose on a revolving shaft. Of course, in time there will be an appre-

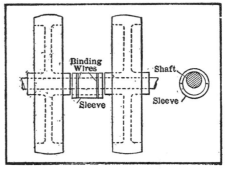

To Save Belt Wear

ciable wearing away. Better take two wood bushings a little larger than the shaft and bind them on with soft wire at the place where the belt will rest when idle. The cut, by courtesy of the American Machinist, shows this device very plainly.

Handy Taper Reamer for Roughing out Holes

A first-class reamer for roughing out all kinds of tapered holes for valves and

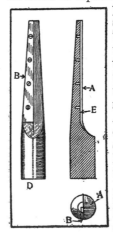

pet cocks is made as shown in drawing. The shank and cutter holder, D, is turned from tool steel to within 1-32 in. of the size wanted, then milled as shown at A. A second cut is taken on the milling machine as shown at E, leaving a recess to take the cutter blade, B. The screw holes in blade should be a little large to allow adjustment for wear, which can be taken up with strips of paper inserted behind it. The holder and blade must be hardened and ground to size.

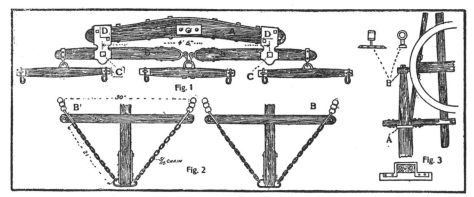

Fig. 1

Fig. 2

Fig. 3

How to Make a Three-Horse Evener

A good way to make a three-horse evener to be used on a truck wagon for heavy work is shown in Fig. 1. The doubletree, A, is made like any other doubletree for a two-horse wagon, except that it is longer, and, of course, somewhat heavier, being 4 ft. 6 in. long. The eveners, B B, are 33 in. long, and divided so that two-thirds of their lengths are inside the drawpins, C C. The two clevices, shown at D D, are made of $4\frac{1}{2}$ by $\frac{5}{16}$-in. iron, and, to give to them a neat appearance, the top side is cut out with a gouge and rounded at the points as shown, says The American Blacksmith. A heavy plate 2 by $\frac{5}{16}$-in. is fitted and bolted to the back of the doubletree, and a hook is to be turned up on each end to keep the clevices in place. These eveners could not be used with one pole only in the center, because the middle horse is placed in front of the center of the wagon, and for that reason two poles are used. Three-horse trucks are sometimes built with a double set of hounds, but any two-horse truck can readily be converted into a three-horse truck and still be available for two horses by simply changing the doubletree and pole. In Fig. 3 is shown the attachment and the way they are put on. A socket, A, is bolted to the splinter bar and made to fit the pole. Another socket, B, for the back end of the pole is bolted to the side hound as shown. No neckyoke is used, the pole-chains answering the purpose of holdbacks, the two inside pole-chains shown at A, Fig. 2, being attached to the middle horse. To prevent the chains from pulling the horses together a spreader bar is made, 30 in. long. This is cut down at the ends to fit the long links of the chain at B, Fig. 2. A pin is inserted in the hole outside of this link as shown.

Boring Hole Through Wheel

Many times when boring a hole for the shaft of a wood pulley or when filling the old hub and reboring, if a lathe is not at hand, a brace and bit has to be re- 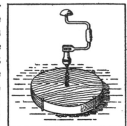 sorted to and the hole bored is quite likely to be anything but square with the wheel. To bore square and straight, lay the wheel flat on the floor and drive about it three or four spikes so that it may be turned. Place your bit in center found by compasses or square and begin boring, holding brace as you think about straight above the wheel. While you are boring let another person be continually turning the wheel. Bore half way through, turn the wheel over and finish the hole in the same manner, and when finished the hole will be true with wheel.

Home-Made Medicine Cabinet

A cabinet for medicine can easily be made by using an old clock. After removing the works, shelving may be placed in it suitable for bottles and a drawer or two may be added for

Medicine Cabinet

smaller articles. The one shown in sketch is the way I arranged the drawers and shelves. It answers the purpose of one that would cost several dollars.—Contributed by G. C. Murphy, Owensboro, Ky.

A Simple Anvil Shears

I have never seen any tool as handy as this one, says A. S. Primmer in American Blacksmith. I learned its

use in a railroad shop. It is a pair of shears for use on the anvil. It is made of steel and is forked to fit the size of stock to be cut. But small iron can be cut in a large tool. The top tool need not be so deep as the bottom. One good heavy blow with sledge of 12 or 14 lb. will cut ¾-in. round. It can be made with a spring or, if a helper is handy, a handle same as on a chisel or fuller is best. Be careful to temper the inside of the fork for cutting and you will have no trouble. It is tempered same as a cold cutting chisel, but in the center of fork. Be sure to bring the two straight sides of both tools together. I have seen this shear do some very heavy work. A size for each rod is best, but you can make one do for several sizes of stock.

To Stop Leak in Suction Gas Producer

The top plate of our gas producer is cast iron and somewhat over 4 ft. in diameter. The fire having been allowed to burn out over Sunday, to give a chance to clean out the producer, the top plate became unusually warm and then cold, so that the expansion and contraction caused it to crack. The iron was of too hard a quality, and the crack extended right across the top and opened up nearly $\frac{1}{16}$ in. The engineer, not noticing the crack, started a new fire Monday morning, and the engine ran all right until it had sucked all the gas out of the scrubber. Then it slowed down and finally stopped, for it was sucking air through the cracked plate instead of gas from the coal. By closing the air-mixing valve on the engine we got it started again, but the supply of air through the crack was still too great.

In this emergency I took some clay, used to babbitt bearings, thinned it with water, and let it drop slowly on the crack. As the suction of the engine drew the clay gradually into the fissure, the heat baked it so thoroughly that the leak was effectually stopped and everything worked as well as ever. As the crack closed it was necessary to open the air valve gradually to compensate.—Contributed by J. A. Manning, Owen Sound, Ontario.

Tempering Color for Tools

After hardening a tool should be polished and drawn as follows:

Lathe, planer and boring tools—Light straw.
Reamers, taps, scrapers—Dark straw.
Drills—Brown.
Wood bits, slitting saws, etc.—Light purple.
Wood saws, screwdrivers—Dark purple.
Cold chisels, punches—Blue.

DESIGNS FOR PANELS—From Decorator and Painter's Magazine, London

Coloring Putty

Ordinary painters' colors in oil, preferably transparent colors, such as burnt and raw sienna, burnt and raw umber and lampblack, are best for coloring putty. Make the putty several shades darker than the wood, says the American Carpenter and Builder, as all wood grows darker with age.

Noiseless Exhaust for Motor Boat

Everyone who rides in a motor boat will be indebted to the Motor Boat magazine for suggesting this method of abolishing the nuisances of the exhaust. It is simple enough—when you know how.

Run the exhaust pipe overboard at a point one-half foot above water line, and there screw on an ordinary elbow, leaving it free to turn. Into the elbow screw solidly 4 ft. of 1½-in. pipe, and to this attach a wire or cord by which the end may be held up out of the water. Now, with a little practice, you can master the problem of a noiseless, odorless, heatless, sprayless exhaust.

With the hinged pipe drawn up out of the water, start your engine. As soon as the boat gains headway drop the pipe in, and you will be delighted to discover that your boat is actually going faster and your engine running freer, and without noise or smell.

The reason is evident. The water rushing past the open end of the pipe produces a suction which makes the exhaust more perfect, emptying the cylinder of all exploded gas after each stroke of the piston, so that the next explosion has full effect. On account of varying speed at different times a little experimenting may be necessary in order to find just the right depth to which the open pipe end should be dropped. The vacuum may be still further increased, if desired, by attaching a funnel-shaped piece to the open end.

A Handy Balancing Device

I was in a large shop which devotes itself to the manufacture of heavy transmission machinery, when I noticed a 6-ft. pulley being balanced on a mandrel which was so far from the horizontal that the eye 10 yd. distant could detect the deflection, says a correspondent of The American Machinist. My first thought was that some apprentice new to the job was responsible for such a state of affairs; but when I pointed it out to my friend the superintendent, who was with me, he went over and showed me that ends of the mandrel, instead of resting on parallels, were between and on little steel wheels (Fig. 1). These wheels or rollers ran on carefully ad-

justed ball bearings (see Fig. 2), giving a minimum of friction. Each set was blocked up on anything handy until the rim of the pulley cleared the floor. The castings holding the rollers were rough all over outside, and it did not appear to matter whether they were used in a perfectly vertical position or not.

I expressed my surprise at such a method, but was assured that wheels balanced in this manner were as well done as by the ordinary method.

Managing Saws with Broken Teeth

Roughly-sawn stock is frequently claimed to be caused by one or more

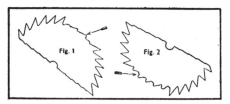

"Set Stubs to Same Gauge as Good Teeth"

teeth being broken out of the saw used. We find sawyers retoothing saws when a few teeth are gone, because they think a saw in that condition cannot be made to do good work, says J. B. Harland in The Woodworker. There is really no excuse for rough sawing because a tooth or two have been broken out. Just set the stubs to the

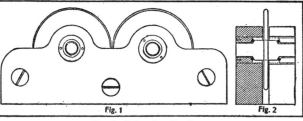

Handy Balancing Device

same gauge as the good teeth, and go ahead. If the stubs are too short to be spring-set, grind or file the throats until they are long enough. If the points of the teeth are swaged, bending the stubs alternately, so that they project just as far as the corners of the swaged teeth, will be all that is necessary. The sketches show cut-off saws thus treated, but rip saws may be handled in this manner to even greater advantage. I know a barrel-heading saw which is doing smooth work notwithstanding eight teeth are broken out, five of them in direct succession, the others in different places. The theory of this treatment is that bending the stubs so that they give the rim of saw plate the same support in the cut that the rest of the plate has, prevents the teeth following the broken ones from dodging, and insures smooth sawing.

Emergency Steam Blower when Stack Fell

A stack was blown down at a lighting station and as the plant had to be in condition to run the same night, a steam blower was made to serve the purpose.

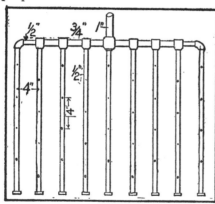

Steam Blower

A steam fitter constructed one like that shown in the accompanying sketch, the vertical pipes being $\frac{1}{2}$ in., 4 in. apart; the holes were $\frac{1}{16}$ in., 4 in. apart. This was applied to the boiler, says Power, and the station started up on time. This blower continued to furnish blast for the boiler for a period of six months.

It is estimated that 50,000,000 bbl. cement will be used this year.

Jointing a Saw

A good method of jointing a saw, particularly a large one, is shown by Fig. 1, in which a piece of emery wheel is shown standing on the saw table. To use the stone grasp it firmly with both hands, and tip the top edge toward

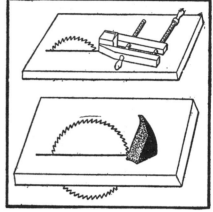

Jointing a Saw

the saw until the stone barely touches the teeth. Watch very closely when the fire begins to fly, for that is the guide to go by when rounding or jointing saws, says Wood Craft. There is no danger of cutting too much off the teeth of the saw, when the sparks are watched closely, for the jointing should be stopped the instant all the teeth are brought to an even length, and when the fire flies from all the teeth they must be all the same diameter and the emery should be removed.

When the fragment of emery wheel is very small, it is not a very desirable operation to hold it in the hand and press it against the fast running saw. In this case, catch the bit of stone in a pair of hand-clamps, square up the stone so it will stand square with the clamps and when they are laid on the saw table the stone must necessarily stand "square with the world." With the clamps, the stone can be fed against the saw in a manner perfectly under control and the method is preferable to the first method of holding the stone in the fingers..

Swinging Doors for Boat-House

Owners of motor-boats will appreciate boathouses supplied with swinging

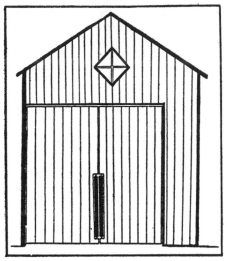

Swinging Doors for Boat-House

doors, as shown in sketch. The doors are each fitted with spring hinges and a set of rollers arranged vertically on the edge where they swing together. On entering or leaving the house simply steer the boat between the rollers and pass in or out without hindrance, says The Motor Boat, the rollers rolling easily along the gunwale. The rollers may be of plain wood but can be covered with felt or rubber, if desired.

◆ ◆ ◆

Handy Shear for Light Metal

A good home-made shear for light metal is described in the American Blacksmith: It will cut hot metal $\frac{1}{4}$ in. thick and $\frac{1}{4}$ in. wide. To make it, take a piece of stock 2 in. by $\frac{1}{4}$ in.

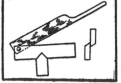

and steel its edge with a strip of old rasp. Then weld on shank to fit in hardie-hole of anvil. Now make the lever of same stock, weld on handle of 1-in. or $\frac{7}{8}$-in. round and drill $\frac{5}{8}$-in. hole in end. Then temper.

Antique Finish on Copper or Brass

Every one who is at all observing has seen and admired the various articles finished in antique copper or brass that are in nearly every office and store. It is one of the prettiest as well as the cheapest finishes known to the metal worker, and is used on hinges, gas-fixtures, transom lifters, trays, and the thousand and one articles in the hardware line. This finish is also known as "oxidized" work and is produced on both copper and brass in exactly the same way.

Suppose you have a small piece of copper that you wish to finish in this way. First mix a strong solution of potash or lye, using about two tablespoonfuls to a quart of hot water.

Then put 5 cents' worth of sulphuret of potash into two quarts of hot water. Also have a bucket of clean hot water handy.

Now take the piece of copper and fasten a short piece of wire to it for a handle, and dip it into the lye, working it up and down to remove all grease and dirt. Then rinse in the bucket of hot water and dip into the sulphuret solution till it is a good, sharp black (brass is a grayish black). Then again rinse in the hot water and hang up to dry. When thoroughly dry, buff all over lightly on a soft cloth buffing wheel, and then buff through to the copper in spots. A little practice will enable one to buff a piece so that it will look as well as if done by an expert.—Contributed by E. V., Menomonie, Wisc.

◆ ◆ ◆

Brazing Cast Iron

To braze cast iron take 1 lb. boracic acid, 4 oz. pulverized chlorate of potash, 3 oz. carbonate of iron, 2 lb. fine brass spelter. Mix well. Heat casting to a brazing heat before applying. Then lay on liberally and work it along the break with an iron rod flattened on the end. Use a gas, gasoline or coke fire, but do not use coal.

How to Determine Speed of a Machine

A very simple way of getting at the speed of any machine you are about to start, and which has an intermediate or countershaft, is to draw a perpendicular line and put the speed of line-shaft and all sizes of the drivers on the left-hand side of the line, says Dominion Mechanical News. Then put all the sizes of the driven pulleys, with X for the required speed, on the other side of the line. Thus: take the speed of a line-shaft at 300 which has a pulley 20 in. in diameter, driving tight and loose pulleys on a countershaft which is 10 in. in diameter. This countershaft has a pulley 18 in. in diameter, driving a cutter head whose pulley is 3 in. in diameter. What is the speed of the cutter-head? By putting the figures representing the driving speed and all the drivers on one side, and all the driven on the other, and working by cancellation, we find that the required speed of the cutter-head is 3,600, thus:

$$\frac{300 \times 20 \times 18}{10 \times 3 \times X} = 3,600$$

This same rule is equally handy for the determination of the size of any drivers or driven pulley driving or driven speed. It is a simple and direct method, and it is accurate and quickly learned. It beats guessing all to pieces.

Packing Pump Piston Rod

I have used a piece of new leather shoe lace for packing a pump piston rod, with excellent results, and for pumping cool water it is hard to beat. —A. L. White, Cresco, Iowa.

A mixture of 4 oz. benzol, 3 oz. fusel oil and 1 oz. of alcohol will remove varnish, paint, tar or lacquer from any varnished or painted surface in less than ten minutes, or restore a hard paint-brush after an hour of soaking in the mixture.

Straightening a Brick Stack

A certain brick stack 75 ft. high, 8 ft. square at the base and 4 ft. 6 in. square at the top, was straightened by the method as described in sketch. The stack was 3 ft. out of plumb and looked as if it were going to fall, says a correspondent of Engineers' Review.

Two good brickmasons and several helpers were secured and the job was completed in just 10 hours.

First, they cut three holes through the north side about 4 ft. above the ground, as in Fig. 1. Through these holes they put three timbers, 16 by 16 in., about 15 ft. long. Back close to

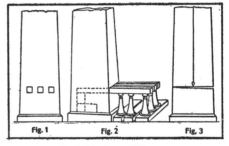

Fig. 1   Fig. 2   Fig. 3

Straightening a Chimney

the inside of the south wall the timbers were blocked up so they were about level while resting on the jack screws on the other end, as shown in Fig. 2. Under each timber was placed three jacks resting on suitable blocking. He then nailed a block on the east side of the stack about 30 ft. from the ground and in line with the center of that side; from this block a plumb bob was suspended as shown in Fig. 3. The stack was out of plumb 18 in. in the 30 ft.

The jacks were then screwed up until there was a good strain on them, while the masons took thin chisels and drove them between the bricks even with the top of the timbers, on the northeast and west sides, while the helpers kept the jacks going up slowly.

In a short time the bricks began to open, and the opening followed the course as straight as if the stack had been cut into with a saw. The opening on the north side was large enough to insert an extra course of brick with ease (see Fig. 3). The brick was then laid between the timbers and on the east and west sides the timbers were removed, the holes bricked up and the job was completed and has never given any trouble since.

Saw Gauge

A very useful gauge for measuring the set of saw teeth is shown in the accompanying sketch. It consists of a 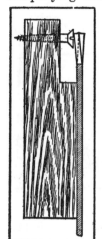 small strip of hard wood with one corner cut away as shown, and a small wood screw. The screw may be adjusted by means of a screwdriver until the head just touches the edge of the tooth as shown. Then by keeping the edge of the wood against the side of the saw and moving the screw from one tooth to another the teeth that are not set properly can be quickly found.—Contributed by M. J. F., Philadelphia, Pa.

To Examine Own Eye

The accompanying cut shows how a magnifying glass and mirror may be used by one's self to locate emery or 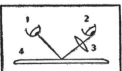 similar substance that may be lodged in the eye.
Beside magnifying the object, the lens, 3, shuts off the vision of the affected eye and enables one to see it plainly at a convenient angle with the unaffected eye.
Explanation of figures in illustration: 1 is unaffected eye; 2, affected eye; 3, lens; 4, mirror. A small reading glass will answer nicely for the lens.—Contributed by Frank Setton, San Jose, Cal.

Home-Made Wheel Bench

The wheel bench is so well illustrated as to need little or no explanation, says American Blacksmith. The rod is adjustable, as shown at A. The rod which supports the spoke is also adjustable for the regulation of the dish. The rod B is fastened at the bottom end to a lever, C, which is operated by the foot. This lever is hinged at the side of the bench, opposite the operator.

Serviceable Wheel Bench

The clip tongs are fashioned from an old buggy top prop iron. In selecting the material for this tool, be sure to have plenty of stock on each arm of the joint.

The other tool is for pulling broken tenons out of hubs. It consists of a lag screw, the head of which is replaced by a piece of $\frac{5}{8}$-in. round stock, sufficient to make the entire tool about 18 in. long. To enable the operator to get a good hold on the tool after screwing it into the broken tenon, the handle end is bent, as shown in the engraving.

One way to impart a deep blue to polished steel is to place it in sand and heat until the color is obtained. Or, paint it with blue lacquer, which is more usual.

How to Grain Pitch Pine

To prepare the ground color for pitch pine it is best to work off a light oak ground color, made by mixing white lead and chrome yellow with a little burnt sienna and patent driers and equal parts of turpentine and oil. The graining is done best and easiest in oil color, which should be mixed the same as for oak, but in place of the umber a little burnt sienna or Venetian red should be employed. The color should be used thin, with equal parts of boiled oil or turpentine, a little patent drier being added, as well as a little megilp. These ingredients should all be thoroughly mixed together in the can, says The Decorator. It may be mentioned here that the megilp is made from the best beeswax melted down in turpentine with a little boiled oil.

Having the graining color ready, prepare a similar color, but quite stiff, and place it on a palette board; then commence by forming the heart of the wood and taking a small flat sable hair fitch, dip it first into the thin graining color in the can and then in the stiff color on the palette. Now, with the fitch full of color, work out the heart from the center of the panel upright in curls and twists. With the same fitch the fine parts of the heart can be worked out, and by holding the fitch on the flat side one can get the broad parts of the curl. The center of the heart must be kept open, but farther apart from each other and darker in color. Then work the veins out finer to each side of the panel, with a lighter shade of color, and with a badger hair softening brush very lightly soften the upright lines, being particularly careful not to let the veins run into each other.

For the stiles or rails of a door, etc., use a 2½-in. thin oak overgrainer. Dip into the thin graining color and pass the hairs through a dividing comb, so as to keep them straight and open. Commence at the top and draw the overgrainer down to the bottom of the stile, then soften the work with a badger very lightly up and down.

How to Make a Concrete Stove

A cement residence in which the building, roof, chimney, porch, and a good portion of the interior finishing was made entirely of cement, led the owner to build a cement stove with which to heat the conservatory. We do not understand that any heating advantages are claimed over an iron stove, but the novelty of the thing makes it interesting.

Reinforced Concrete Stove

The stove was made in three parts, the base, the body and the top. The base was made with concrete grate bars in an ordinary box, the top was made in a round form with a piece of sewer pipe put in for the base of the stove pipe, the hole in the top was made by setting a tin pan, bottom of which was covered with oiled paper, right in the form. The body of the stove was made by setting a small barrel inside a large one and filling the space between the two with concrete, the door being blocked out in the barrel, hinges set in while the concrete was wet. The whole stove was reinforced with "lock-woven steel fabric" at a cost of about one-sixth of what an ordinary iron stove would be.

Economy Ice Box

Scarcely has the last coal been paid for — perhaps before that — when the ice question must be considered. Here there is usually a big leak, both figuratively and literally, for much good ice water is allowed to run to waste.

The ice question has two equally important parts—first, get the weight you pay for; second, get the full benefit of it. It is a safe estimate that half the good of a cake of- ice is lost by the usual method of keeping it in the top of a refrigerator. The economical way is to get an ice-box large enough to hold 200 lb.; it costs about half the price of the ordinary 50-lb. refrigerator.

Take the wooden frame (on which the ice is to rest) out of the box and saw it across into halves. Get an ordinary spool and whittle one end to fit the outlet of the box watertight. It may be necessary to wrap a layer of thin cloth around the end of the spool to secure a tight fit. Having driven the plug in, but not so hard as to strain the metal bottom, put in half the wooden frame, and pour in cold water until it begins to run out through the hole in the spool; but the top of the frame should be out of water. If it is not, nail strips under it.

Order 100 lb. and see that you get it. Have it set on the frame, in one corner of the box, and wrap it on all sides except the bottom with a thick woolen cloth previously dipped in cold water. Now you have an arrangement which will make 100 lb. last a week in ordinary summer weather and at a cost of 35c. Furthermore, you have a splendid tank of ice-cold water all the time in which to set bottles of milk, filtered water, etc., while the food set on the shelves of the box will be almost frozen. Last, and not least, every time you open the box, your cold air will not all spill out, as it does from a refrigerator.

At least once a week the plug should be pulled and the box given a thorough scrubbing with hot water, and left open for a half-hour. Leave the half-frame out to dry and use the second half. In really hot weather the box should be covered on top, back and sides with a heavy woolen blanket, held in place by a few tacks. If the box cover is too heavy for lifting, part of the weight may be carried by a rope attached to the front edge and passed over a pulley to a small weight.—Contributed by Dr. C., Chicago.

For Burns

A good practice in foundries, where burns are frequent, is to put on thick soap suds. It beats all the patent compounds ever gotten up, and besides soap is obtainable anywhere at any time. The lather keeps out the air and draws out the inflammation. After a few minutes the burn, if a bad one, may be wrapped up, but if just an ordinary burn, an occasional application of lather is all that is needed.

Soap and Alum Waterproof Cement

The cement reservoir of the new water system at Uxbridge, Mass., which leaked water at the rate of 25,000 gal. a day, when tested, has been treated with an inside coat of a composition of soap and alum. The composition is made by heating soap, alum and water in a kettle until the mixture is the thickness of a paste, says Cement Age. It is believed that this will fill the pores in the cement and prevent the water from leaking through. This process has long been known to engineers, and, in spite of the theory of some that it will not last, has given entire satisfaction on more than one occasion.

A Hard Drill

If you have a job that requires an unusually hard drill, heat the drill to a nice cherry red and dip about a quarter of an inch of the end in common soldering acid (muriate of zinc).—Contributed by E. Viall.

SHOP NOTES

To Reverse a Chain Drive

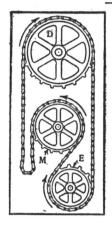

Sometimes it is necessary to run a shaft in the opposite direction from the drive shaft, using sprockets and chain transmission. A simple arrangement of the sprockets as shown in the accompanying cut will give this result, says American Miller. In driving some elevators one extra sprocket wheel, E, was added, which caused the sprocket wheel D on the shaft to be driven to turn in the opposite direction from the sprocket wheel M, on the main shaft.

Extra Seat Attachment for a Bicycle

Take an old bicycle front fork and fit it on the rear axle of the bicycle outside the frame braces. For a brace to hold the seat in position I used a heavy piece of wire, as shown in the illustration. A seat and seat post were fitted in the fork just the same as in the bicycle frame.—Contributed by Randolf W. Seaman, Brooklyn, N. Y.

Showing Extra Seat Attached

A Lawn Mower Feed Cutter

When your lawn mower is not otherwise needed, clamp it to a post with cutting knives upward and build a box to fit up close to the cutting edge, as shown in cut. A belt wheel to drive the mower may be placed on both ends of

Cutting Feed with Lawn Mower

the shaft, but one will do, with a crank to turn it. Feed the material at an angle.

A Novel Cooling Device

A simple but effective method of securing a cool atmosphere in a certain basement, which is used for the storage of wine, has been adopted by the proprietor.

A substantial barrel is placed on top of a water-tight box of sufficient capacity to accommodate the drip from the melting ice, and three or four hundred

pounds of ice are placed inside of the barrel. The latter is provided with a couple of auger holes in the bottom, to permit the escape of water, and a small opening measuring about 8 in. square is cut in the side of the barrel, just high enough from the bottom to come directly opposite the blades of an ordinary 12-in. electric fan, supported on a shelf across the box. When in operation the fan draws a current of air down through the open top of the barrel and out through the square opening. The fan blows this chilled air through the basement and maintains a constant circulation, says the Electric City. The barrel is filled with ice once a day, and the result secured is satisfactory, the temperature of the basement being from 20 to 40° lower than that of the outside air.

A Kink for the Shaper

To shape a punch and leave a shoulder, set the work in the shaper vise with face outward and set stroke of

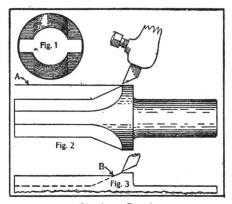

Shaping a Punch

the machine as shown by line at A, Fig. 2. When one cut has been taken and tool lowered for the next it will not begin to start the second cut until it reaches the point B, Fig. 3. Fig. 1 shows end view of the punch completed. This is a good kink for those that do not possess a milling machine. —Contributed by Arthur Benson, Chicago, Ill.

The ink of any steel engraving, no matter how old, will smear if exposed to the slightest friction.

Illuminating a Gauge Glass

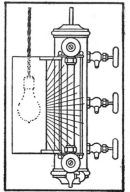

A method used by a writer in The Engineer for lighting up a gauge glass is shown in the sketch. A tin tube 3 in. in diameter and 12 in. long, having a slot ⅜ in. wide by 8 in. long in the side next to the gauge glass, is used. An 8-cp. incandescent lamp is placed inside the tube and throws a powerful light on the glass only.

Water Supply System

The accompanying sketch shows the plan of a water system I have used for the past two years which has given good satisfaction.

I can pump cold water to the reservoir on the stove, hot water from the reservoir to the bath tub or cold water from the cistern to the bath tub. Two globe valves are placed in the pipe as shown at A. One check valve is used at B.—Contributed by Laurice E. Fry, Mt. Sterling, Ill.

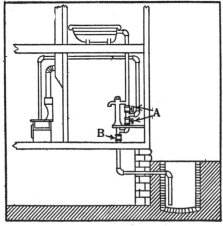

Convenient Water Supply

Repairing Plaster Casts

The following method for repairing plaster casts of all kinds has been tested by years of use. Coat the broken surfaces with thick shellac and expose immediately to alcohol flame until the alcohol in the shellac is nearly all burned out. Then apply the broken parts accurately to each other with slight pressure for a few minutes.—Contributed by Dr. C. E. Fraser, Jr., Rome, N. Y.

Adjustable Hand Gauge

For large duplicate work or to use in connection with turning blanks for twist drills or any large cylindrical work a gauge can be made amply large

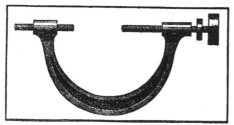

Gauges Work up to 3½ In. Diameter

enough to take this work in and be adjustable to the smaller sizes as shown in the accompanying cut. The main frame is made of cast iron, using ½-in. cold rolled steel with about 20 threads to the inch for screws. On the longer screw fasten a milled head and place a lock nut between head and frame. While the gauge may be of any suitable size the one I made will gauge work up to 3½ in. in diameter.—Contributed by S. H. Heller, 723 Grant St., Akron, O.

Deodorized Glue

One authority recommends the use of a teaspoonful of saltpeter to a pot of glue as a deodorizer, says Wood Craft. It is further claimed that it helps the glue to dry faster and become harder, nor is the strength and tenacity impaired in any way.

A Wooden Boiler

This is a novel way of using a wooden keg for a steam boiler. While it may seem absurd, I have one in good working order, says a correspondent in Engineers' Review.

I took a beer keg and ran a ¾-in. pipe out about 3 ft. and bent it to return,

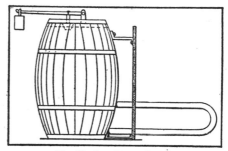

Keg Used as Steam Boiler

as shown in the illustration. This pipe was shoved into the kitchen stove which generated the steam. We ran a ¼-hp. engine attached to a small grindstone which was used to sharpen mowing machine knives on and it saved many a blistered palm.

While this was boys' work, it was more practical than many would think. The boiler was equipped with safety valve having an iron weight. Between the boiler and the stove a partition of asbestos was put in place to protect the boiler.

Charging Small Storage Batteries

A simple way to charge storage batteries such as are used in automobiles

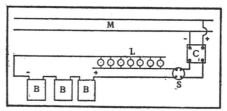

Wiring Diagram for Charging Batteries

and for small electric motors is shown in the sketch. From the main wires, M, connect through a cut-out, C, then to a switch, S. A number of lamp sockets, L, are connected in parallel so that any amount of charging current can be obtained by inserting one or more 16-cp. lamps, says a correspondent of The Practical Engineer. If only $\frac{1}{2}$ ampere is required, insert one lamp; if two amperes is required, insert four lamps, and so on.

Screwing Flanges on Pipe

In our August number we described and illustrated "Screwing Flanges on Large Pipe." The following is even a better plan: It is unnecessary to tie the handle of the chain tongs to a post. The practical way to arrange the pipe and tongs would be to place the tongs as shown in Fig. 1,

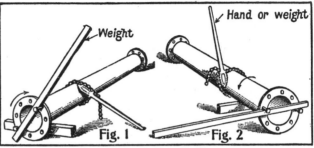

Use a Timber to Turn the Flanges

so that they will hold the pipe from turning, and then allow the handle of the tongs to rest on the floor, using the timber to turn the flange, says a correspondent in the Metal Worker.

Another way would be to allow the end of the plank to rest on the floor, and the workmen could use the tongs to turn the pipe into the flange, the flange being held stationary by the timber, as in Fig. 2.

A Rope Conveyer

A temporary conveyer which can be used in some cases by millers, especially in experimental work, when a regular conveyer is not at hand, is shown in the

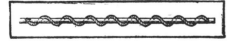

Conveyer May Be Any Length and Size

accompanying sketch. This simple way of making a conveyer is quick and will answer every purpose until a better one takes its place, says American Miller.

The conveyer can be made any length and size to suit the purpose. The shaft can be made of steam pipe. Fasten the rope with a crooked hook and nut. It will stay tight.

A Substitute for Back Plaster

In the construction of buildings it is always desirable to have a dead-air space in the walls, which is usually obtained by putting in back plaster. A good heavy paper that is tough enough not to tear easily will serve the purpose just as well. Two ways are shown how this may be done. To use 32-in. paper and put it on vertically, as in Fig. 1, will cover two spaces. All laps should

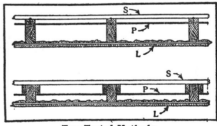

Two Tested Methods

be on solid bearings, says American Carpenter and Builder. Then strip with $\frac{7}{8}$-in. pieces and put on the sheathing S in the usual manner. Fig. 2 shows another plan, but is not so good, as the paper, P, must be cut to fit the spaces.

Clean soiled playing cards by rubbing with soft rag dipped in a very little camphor solution.

A Device for Spacing Holes in a Belt

Use for a handle a piece of metal to which is soldered spring wire fingers, as shown in cut at A. These fingers

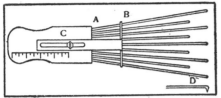

Can Be Set for Any Width Belt

pass through a sliding gauge, B, and can almost instantly be set for any width belt by the thumb nut, C, and scale marked on the handle. When set the fingers are at equal distances and are ready to be struck lightly or drawn over belt for marking. The ends of the fingers are turned down and sharpened, as shown at D, to give a point for marking.

Smoking Meat without Smoke House

A novel way of smoking meat without a smoke house is shown in the sketch. Take a box about 4 ft. high and 2 or 3 ft. wide and remove both ends. Dig a hole in the ground about 2½ ft. deep and from this hole dig a trench the length of a stove pipe and 8 in. deep. At the other end of the trench dig a small hole and place over it the box. Put a joint of old stovepipe in the trench and cover it up, and bank up the box with earth, says the Dakota Farmer. Make a cover for the large hole from a piece of tin or an old stovepipe uncoupled and flattened out. After the meat has been in the brine

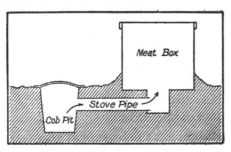

about two weeks take it out and put it in a tub of cold water for a day and night and then it is ready to place in the box. A fire made out of a few cobs in the large hole will do the work equal to a smoke house.

Repairing a Broken Cylinder

An engine cylinder that was cast to the main frame as shown in cut was broken at the point A right on top of the port, where the metal was so thin that it could not be repaired by putting on a patch. A cylinder head was cast with an extension, B, and by using some long stud bolts that screwed into the steam chest the crack was closed

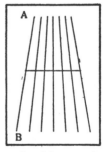

How the Crack Was Closed

and made the cylinder as good as new.
—Contributed by C. R. McGahey.

How to Make a Special Divided Rule

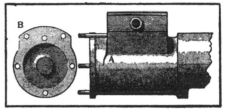

Take a piece of paper and lay out as many equal divisions as you wish the inch to have, making at point A less than an inch and at point B more than an inch in width. Draw lines between each corresponding point and with a rule find the width of an inch and cut the paper at this point.—Contributed by Allen Casey, Windsor, Conn.

Iron and steel may be cleaned of grease or paint by boiling in a solution of ¼ lb. caustic soda to 1 gal. of water. Mixture can be used several times.

Quickly Made Counter-Bore

Use a piece of round stock, as shown in cut at A, that will fit the hole in the work, C, and place in the drill chuck. Take a piece of square tool steel, B, the size of which is to be determined by the hole wanted, and clamp to the side of the round stock with two lathe dogs, as shown. The end of the tool steel, B, must be ground with clearance. This not only makes a counter-bore but serves to dress the work around a bolt hole to form a level seat for the bolt head and nut.—Contributed by Charles W. Partridge, New Haven, Conn.

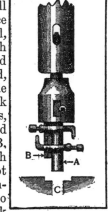

Bending Angle Iron

To accomplish the bending of a considerable number of angle irons ranging from 2 by 2 in. to 6 by 6 in., and to a radii ranging from 18 in. to 10 ft., some cast-iron plates were made 2 in. thick and about 3 ft. long, says a correspondent in the Blacksmith and Wheelwright. Three plates were found all that were necessary, and they were fastened together, as shown in Fig. 1, the plates being held together by two large bolts, and three set screws also being put into each of the outside plates, so the distance between each of the plates could be adjusted at will. Holes were cored through the cast plates, which had no machine work whatever, and the clamp, A, is shown placed in one set of the holes. The other holes permit the clamp to be attached almost anywhere along the circumference of the jig. A piece of 3-in. shaft was put through another hole, B, which was located in the balance center of the jig. Blocks placed under the shaft, as shown by sketch, Fig. 2, permit the jig to be revolved so any desired portion can be brought uppermost.

In bending a piece of angle iron a portion of the jig is selected which is of the desired radius, the clamp is set, the angle heated, slipped under the clamp at one end and the flange is quickly hammered down to the desired degree of curvature. The distance between two of the plates is adjusted by means of the set screws, so that the web of the angle will just go between the plates. Then, when driven down by blows on the flange, the web is kept straight and in its proper shape by being forced between the iron plates.

When it is desired to bend the angle with the web outermost the jig is revolved bottom side up and the angle is heated and clamped as before and driven into that portion of the jig which is of the right concavity.

If a belt persists in slipping, hold a piece of tar soap on the inside of the belt while it is running.

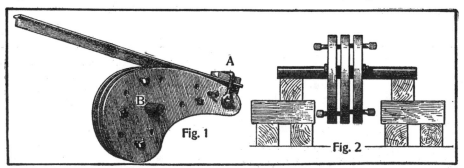

Bending Angle Iron to Various Radii

Another Way to Ground a Wire

Having read in Shop Notes the best ways to fasten a ground wire to the ground, I wish to submit my plan. I simply take a piece of small pipe, say $\frac{3}{4}$-in., and long enough to reach the damp earth. Bend a hook in a piece of heavy wire and hook into the bottom of the pipe and drive both into the ground, as shown in cut. Either lead this wire to the desired place, or solder onto it, which can be done with less danger 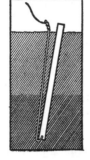 of a loose connection and a poor ground than by soldering to a piece of pipe.— Contributed by H. C. Gamble, Keifer, I. T.

Old Boiler Used for a Forge

A forge to be used for heating large parts can be made from a section of

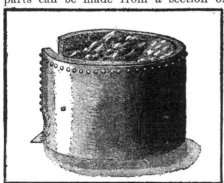

For Heating Large Parts

an old boiler, which can be obtained at a very low cost, says Street Railway Journal. The boiler used in this instance extends about 4 ft. under ground and is left unfilled up to the fireplace. The brick lining is held up by cross bars supported from the rim of the forge. The grate was formed of the perforated plate of a Providence car fender. A motor-driven blower placed overhead supplied air to the forge through a square wood pipe.

How to Find the Positive Wire

To distinguish the positive wire of a direct current from a negative wire, put a tablespoonful of salt in a glass of water and insert the free ends of the wires so they are an inch apart and do not make a short circuit, then

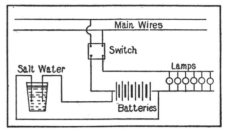

To Find Positive Wire

turn on the current. Fine bubbles will be given off from the negative pole, and therefore the other wire is the positive. It is always necessary to know the positive and negative wire in charging storage batteries. The cut shows the proper connections, which should have six 32-cp. lamps in parallel with the batteries.—Contributed by I. L. Powers, 326 E. Walnut St., Lancaster, Ohio.

A Belt Supporter for Trousers

As I had considerable trouble wearing a belt on trousers that had no belt straps attached, I made a substitute out of some strips of sheet iron which were about $2\frac{1}{2}$ in. long and $\frac{1}{4}$ in. wide and cut to a shape as shown in Fig. 1. I bent them at the points marked by the dotted lines and shaped them as shown in Fig. 2. After putting them on the belt I clamped them tight, leaving the 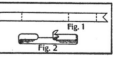 prongs to hold in the cloth of the trousers.—Contributed by Ralph E. Briley, Ames, Iowa.

Temper can be drawn from brass by the same process by which it is put into iron — by heating to cherry-red and then plunging into water.

Quickly Made Support or Bracket

To an upright piece and where wanted bolt two pieces of iron bent in an angle which is drilled to take the size of pipe to be used, as shown at A

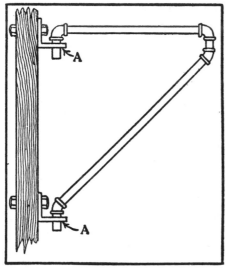

Bracket Made of Pipe and Fittings

in sketch. Any size pipe may be used, and with three nipples, two elbows, two 45-degree elbows and two pieces of gas pipe cut to fit, will form the bracket as shown when screwed together. The support can be put on upside down by changing the nipples and angles a little, which will make a good hanger.— Contributed by Carson Birkhead, Indianola, Miss.

Shearing Value of Rivets

The materials from which boiler rivets are manufactured today are of very uniform grades, and their strength in shear has been definitely determined. The results given below were obtained by the Master Steam Boiler Makers' Association in their tests made about a year ago and are probably the most reliable of any:

	Lb. per. sq. in.
Steel rivets in single shear	45,000
Steel rivets in double shear	88,000
Iron rivets in single shear	42,000
Iron rivets in double shear	80,000

How to Build a Refrigerator

In constructing a refrigerator there is no necessity of charcoal, or any filling whatever. Simply construct two or more perfectly air-tight walls, with dead-air chambers between them, which makes the best possible insulation, as air which is absolutely confined is the best insulator. Three air-tight walls with ⅛-in. space between will make a good refrigerator, says American Carpenter and Builder. A cheap way to obtain this would be to build the outer wall and cover with good two-ply red rosin-sized building paper. This should then have a coat of linseed oil to make it air tight and durable, then strip this with ⅛-in. strips, ceil again, cover with paper as before, as shown in cut at C, being sure that all joints are stripped down and air tight. Next cover the strips with paper as before (this may be oiled and dried before applying) and finish with the inner wall of ceiling, which can be best coated with shellac. To make a job which will economize ice this should be the construction of floor and ceiling as well.

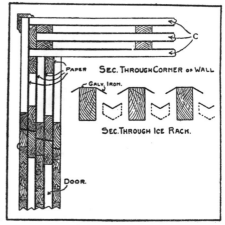

Details of Home-Made Refrigerator

All that is necessary to form an ice shelf is a rack which will support the ice wanted and at the same time give free passage of the air down through and around it and at the same time carrying the water off perfectly. This may be secured by taking 2 by 4 in. pieces and arranging them side by side on edge, 4 in. apart, and covering them with galvanized iron so it will project 1½ in. on each side and bend down at an angle of about 30°; then place a series of troughs between the 2 by 4 in. pieces to carry off the water into another trough at the ends of these and connect to a drain pipe, which should be trapped so the air can not pass back through it into the cooling room. The rack should be placed at the top of the room, as cold air descends, keeping up a circulation.

Supporting Electric Wires on Trees

A good device for supporting power, electric light and telephone wires on trees may be made from a piece of metal as shown in the sketch herewith.

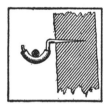

A piece of rubber hose is slipped over the hook part, to form an insulator for the line wire. The shank can be about 8 or 10 in. in length, while the hook need not be over 4 in. The line wire can slide in the hook, no matter how much the trees sway, and if fastened to every third or fourth tree it will insure steadiness along the whole line. —Contributed by Charles Vivier, Santa Anita, Cal.

To Use Common Vise as Pipe Vise

A very satisfactory pipe vise can be made from a common steel vise by taking a piece of coarse sandpaper about 3 in. by 6 in. in dimension and after doubling it, place it around the pipe, then place the part with the sandpaper on it between the jaws of the vise and tighten. The pipe may then be either threaded or cut without difficulty.— Contributed by P. O. Ward, Johnson City, Tenn.

A Home-Made Sink Trap

Your magazine has shown many kinks in the past for helping out the engineer and fireman. Perhaps the following may also prove a help to some one: In a certain steam plant

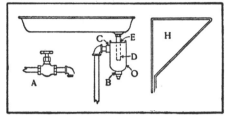

Sink Trap Made of Oil Can

the superintendent agreed to give the engineer a sink if he could find the necessary material to put it in place. For the faucets he used globe valves with a nipple and elbow, as shown at A in sketch. The sink trap was constructed out of an old oil can, O, leaving out the spout. A coupling was soldered in the can where the spout screwed in and a plug turned in the coupling, B. Another coupling was soldered in the can at point C and a pipe connected from this to the sewer. The can takes an inverted position and the pipe, D, leading from the sink runs down into the can as shown, and is soldered at point E. Two brackets were formed by bending ¼ by ¾-in. band iron, which made the supports, H, for the sink.—Contributed by J. Ellethorn, Toronto, Ont.

To Remove Fountain Pen When Stuck

When a fountain pen becomes stuck so it can not be unscrewed with the fingers, a good plan is to place a strip of fine emery cloth around the part to be unscrewed, with the emery side in, and clamp the ends in a vise or pliers.— Contributed by Charles Partridge, New Haven, Conn.

A Hardening Furnace

If the tool has been forged and allowed to harden afterward, it is well to heat the whole tool and afterward anneal the shank or neck, so as to secure the greatest possible toughness at that point. In the case of drills and reamers made of unannealed stock this is rarely necessary, if the 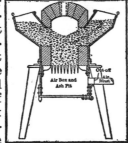 hardening heat is kept out of the shank. For this purpose the tools may be suspended through the top of the furnace, says American Machinist, when the latter is so designed as to permit of it, with the part to be left annealed projecting outside. The device consists essentially of a cover provided with holes of appropriate size, through which the tools are lowered. The tools are secured by clamp tongs or handles with eyes, and set screws at one end. A coke furnace as shown in the cut could be fitted with a device serving the same purpose, with little trouble.

Hints on Buying a Second-Hand Engine

How to Detect the Weak Points

The fact that a second-hand engine is on the market may be due to many reasons. In any case the buyer should make a complete and thorough examination. If it is possible to trace the history of the engine, so as to determine the exact reason for its rejection by the original owner, the buyer will then know where to look for defects.

Lubricating devices frequently become inoperative, stoppage of the oil ducts or pipes, or damage to the engine itself. The surface of the cylinder barrel and the valve seats and faces can be examined only by removing the cylinder head, the steam chest cover and the valve; or the valve bonnets and the valves in the case of the Corliss engine. The failure to lubricate these does not show the damage as quickly as the external parts, so the valve, valve seat and cylinder are liable to be badly scored. These parts should always be looked after first. If they are scored, leakage is bound to occur, and leakage at these points cannot easily be detected. Leakage of steam may also occur past the piston, due to the cylinder being worn somewhat oval. These defects may be determined by using calipers and a straight edge.

If cutting or scoring has occurred the marks will plainly show. Where the damage is very great, it will be necessary to have cylinder rebored. The straight-edge should also be applied to the valve seat and face, in the case of the flat slide valve. Rotary valves should be tested by blocking the piston in position and turning steam into the steam chest.

The exterior should be given as much careful scrutiny. Cracked flanges should be looked for and stud bolts in the cylinder should be examined. The precaution of examining the cylinder for cracks should be extended to take in all cast parts, including the main frame or bed.

The various rods and shafts about the engine should be thoroughly inspected for bends, twists and cracks.

The piston rod and valve stems should be examined to see if they have been scored and also note if they have been bent.

All journals, pins and bearings should be inspected for wear. The eccentric and eccentric strap should be gone over carefully to discover if there is any wear.

After the engine has been given a complete inspection, the cost of repairs necessary to put it in proper condition should be estimated and considered in the price asked for it. The foregoing is condensed from an article in the Practical Engineer.

"Oak and Ivy" Design for Frieze—London Decorator

Finding the Speed of an Engine when Shut Down

It becomes a simple matter to determine the revolutions per minute of an engine which is not running when the following method is employed. It is given in the Practical Engineer and assumes that the steam is controlled by a fly-ball type of governor.

Examine the vertical shaft between the stop collar, A, and the sliding sleeve, B. If the engine has been run for a short time a ring will be found marked on the shaft. If the engine is new, lay off about five-eighths of the distance between the stop collar and the sliding sleeve, as indicated by the point H in the cut.

Remove the belt from the governor pulley, D, and secure some sort of a handle to the wheel. A piece of broomstick lashed to the rim with stout twine serves very nicely. Next revolve D until the balls have drawn the sleeve, B, up to the mark H. The pulley, D, is then running at the same speed it would if the engine were working. Therefore to determine the total revolutions per minute of the crankshaft, count the number of turns per minute that D makes to keep the shaft sleeve at H. Multiply this number by the diameter of D and divide by the diameter of the governor belt wheel on the crankshaft. The result is the speed of the latter pulley and of course the engine itself.

While revolving the pulley, D, the wrist plate should be placed on the center marks to avoid interference with the knock-out knuckles. This method will approximate very closely to the number of revolutions per minute of the engine.

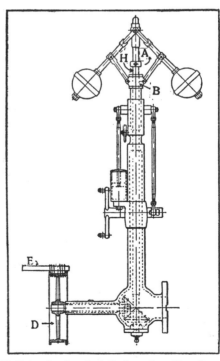

To Determine Speed of Engine when Shut Down

How to Make a Gasoline Brooder

In building a brooder to use gasoline as fuel, make a sheet-iron arrangement around the burner or the lamp box, which should be underneath the poultry house. The heater drum should come through the floor of the house and rest

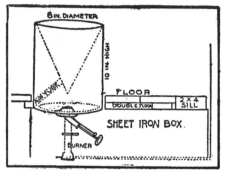

Gasoline Brooder

on the sheet-iron lamp box with a packing of asbestos paper between the wood and the burner box as well as heater drum.

You can see from the accompanying cut the drum is composed of two cylinders, says The Rural New-Yorker, the inner one V-shaped, with the large end the same size as the outer one, to which it is fastened airtight. From near the bottom of the V a small tube runs out through the outer cylinder and takes the fresh air from behind the lamp box underneath. The edges wherever joined should be rolled as well as soldered. The double floor shown in cut is just to bring it level or even with sill.

To Insure a Non-Short Circuit Between Dry Cell Batteries

To prevent short circuits between dry cell batteries where they are in a damp place or in a crowded place where they are liable to come in contact with one another, procure one or two inner tubes of quite large diameter of old bicycle tires. Cut them in lengths about 3 in. longer than the battery cell, pull the piece over the cell, only leaving the

connecting wires through end of tube. With a piece of strong cord wrap and tie tight each end of the tube. Place one of these on each cell and you will have no trouble with wet weather affecting your cells or short circuiting by cells coming in contact.—C. B.

How to Caseharden Soft Steel

Place the steel to be hardened in the furnace and heat to a cherry red. Then apply cyanide of potassium to cover the entire surface, and see that it fuses. Return to the fire and heat again and then plunge in cold water.—Contributed by H. M. Dinsmore, 13 Frederick St., Providence, R. I.

An Early Riser Alarm

The early riser is a simple device which rings a bell and turns on the light. A porcelain base lamp socket is fitted on a block of wood the right height so its key will be in line with the key of the alarm clock, as shown in the sketch. A piece of wood with a notch cut in either end to fit the socket and alarm key fastens together these two keys. This socket is then connected by wires through the wood block and a board used as a base to a socket and lamp placed in front of the clock. A flexible wire connection with a plug at both ends will attach this device to any lamp socket. The alarm is wound up by turning the piece of wood connecting the two keys. When

Rings Bell; Turns on Light

the time set for the alarm comes the bell rings and the light is repeatedly turned on and off.—Contributed by John Cook, Allendale, N. J.

How to Put Brass Cogs in a Wheel

First, cut and dovetail where the cog broke, about ⅛ or ¼ in. deep, according to the thickness of rim of wheel; then bore two holes in the cut and cut threads in them; cut threads on rod and screw in tight. Then cut the rod off about ¼ in. shorter than the height of cog. The rod must be so that the brass covers it, says J. F. Koenig in American Blacksmith. Now take two plates the height and width of the cog and shape the same as the other cog. Then set the plates on the edge of the cut to get the right thickness of cog. Now take two more plates, place them on the sides and clamp all together with clamp screws. Now fill the space between the plates and other cogs with clay to keep them in place. Then take a plumbago crucible and put in your old brass and melt it to a very bright heat, so that it flows very freely. Now pour in quickly and, after it cools, take away the plates and dress down edges with a file, and you will be delighted how nice a cog you have. I charge from $1.50 to $5 per cog, according to the size.

Line Wire Hoist

It is sometimes very difficult for linemen to hoist a wire on account of trees and rubbish being in the way. A device that is simple and easy to carry in a wagon is shown in the accompanying sketch. A cross section view of the handle and upper end is shown in Fig. 2 and Fig. 3. A projection is made on the handle, Fig.

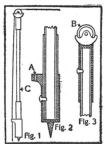

2, in which is drilled a ¼-in. hole, A, for the line wire to pass through. A 3-in. brass wheel is placed in the upper end, B, Fig. 3. The complete device is shown in Fig. 1. The handle is constructed so as to make the main rod C extend or shorten.—Contributed by Clifford B. Brainerd, Chevy Chase, Md.

Photographing Wood Grain

Of course a block of wood can be photographed the same as anything else by direct light, but the grain will be brought out much better by using transmitted light. Obtain a thin veneer of the wood to be photographed, back it with a sheet of ground glass, and allow strong direct light to fall on the glass. The picture will be more perfect if some light is allowed to fall directly on the surface of the wood, but most of it

From a Photograph

should be transmitted. The results are shown in the accompanying cut by courtesy of "Camera Craft."

While this may be a good way of reproducing the grain in small pieces of wood, it would not be practical for securing grain of wood where it is made up in furniture, etc.

This can be done at the time the wood is prepared for the filler. As soon as the camera is ready, with a large brush dash a good quantity of gasoline on the object to be photographed and quickly make the exposure.

To Stretch Screen Wire on Frames

It requires some time and patience to put screen wire on frames and get good results. A method used by a correspondent of American Carpenter and

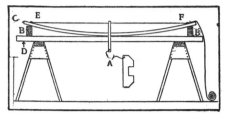

Frame Clamped for Attaching Wire

Builder is illustrated in the accompanying cut. Take two 2 by 6 in. pieces, D, a little longer than the frame and place them on two horses so they will be far enough apart to be the same width as the frame. Place two pieces of wood, B, across the pieces D as shown. Put the frame, C, on the pieces B and apply the clamps, A. Fasten end of screen wire at E, using care to get it to run parallel with the sides of the frame. Draw screen wire reasonably tight and fasten at F. After clamps, A, are removed fasten screen wire to the sides of the frame.

Substitute for a Post-Hole Auger

In constructing a piece of backyard fence I keenly felt the lack of a fence post hole auger or digger. The extent of the work did not warrant the purchase of such an implement. Doubtless many of your readers have been in a similar predicament, and they are welcome to my experience. I found that a most efficient tool to dig these holes was made by putting a small rope or noose around a

shovel and spade, near the middle, so that the ground could be lifted out of the holes by prying the two apart on the top. Any depth hole can be made in this way. For holes of small depth, the hand can be used to hold the shovel and spade together.—Contributed by Charles Voigt, Sheboygan, Wis.

Field Glasses for Line Inspectors

Instead of climbing the pole, line inspectors can relieve themselves of a large amount of physical labor, if they will use a plain hand mirror and a small field glass in connection with their work. When a day is sunshiny, the lineman can take a position on the ground beneath the wires and reflect so strong a light upon the insulators, cross-arms, or pins, that small defects, which might become serious, can be detected through the field glasses almost as well as though the observer were at the top of the pole.

To Grain a Plastered Ceiling

A plaster ceiling is easily grained, and where a room is finished in the natural wood, or grained, it presents an appearance which is superior to almost any other form of decoration. "Too little attention," says the Modern Painter, "is paid to the decoration of the ceiling in the average house of the better class. Great pains are taken to have the furniture, hangings and wall paper harmonize, while the ceiling is often left a blank white, or merely tinted, with no attempt at decoration."

One of the simplest forms of graining for the ceiling is to lay it off to represent sheathing, or a more elaborate plan is to decorate it with panels and mouldings, conforming to the architecture of the room. It is a good idea, if the latter is used, to grain all the flat surfaces first, leaving the mouldings to the last, which avoids the possibility of ragged edges.

Care should be taken to keep the colors light, as a ceiling grows dark more rapidly than the side walls. Three coats of good paint, smoothly applied, are required to produce a proper foundation. After the graining color is thoroughly dry, it should be given a thin coat of varnish which has about one gill of raw linseed oil to the pint. This makes the varnish less likely to crack. The latter is only necessary to facilitate cleaning, for now the ceiling can be sponged over and washed, whereas if the graining were left unprotected it would be a difficult matter to do this.

A Buggy Jack

A cheap and handy buggy or wagon jack can be made from 1-in. boards as shown in cut. For large vehicles it should be made of heavier material. The main post is tapered to the top and is 4 in. wide at the lower end,

where two cross pieces are fastened for the foot. The lifting piece should be p i v o t e d at a height of one-half the sum of the radii of the front and back wheel from the base. A wire loop that is used to hold lifting piece is made to fit the notches in the main post and has an eye at the end for the finger to use in changing from notch to notch.

An Adjustable Sandpaper Block

An adjustable sandpaper block that I find very useful for hollow work is made by gluing a piece of rubber packing to a block of wood $1\frac{1}{2}$ by $2\frac{1}{2}$ by $3\frac{1}{2}$ in., says a correspondent in Wood Craft. When dry pass it over the ripsaw a number of times, cutting grooves about $\frac{3}{16}$ in. apart in the wood and to within $\frac{1}{8}$ in. of the packing.

For gold ink rub together 2 parts mosaic gold and 1 part gum arabic.

A Multiple Film-Developing Machine

Where I had a large number of films to develop the old method seemed to be too slow for me, so I made an arrangement as shown in the sketch to develop

Develops Several Films at a Time

several at a time. I placed a roller on two adjustable end pieces which is turned by a small electric motor. Underneath the roller I use a long tray for the developing solution, in which is a small roller for the films to turn around. As the ends are adjustable any length roller may be used for either 6 or 12 exposure films.—Contributed by Joseph Bell, 411 Herkimer St., Brooklyn, N. Y.

Home-Made Tongs for Handling Fuses

To replace burned-out fuses of the cartridge type where it is necessary to reach past exposed bars that carry high voltage while current is on, necessitates something to do the work besides the

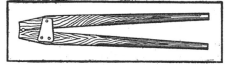

Made of Wood

bare hands. To avoid accidental shock, says a correspondent in Power, we have had some wooden pliers or tongs made, to handle the fuses with, as per the accompanying sketch. The tongs comprise two pieces of oak, 1 in. thick and 1½ in. wide, the handles being rounded with a plane. The jaws are tapered for a distance of 3 in. to about 1 in. at the ends. The pieces were clamped together, and a hole bored laterally through the jaws, near the end, as indicated, so that half of the hole is in each jaw piece. This hole is just the size of the smallest fuse. A piece of strap-iron was riveted on each side to form the hinge, there being two rivets in one leg to keep the parts from "sawing" back and forth.

Piping Gasoline Engine for Kerosene

Under certain conditions kerosene is as explosive as gasoline and can be used in engines of the explosive type

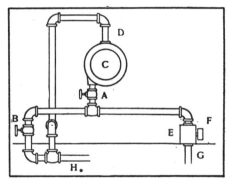

Burns Kerosene Instead of Gasoline

for power if those conditions are applied. We were told that if we could get the cylinder hot by first using gasoline to start we could turn on the kerosene and use it the same as gasoline. We made this change in our engine at the expense of about $10, including a small tank for kerosene, says a correspondent in the Grain Dealers' Journal.

When starting, valve A is opened to pump the cylinder jacket full of water, the water running back into pump to prime it. Closing the valve also holds the water in the cylinder when it is necessary to stop; keeping the hot water in the cylinder does not require so long a run on gasoline to start.

After starting, the engine is run on gasoline until the water in the jacket gets hot, the water from the pump being run to waste pipe. The flow of water through the jacket of the cylinder is regulated by the globe valve B, after turning on the kerosene. By means of the two globe valves, A and B, the amount of water passing through the engine can be regulated almost to a drop. Valves A and B are the 1-in. size and we use an inch pipe from pump to engine, and 1½-in. for the overflow.

For piping the kerosene (not shown) we use a quarter-inch pipe attached under the gasoline pump; and on the oil overflow we have a three-way connection, ⅜-in.

We have run as much as five hours at a time handling grain, leaving the throttle that furnished the gasoline at the same mark in using the kerosene. We find that kerosene does not require so much air as gasoline, and this is regulated by using a cut-off, which we experimented with until we got the required amount.

The engine should be stopped on gasoline as well as started, so as to leave the pump and pipes full of gasoline ready to start on.

Corner Brace for Wire Fence

A good way to make a corner brace for a fence is shown in the accompanying cut. The top cross pieces are made from 4 by 4 in. material about 8 ft. long. The brace wires are constructed by winding together eight wires.—Contributed by G. A. Fullwood, Turnersville, Tex.

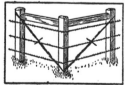

To make a mirror brilliant rub with a ball of soft paper slightly dampened with wood alcohol, sprinkle with a little whiting and polish with tissue paper.

SHOP NOTES

A Hinge Joint That Will not Slip

To make a hinge joint that will not slip, yet must be adjustable, use round stock and cut threads on one end of

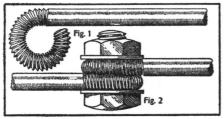

Adjustable Hinge Joint

each of two pieces. Bend an eye in the end, as shown in Fig. 1, where the threads have been cut. Clamp the two ends thus bent together with a bolt, as shown in Fig. 2.

A Blacksmith's Tool Table

A very handy revolving tool table can be made by using an old buggy wheel fixed on a pedestal as shown in the illustration. Nail two $\frac{1}{2}$ by 2-in. pieces parallel, which are cut mitering to fit between three spokes, leaving a space for hammers, hot and cold cutter, top and bottom swages, etc. Around the hub nail four small, wooden boxes

The Revolving Table

for your punches and chisels, says the Blacksmith and Wheelwright. The spokes provide a fine place for tongs. Your tools are all in sight, and when you can't reach what you want catch the rim and turn it to you.

Home-Made Water Cooler

A cheap and serviceable cooler for shop use can be made in the following way: Take a nail keg and a pickle jar, the jar being about three-fourths the size of the keg, and pack a layer of old newspapers in the bottom of the keg. Set the jar in the keg and fill up the space between

with old newspapers, packed tightly with a stick. Make a heavy wooden cover for the top and you have a first-class cooler that will save ice.—Contributed by J. H. Hecker, New Orleans, La.

Door Holder for Carpenters

The accompanying sketch shows the construction of a door holder that I use while fitting them.

When I want to hang a door I get

It is Quickly Made

a piece of board (any scrap will do) about 10 by 24 in., and two pieces of 2 by 4 about a foot long, and nail them across the board, using eight-penny or ten-penny common nails, and have the nails go through the board so that the points of the nails will catch the floor when the door holder is laid flat on the floor, says a correspondent in Wood-Workers' Review.

This sort of door holder can be made in a very few minutes, and the material can be found in any scrap pile; can be moved around the room with ease, and will stick to the floor wherever it is placed. By placing a little strip of board or block under the other end of the door, keeps it off the floor out of the sand and dirt.

An Alarm for a Break in Line Wire Circuit

Use an ordinary magnet, M, from an electric door bell in series with an 8-cp. lamp, L, as is shown in cut. The magnet will hold the small lever, A, while the lamp is lit. When the current is broken by opening the switch at the

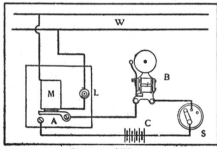

Diagram of Wiring

plant, or from any other cause, the lever, A, is released, making contact with the line in which an ordinary door bell, B, is in the circuit, ringing bell until circuit is restored on power line or switch is opened in bell circuit.—Contributed by B. C. Thomas, Valparaiso, Ind.

Black Mortar for Concrete Blocks

To obtain black concrete mortar add 2 lb. excelsior carbon black to the mixture, for every 100 lb. of cement used. To make it dark gray, add only $\frac{1}{2}$ lb. black to each 100 lb. of cement.

Method for Reducing Play in Steady Rest Hinge

The steady rest as at B, you will notice, is machined straight across, while the bolt at A is usually a loose fit, says the American Machinist.

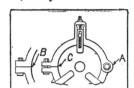

Therefore, to take up the lost motion it requires the upper jaw to be screwed down very tight; whereas, if it should be cast or cut away in the manner illustrated at C, the mere act of tightening the bolt in C would take up the lost motion at bolt A. Thus the upper jaw need only be tight enough to hold the work in place.

A Gasoline Reserve Supply

It is well to have some simple means of fitting a reserve tank in an automobile so that an emergency supply of gasoline can always be carried. The accompanying sketch shows how a reserve can be kept in the same supply tank.

There are two connections or supply outlets from the tank, one of which reaches up 3 in. above the bottom of the tank, while the other is level with it; the latter constitutes the draw-off for the reserve supply while the former is the regular supply outlet. The valve A is allowed to remain open at all times, while that in the emergency pipe is kept closed. By turning the valve B, a 6-gal. reserve supply is tapped, which is usually sufficient to reach a

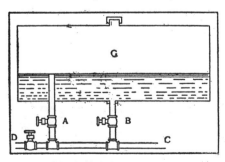

Valve B Taps Reserve Supply

supply station, says Automobile. The pipe C is connected to the carburetter, while D is used for a drain.

A Device for Turning Breeze Through a Window

The accompanying sketch shows how an arrangement can be made that will be appreciated by those who have to work in a room where the windows are all on one side and where the breeze at times passes the windows instead of coming into the room.

The post A is a piece of wood 1 by 3 in. and is cut as long as the distance that the sash can be raised. A notch

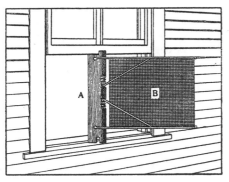

Turns Breeze Into Window

is cut in both ends to fit the bottom of the sash. These notches are cut opposite each other in order to give different angles to the wing.

The wing, B, is a piece of close woven cloth fastened to a rib of an old umbrella at each end. Notches are cut in the edge of wood, A, as is shown, to adjust the short part of the rib, which will stretch the cloth. When not in use it can be folded and laid aside.

How to Color Old Window Shades

Mix a sufficient quantity of wall paint, which may be of any color desired, and after placing the shade on a flat surface paint two coats with a brush, putting it on with strokes crosswise. When dry the shade will be like new.

A Paint Brush Keeper

After using a paint brush it should be cleaned and placed in water so it will be ready the next time when needed. A correspondent in The American Blacksmith says: We took a common ordinary candy pail, which we secured from the grocer,  and painted it inside and out with two coats of paint. We then put a row of hooks on the inside of the pail about 2 or 3 in. from the top. When through using a brush we simply hang it in the pail into which a sufficient quantity of water has been poured to just cover the bristles.

It is well to say that to place a brush in water before it has been touched by paint is to ruin it. The water will make it soggy and practically unfit for painting use.

A Handy Coal Bin

Where small quantities of coal are purchased at a time the usual way is to put it in a corner of the basement, a stall in the barn, or on the ground. A good plan is to make a bin constructed as shown in the illustration.

The dotted lines show how the bottom of the bins are made sloping toward the doors. One bin may be used for hard coal and the other for

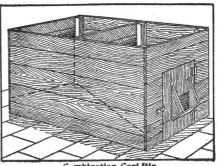

Combination Coal Bin

soft coal, while the space beneath the bottoms of the bins will make a place for wood or kindling and a door can be provided for it. A spout of suitable size is made on each coal bin door, which prevents the coal from dropping on the floor and still have a supply in the spout.—A. H. Osterman, Sandusky, Ohio.

A Cement Watering Tank

For a number of years we had to go to the well and pump water by hand, and drive the stock there through the storm and mud, but now we have a

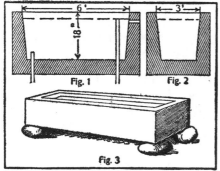

Fig. 1   Fig. 2   Fig. 3

Cement Watering Trough

cement trough built near the barn which is kept full of water by a windmill, says a correspondent in Hoard's Dairyman.

It took two of us one day to make the form and build the trough complete with pipe connections. It required ½ ton of Portland cement, ½ load of

gravel and ⅔ load of sand. The entire cost of the trough, not counting work, was $5.55.

Figs. 1 and 2 show the trough in section, which is 6 ft. long, 3 ft. wide and 18 in. deep, inside measurements. The top edge of the cement should be 4 in., while the bottom is 10 in. thick. The intake pipe, A, Fig. 1, does not project in the tank more than 3 in., while the overflow pipe, B, comes within ½ in. of the top.

How to Bore a Conical Hole

When you have a conical hole to bore, such as for a handle hole in a wooden maul or other similar places, leave the cutter of an expansive auger bit a trifle loose and begin boring at the side where the smallest end of the hole is wanted. The inner edge of the cutter lip being angular, the cutter will gradually draw itself out from the body of the bit, making the hole larger as the bit goes into the wood.

How to Make a Windmill Quadrant

When it is necessary to pump water at a distance from the windmill a quadrant may be used, constructed as shown in the sketch. Out of a piece of wagon tire iron form the angle piece, A, and with another piece of iron, B, connect the ends of A. These should be securely fastened with bolts.

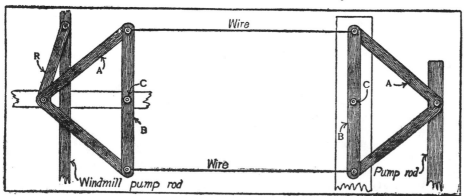

Quadrant for Working Pump at a Distance

Drill holes at the centers, C, and bolt onto a cross timber or to a post. Connect one to the windmill rod with a connecting piece, R, also made of a piece of the same iron. The other may be connected to pump rod as shown.

How to Make a Ladle for Melting Lead

The illustration shows how a baking-powder can cover can be used for melting lead when no ladle or iron spoon is available. Bend the edges of the cover inward, as shown, until the proper point is secured. This will make the opposite side flat. Make a handle of hardwood, or some wood which will not burn easily, and drive two small nails through the flat side into one end of the handle. This makes a very durable ladle.—Contributed by Stephen B. Mastick, Lake Bay, Wash.

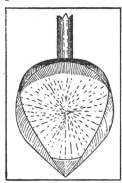

Support for Shaft when Babbitting

To babbitt boxes for shafts drill two holes about 90° apart and about $\frac{1}{4}$ in. from the outside end of the boxes. Tap these holes for countersunk head screws. When the shaft rests on the heads of these screws it can be lined up by turning the screws. After the babbitt is poured, the screws can be removed, says Machinery. The convenience of this method is that after lining up shaft it can be taken out, warmed up and replaced before pouring the babbitt with the assurance that it will be in line.

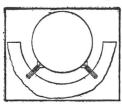

Iron Punching Machine

The accompanying illustration shows how an old hand punch was converted into an air operated machine by means of a 7-in. brake cylinder. The power is controlled by a straight air engineers'

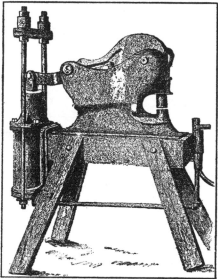

Home-Made Power Punch

valve placed in a convenient position for the operator. This machine, says Street Railway Journal, was formerly operated by a man and a boy. The man now attends to it alone.

A Hand Tapping Device

A simple device which I have found to be a very efficient fixture for the tool room was built as shown in the sketch, says a correspondent in American Machinist. This design can be made in various sizes.

The base, A, is of cast iron, having the upright, B, firmly fastened to it as shown. The arm, C, is clamped to the upright, but can be adjusted if special length of tap or height of work

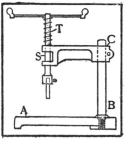

necessitates. The spindle, S, is a free fit in the arm, C, and the spring, T, is simply stiff enough to carry the weight of the spindle with ordinary chuck and tap.

How to Wind Irregular Shaped Springs

Some time ago the question, "How to wind springs shaped like those on

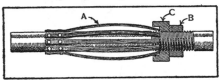

Making Irregular Springs

stove lifter handles, stove doors, etc.?" was asked. I have made a tool as shown in the illustration and used it in my lathe with good results.

Each piece A is made of spring steel and riveted to a shaft with two rivets on one end, while the other end fits into an individual notch in the collar, C. This collar is kept from turning on the shaft by a key. Turning nut B up against the collar pushes on the ends of the springs, causing them to bulge outward in the middle. When the proper size is secured on these springs one end of the wire is fastened to it and the coil is wound.

When through winding loosen the nut and slip the finished coil over the opposite end of the shaft from the collar.—C. T. A.

How to Enclose Coin in a Letter

Cut through the writing paper with a knife a cross, making the cuts no

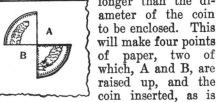

longer than the diameter of the coin to be enclosed. This will make four points of paper, two of which, A and B, are raised up, and the coin inserted, as is shown in the sketch, and the other two points remain back of the coin, holding it firmly in place.

Painting an Old Brick Wall

The first thing to do is to get every particle of loose stuff from the walls, which may be done with a coarse fibre brush; then dust off clean. If you have a lot of old paint and enough to do the job, thin it down with oil and a little benzine, strain, and apply quite thin to the wall, says Master Painter. Brush this well into the surface, and let it have several days to become hard. The next coat should be a lead paint, of fresh materials, with raw oil and just enough driers to dry it well in reasonable time. A little turps also will be an advantage. This will now give you a good foundation for whatever color of paint you may want to apply.

A Wire Fence Splicing Tool

Where a wire on a fence breaks after it has been securely fastened at the

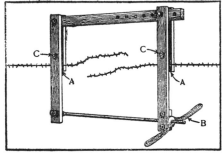

Splicing a Break

end or corner post, it causes a great deal of work if one end must be loosened and the wire spliced and then stretched again and fastened to the posts. A tool for pulling the ends together and holding the wire tight while it is being spliced can be made as shown in the sketch.

The frame may be made of iron or wood, which depends on the tools at hand. If made of wood then iron plates must be placed at A, where the wires are held in the clamp. The hand burr, B, is then turned to the end of the rod and the loose ends of the wires are inserted in the clamps, which are held by the bolts, C. The hand burr is then screwed up, drawing the ends of the wire together and holding them until they are twisted. When the clamps are loosened the wire will be tight and a quick job has been accomplished.

How to Make an Expansion Bolt

Secure a piece of pipe the size and length of the bolt that is intended to

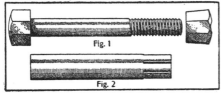

Expansion Bolt

be used. With a hacksaw slit one end of the pipe about $1\frac{1}{2}$ in. deep in eight equal places around the pipe, as shown in Fig. 2.

Take a hexagon nut and file each face on one edge, only making it conical as shown in Fig. 1, so the small end will just start in the pipe. Place each corner of the nut in one of the slits cut in the pipe. When the bolt is screwed in, the eight wings of the pipe will be forced outward.

Oil Tempering Bath

If much hardening of tools is to be done, oil should be used. Fish oil or any other of the cheaper grades answers every purpose, says American Machinist. For use in a shop making few tools no apparatus other than a suitable tank to hold the oil is necessary. If a 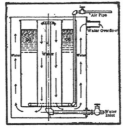 great many tools are hardened it becomes necessary to keep the oil stirred up and properly cooled. In such a shop air and flowing water are generally at hand and these offer the simplest means to accomplish this end. A suitable arrangement is shown in the accompanying cut, where an outer tank containing water is used, within which is supported a double cylindrical oil tank; the inner cylinder opening into the larger tank so as to allow the water to circulate freely in both. The water inlet reaches to the top of the inner cylinder and has an overflow near the top of the outer, so that as long as the inlet valve is open, water will circulate around both sides of the oil holder. A circular pipe is provided at the bottom of the oil holder with suitable number of holes, from which air from a blower or compressed air tank bubbles up, keeping the oil well stirred.

How to Sharpen an Air Brush Needle

Take a piece of bristol board, or something about as tough, and cut out a round piece about $1\frac{1}{4}$ in. in diameter and cut a hole in the center just a

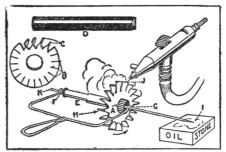

Sharpening an Air Brush Needle

trifle smaller than the needle. Cut slits in the edge of the wheel, as shown in sketch at B, and twist each section crosswise of the wheel like those shown at C, and you have a small turbine wheel. Set the shoulder shown at A so that it will fit close.

Remove the black handle of the air brush, D, also the needle set clamp, E, with the needle in it.

From a piece of wire 10 in. long and about 24 gauge make a fork with a small eye at each end, F and G. Put on the wheel, as shown at H, insert the needle first at G, and spring F over the other end of the needle, K.

Place an oil stone on the table and hold the fork so the needle will rest lightly on it. Take the air brush in the other hand and blow at the top of the wheel, J, to make it spin.—Contributed by E. Stanton King, Minneapolis, Minn.

A Home-Made Generator

An acetylene generator for use in an automobile may be constructed as shown in the sketch at small expense. It can be made by a good tinsmith from galvanized iron. The tank A is 5 in. square and 10 in. high, the top has a circular hole 3¾ in. in diameter. The

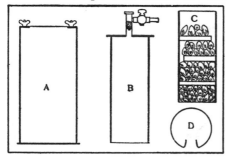

Plan of Generator

bell B, which contains the carbide holder, is open at the bottom, is 3½ in. in diameter and about 9½ in. high. A tube, fixed in the top with stop cock, takes the gas to the burner; solder a wire across this tube, placing a wad of absorbent cotton above it to prevent any water passing to the burner, says The Motor Way.

The carbide is placed in a tin cylinder C, 3 in. in diameter and 7 in. high. Pierce three or four holes in the bottom of the tin to let the water in; place the carbide in as shown with discs of wood in between to prevent all the carbide getting wet at once. Fix carbide holder C in the bell B by spring D made of a strip of brass bent into a circle; by pinching the end with the fingers, it is inserted in the bell. A reserve carbide holder can be kept ready charged in the car for use when needed.

The bell B is attached in tank by two screws and thumb nuts at opposite corners of tank A, which will leave an open joint allowing any superfluous gas to escape. Fill the tank half full with water; as gas is generated, it forces the water out of the bell holding the carbide and gradually works up as the carbide is used.

A Handy Clamp for Die-Makers

For holding work of different sizes and diameters a correspondent in the American Machinist constructed a clamp which could be adjusted to the work in a few minutes' time. Referring to the sketch, the clamp screw, A, passes

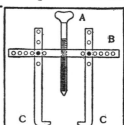

through a threaded hole in the metal, B. The jaws, C C, have holes in their upper ends, as well as the ends of the metal, B, for adjustment. Two pins or bolts fitting these holes complete the device.

A Surface Plate Jack

In laying out keyways at different angles on a large shaft, about 7 ft. long, which weighed several hundred pounds, I did not have a suitable jack to use in lifting the out-bearing end on the sur-

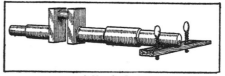

A Handy Jack

face plate. I used for this purpose an ordinary carpenter's wood clamp, removing one jaw and placing both screws in the other, which made a quick way to center up and a very sensitive adjustment.—Contributed by F. V. T., Lansing, Mich.

If a round brush spreads too much, slip a rubber band over the upper part of the bristles.

How to Make a Wiped Joint in Cable Splicing

When the cables are in position and ready for splicing, the ends should be marked at the point to which the lead is to be removed and scored or cut entirely around. This may be accom-

Wiping the Cable Joint

plished by a plumber's chipping knife and hammer, marking the lead, but being careful not to cut entirely through to the insulation, which might thus be damaged.

The lead is then cut lengthwise from the circular score to the end by the chipping knife and is removed with a pair of pliers. In making this longitudinal cut great care should be used not to injure the insulation, cautions the American Telephone Journal. The knife should be held at such an angle as to pass between the lead and the insulation, but not cut the insulation.

When the lead has been removed the parts where it has been scored should be examined carefully and all rough or sharp edges removed. It will be well also to "bell" the lead slightly with the handles of the pliers or some other blunt instrument.

When the lead covers of the two sections of cable have been prepared, as described, the lead sleeve is slipped over the more convenient end and pushed back along the cable far enough to be out of the way. This lead sleeve should be at least as thick as the sheathing of the cable, and in view of its exposed condition may be somewhat heavier to give it greater mechanical strength. Before slipping it on the cable each end of the sleeve is thor-

oughly scraped with a shave hook or a knife for a length of about 2 in., and the cleaned portion thoroughly smeared with some convenient flux, preferably a tallow candle, which, by preventing the formation of the usual film of lead salts, insures a close union of the lead and the wiping metal which is used to make the joint between the sleeve and the cable sheath.

The internal diameter of the sleeve should exceed the external diameter of the lead sheath of the cable by from 1 in. to $1\frac{1}{2}$ in., so as to allow for the splicing and paper sleeves.

After the conductors have been properly spliced, the lead sleeve is brought into position so as to extend equally over the lead on each cable end, and the ends of the sleeve are dressed down close to the lead of the cable, care being exercised to have the lead sleeve concentric with the cable.

The sleeve and the lead of the cable are then joined together by molten solder, as shown in the illustration.

The solder is poured on the joint in the manner shown, and is wiped smooth with the cloth wiper, which is usually made of several layers of ticking sewed together in convenient size. The wipes must be absolutely watertight and should be carefully inspected, especially underneath the joint, which may be accomplished by means of a small mirror, to insure smoothness, solidity and absence of air-holes, as the presence of small blow-holes in wiped joints causes more trouble than any other feature in cable splicing.

How to Make a Folding Oar

For convenience in motor boats a folding oar can be made so as to be

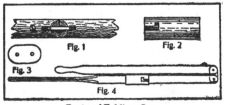

Parts of Folding Oar

carried under a seat or in a locker. Cut a 7-ft. oar in the middle and then make a slot $\frac{1}{8}$ in. wide by $1\frac{1}{2}$ in. deep in both ot these ends. Each end must be cut round or in a half circle, as in Fig. 1. A piece of brass $\frac{1}{8}$ in. thick is cut the same width as the diameter of the oar and both ends rounded, as shown in Fig. 3. A hole is punched or drilled in this brass $\frac{3}{4}$ of an inch from each end. The brass is then inserted in the slots that were cut in the oar and riveted, as in Fig. 1. Take a piece of brass tubing the same size as the oar and about 5 in. long and cut a slot in it as shown in Fig. 2 and slip this on the oar with slot end toward the handle. Place a round head screw in the handle end, as shown, which serves as a lock for the brass tubing and also to keep it from coming off the oar.— Contributed by C. F. Hussey, Portsmouth, N. H.

How to Make a Temporary Street Bridge

City officials in small towns are often called upon to face the problem of providing clear streets for parades, races, etc., yet at the same time not block foot traffic on the main thoroughfares. Temporary bridges are used in Europe and the following is a brief description of how to make one that will serve the purpose very well:

Suppose the street is 40 ft. from curb to curb, and it is desired to have a clear passage 14 ft. high for the procession. Take four 2 by 12 in. planks 28 ft. long, if they can be procured in that length. If they cannot be obtained, secure shorter ones together and they will serve just as well. Cut risers in these long planks for as many steps as desired, and then nail in pairs in the shape of a letter A. Raise them in the air, with one leg on one curb and the other leg on the opposite one.

Nail a horizontal 2 by 8 in. plank 20 ft. long at a height 14 ft. above the ground. This will leave about 5 ft. projecting on each side of the A. Run a vertical brace to the ground from each extremity. Brace the structure laterally and add a floor as wide as desired, and for safety, put a temporary hand-rail on each side. The result is a substantial bridge which serves its purpose and can be taken down and laid away for future use.

How to Make a Wire Straightener

Secure a piece of $\frac{3}{8}$-in. brass tubing about 14 in. long and round out the

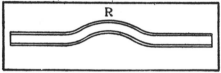

Wire Straightener

sharp edges inside the ends. Fill it with lead or rosin and make a bend in it that has a radii of $2\frac{1}{2}$ in. at point R

Procession Can Pass Under Bridge

in the sketch. After removing the lead or rosin place one straight end in the chuck of a lathe. Speed the lathe to 400 or 500 revolutions and start the wire to be straightened into the tubing by clamping the wire in a hand-vise about 15 in. from the end. Push the wire through the tubing until it protrudes through the spindle of the lathe. Stop the lathe and remove the hand vise and clamp it on the end of the wire that comes out, then pull the entire length through the tubing while the lathe is running.—Contributed by Chas. R. Vollmer, Brooklyn, N. Y.

Soldering Brass to Lead

Scrape the lead clean and tin the brass, using tallow as flux, and muriatic acid for the lead. Use copper cleaned with sal ammoniac and tinners' solder. Be careful not to melt the lead.

How to Build an Ice House

The use of sawdust or any other light non-conducting material is a benefit to the keeping qualities of a wall. In constructing an ice house the walls should have two spaces, the outer one filled with sawdust and the inner one a dead air chamber, says the Metal Worker. In the illustrations, Fig. 1 shows a horizontal section of the corner. The heavy felt paper shown between the sheathing and siding and under the inside set of studding should be lapped solid at the angles.

Fig. 2 shows a horizontal section through the door and frame. The outer boards are shown to fit into a groove plowed in the jambs. This is much better than cleats, as the latter are apt

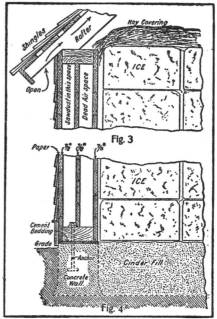

Details of Ice House Construction

to become damaged by the ice in taking out and filling the house. These boards may be put in at the top of the opening, and as the ice is lowered into the house they may be removed and stored for future use. It is a good plan to have the tops of these boards a little higher than the top of the ice.

Fig. 3 shows a vertical cross-section at the plate and Fig. 4 a vertical cross-section at the sill. The boards used in making the partitions are $\frac{7}{8}$-in tongue and grooved material, which makes a tight joint. The cinder filling absorbs any moisture there may be.

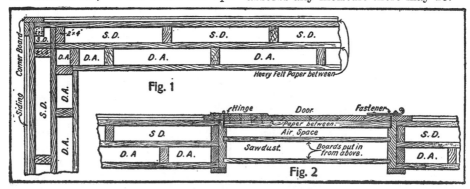

Plan of Constructing Air Chambers

Pipe Joint Mixture

For ordinary pipe joints use a mixture of plumbago and vaseline instead of white lead. This mixture does not dry out and the joint is easily separated when needed.

* ◆ ◆ *

A Home-Made Line Lightning Arrester

On rural telephone lines where protecting devices are not used in the exchange and where trouble is frequently caused by lightning, a simple and easily applied arrester can be made by any

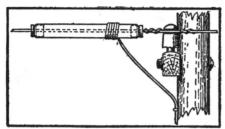

Lightning Arrester on Rural Line

village tinsmith. All the materials necessary are a tin tube 20 in. in length, two No. 4 porcelain knobs and a ground wire.

The tube should be fastened in the same manner as a stove pipe and just large enough to admit the porcelain knobs, says the American Telephone Journal. Insert a knob in each end of the tube and with a pair of pliers or a hammer gently force the tin down into the grooves of the knobs at each end. This will secure the knobs in position.

The completed arrester is then placed on the line wire, one section from the head, by slipping the line wire through the screw holes of the porcelain knobs, in the manner shown. The ground wire should be wrapped around the tube tightly about six times and soldered. It is then run down the pole to a well-made ground. A No. 12 galvanized iron wire serves this purpose the best. All of the arresters on the pole may be connected to the one ground wire.

This comparatively crude arrester, while not making an extraordinarily handsome appearance, serves the purpose of keeping the line discharge below the striking point and of diverting the major portion of any such discharges away from the exchange arresters and the arresters on the telephones.

* ◆ ◆ *

Making a Bevel Pipe Fitting

In a certain place where they used water to prepare coal for the market it became necessary to change one of the large water lines that furnished the water. It had to be fixed in a certain length of time and, not having regular standard length of pipe, when they came to finish they had to have a bevel ring to make the right elevation. There was no time to have one cast in town, and something had to be done and done at once.

After looking around they found a piece of casting that would fill the bill with a lot of work, says a correspondent in the American Machinist. The casting, which was 19 in. outside diameter by 7 in. inside diameter, was placed in the lathe and the inside diameter increased to 13 in. The outside was finished down to 17 in. in diameter and then faced. It was then turned around in the chuck and faced on the other side.

It was then ready to be cut for the

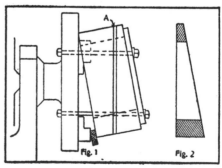

Bevel Pipe Flange

angle, which was done by placing it in the chuck, as is shown in Fig. 1. One edge was placed up close to the face of the chuck and the opposite edge was placed on a block of wood cut to the right size and placed on one of bolts, as shown. A cutting-off tool was placed in the tool post and a cut taken on line A. The result was a bevel fitting like that shown in Fig. 2, with one side an inch in width and the other 5½ in.

A Current Indicator

Some time ago I wanted to find out whether a certain wire had a current passing through it or not, and having no 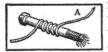 instrument and not wanting to cut the wire, I picked a piece of iron out of the scrap heap and wrapped the slack of the wire, A, around it and used a handful of iron filings to try the magnet thus formed.

Pounding of Engine Heard Through Teeth

A good many years ago the writer was employed in a mill where a great amount of noisy machinery was running night and day. Among other things were four Westinghouse single acting vertical engines, which ran continuously for six days in the week. These engines have a closed crank case in which is kept a mixture of oil and water to lubricate them. The word mixture is unfortunate, perhaps, but the water was used to bring the oil level up to the cranks and the action of the cranks did make a pretty good mixture after all.

Well, the point is that I was over with an old hand to look over the engines and see that they were running smoothly. He wanted to know whether the engine was pounding or not, and I didn't see how he could tell with the whole plant running full blast. It didn't bother him, though. He took a 2-ft. rule out of his pocket, put it between his teeth with one end against the crank case and by stopping up his ears with his fingers he shut out the sounds of the other machinery and could hear through the medium of the rule a steady thump, thump, which in-

dicated that the crank brasses needed tightening up.—Contributed by W. E. Morey, Chicago.

Utilizing Heat from a Chimney

The wasted heat in a chimney of a fireplace may be turned into service without much trouble. Where rooms are directly above the fireplace it may be possible to by-pass the hot gases

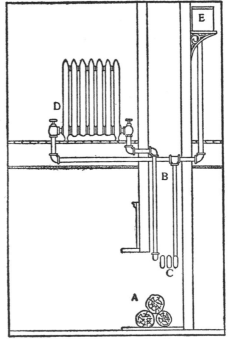

Radiator Heated by Fireplace

in the chimney through an old-fashioned drum, and if the size of the chimney would admit it, it would be a very easy matter to tear out some of the chimney wall and locate a pipe coil right over the fireplace in the chimney so that one or more radiators may be connected with the coil. It will be necessary to use care in placing the coil so as not to obstruct the draft, says a correspondent in the Rural New-Yorker.

The accompanying illustration shows how a hot water system may be installed. A is the fireplace; C, the coil; B, the connecting pipes; D, the radiator, and E, the expansion tank. The pipe connections should be made from one end of the radiator to the top of the coil, and the other end to the bottom of the coil. Any series of radiators in the same manner. The expansion tank is for the expansion of the heated water as well as to keep a head of water above the radiators to keep them full.

◆ ◆ ◆

How to Harden and Temper an Axe

A good clean fire, well coked, large enough and with plenty of depth so no cold air from the blast is likely to reach

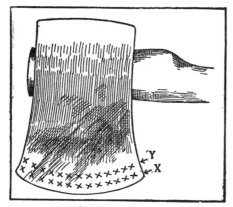

Tempering an Axe

the blade, is necessary. Heat the cutting edge of the axe to a strong yellow. Exercise care, cautions The American Blacksmith, so that the heating will be done evenly and uniformly. Now hammer along the edge of the axe as shown by the little crosses at X in the engraving. After hammering across one side turn your blade and proceed with hammering on the other side. In hammering draw the blade out toward the edge and continue your pounding until the heat begins to get low, but not after that. Now reheat the cutting edge to about the same color as before and for a distance of from $1\frac{1}{2}$ to 2 in. from the edge. After heating proceed with hammering as before, but at line Y, or about $1\frac{1}{2}$ in. back from the edge of the blade. After hammering one side turn

and hammer on the other side of the blade.

At this stage of the hammering the smith will notice that the blade has widened considerably. Do not under any circumstance attempt to hammer it down to the desired width. In fact, it is best to not touch the edges of the axe with the hammer at all.

Heat the blade for the third time and hammer again across both sides at the line Y. This third heat is a very low one, and should be such, so that the hammer will leave a bright gloss on the blade. The superfluous metal at the sides of the blade is now cut off and the edges filed smooth. The blade is now ready to harden.

Heat the axe to a cherry red from its cutting edge for a distance of about $1\frac{1}{2}$ to $1\frac{3}{4}$ in. back. Then dip the blade into the hardening bath and move it up and down. Polish the blade so that the temper color can easily be distinguished, and heat very slowly over the fire until the blade shows a blue. Then cool the blade and grind.

◆ ◆ ◆

Device for Holding Field Coil While Varnishing

To hold a field coil in one hand and apply varnish by means of a brush in the other is not only a sticky job, but dirt and foreign substances a r e liable to be picked up and to give trouble.

A correspondent in Electric Traction Weekly says that he rigged up a device as shown in the illustration to hold the coil. 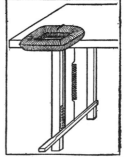 A narrow strip of iron bent in the form of an L passes up through the work bench and holds the coil at the edge of the brush. The strip of iron is attached to a foot pedal which is hinged to one of the back legs of the bench. The strip of iron has a tooth which engages in several saw tooth projections on a metal piece which is fastened to a front leg of the bench.

A coil spring furnishes the pressure for holding the clamp in position. By this device it is possible to apply the brush to about half the surface of a field coil without changing the position. This done, the operator releases the pedal, turns the coil over and applies the varnish on the other side.

Where a large number of field coils are to be varnished it is better to dip them in a tank that has enough varnish to cover the coil and hang over a return drain board with a piece of metal the shape of an S to a hanger bar.

Cooling a Metal Cutting Tool

Cooling the nose of a cutting tool by the application of some fluid to the point where the chip is being removed

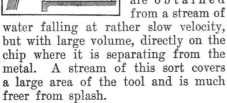

by the tool enables the operator to increase the cutting speed.

Different methods have been employed and the most satisfactory results are obtained from a stream of

water falling at rather slow velocity, but with large volume, directly on the chip where it is separating from the metal. A stream of this sort covers a large area of the tool and is much freer from splash.

About 3 gal. of water per minute is required for adequately cooling a very large roughing tool, say, 2 in. by $2\frac{1}{2}$ in. section, and proportionally smaller quantities for the smaller tools.

For economy, the same water should be used over and over again, and it should be supersaturated with soda to prevent the machines from rusting.

A series of experiments has demonstrated that water thrown on the chip, as shown in the illustration, will give an increase in the cutting speed of

about 40 per cent.—Extract of a paper read before the American Society of Mechanical Engineers.

Hydraulic Elevator for Window Display

A moving device in a show window attracts attention, which, creating interest and criticism, actually sells more

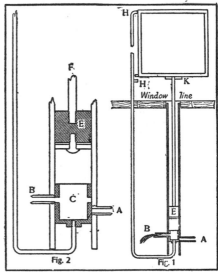

Window Elevator

goods than an ordinary display of stock, even though the model is something foreign to the business.

The following cuts show an hydraulic elevator that moves up and down the guides continually as long as the water cock is open. The device is comparatively simple and inexpensive, can be constructed by anyone, and made as elaborate as the maker desires. The operating valve is the most important part and is plainly shown in Fig. 2.

The jacket is made of $\frac{3}{4}$-in. brass pipe, as long as the rise is intended to be. The top end of pipe can be flush with the window line, which leaves all the mechanism out of sight, the only visible parts being the plunger rod, valve rod and guide bars for the car, which are made of $\frac{1}{4}$-in. square brass rod.

The valve rod can be made of $\frac{1}{8}$-in. round steel rod run in brackets soldered on the car guides, also having two steps, H and I, at the required distances. The plunger rod can be made of $\frac{3}{16}$-in. steel, screwed into brass cap, K, and the other end into E, which is brass with leather washer and plate. The valve is brass pipe, $\frac{3}{4}$-in. outside diameter, with hole drilled in straight line through both walls. Solder a plate on bottom for the plunger rod to screw into. The inlet is at A, which is now closed, and the water is escaping from outlet, B. The car is about to strike step, H, which will reverse the proposition. As the water fills cup C and the jacket the car will rise.

The inlet and the outlet may be coupled to the faucet and sink with a small rubber tube. A tin funnel at the bottom of plunger tube will catch any leakage. The speed of car can be controlled by the inlet cock, which should feed about the same amount of water as will escape through the outlet in the same length of time.

Home-Made Electrolytic Interrupter

It will be recalled that an electrolytic interrupter consists essentially of an aluminum and a platinum electrode 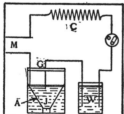 immersed in a solution of ammonium phosphate. It was found necessary to make such an instrument on short notice and with the materials at hand. The ammonium phosphate solution was placed in a 5 by 7 in. battery jar, J, and an aluminum electric light shade, A, as shown in drawing, inverted and placed in the bottom of the jar formed the aluminum electrode. Platinum wire was not to be had, and therefore a piece of German silver wire, G, was fed through a hole in the cover until the end projected about $\frac{1}{4}$ in. below the surface of the solution. The interrupter was

then connected in series with the primary of the induction coil, C, and a water resistance, W, the latter being necessary, as the circuit, M, was 110 volts alternating current. Due to the chemical action, the German silver wire was very slowly eaten off, making it necessary to gradually feed in more wire. This simple instrument gave good service, however, and is still in use.—Contributed by the Auburn Utility Company, Chicago.

Tinting a Cement House

It frequently happens that in building a concrete house the cement will dry out in several colors or shades. It may be desirable to tint the entire surface of a uniform color that shall not be paint, but practically a part of the house itself. This result may be secured by washing the whole house with cement, but there is a trick in doing this properly that is not always understood. The cement wash is made by mixing two parts of Portland cement and one part of marble dust with enough water to reduce it to about the same consistency as whitewash, and is applied with a whitewash brush. The wall must be thoroughly wet with water for several hours before the wash is applied and kept constantly wet during the application, and for at least a day afterward, says American Carpenter and Builder. The important thing to remember is that the wash must not be applied to a dry wall, as it will not adhere. This work will be worth at least a dollar a square yard, or more, according to the price of labor, but the result will fully justify the cost.

Pasting Cardboard to Glass

To fasten cardboard to glass, apply good 30° B water-glass with a soft rag or sponge to the glass (not the paper), and stick the card on immediately while dry. When the solution is dry, the paper cannot be detached. The silicate should be somewhat diluted.

SHOP NOTES

To Remove Rusted Nut

A nut sometimes is rusted to a bolt so solid that it is impossible to remove  by ordinary means. To force it with a wrench would only result in breaking the bolt and causing a large amount of extra work, says The Automobile. The only thing to do is to sacrifice the nut by splitting it with a chisel, as shown in the sketch.

Cement Piers for Scales

The use of a wood frame support for scales if placed in a pit causes too much dampness for the wood timbers and in time they will rot. Fig. 1 shows how a common wood frame support is constructed before placing in a pit. A correspondent of American Miller constructed a support as shown in Fig. 2 with 6 in. by 8 in. sills placed on a brick foundation and with cement piers built in the corners AA. These piers were made 1 ft. high, on which were placed the saucers that hold the balls. Just as the cement was about hard the

saucers were fastened to the cement with lag screws. When the cement set this made the saucers firm and solid.

Special Engine Frame Truck

In railroad shops, where it is necessary to remove a frame from a locomotive and transfer it to another building on the grounds, a truck of some kind must be used. The accompanying sketch shows how such a truck may be

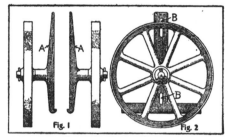

Truck for Engine Frame

made for this purpose. The truck is constructed entirely of iron with cast iron wheels 32 in. in diameter. A wrought iron tire $\frac{5}{8}$ in. by $3\frac{1}{2}$ in. is shrunk on the rim of the cast wheel. The jaw and axle (A, Fig. 1) is made of one forging or casting. It takes very little time to fasten an engine frame between the jaws AA with bolts through the slots BB. A heavy engine frame can be taken any place about a

Construction of Cement Piers for Scales

large shop in this manner.—Contributed by D. H. Utter, Sayre, Pa.

Pulling Arc Light Switch Plugs from a Distance

In a certain place which was a long distance from the station switchboard and where old iron telephone wire was

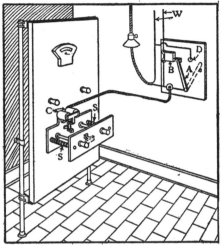

Operating Switch Plugs from Distance

used to close the circuit, an arrangement as shown in the accompanying sketch was made to draw the plugs on an arc light switchboard.

The coils, C, which release the springs, S, on the plug drawing attachment are coils from an old arc light. These coils are operated through a local circuit using an ordinary buzzer, B, for a relay, which releases a small arm, A, operated by a spring, making a momentary contact on point D, thus closing the circuit through the coils. The wires, W, are the iron wires connected to a push button at the house.

This could be used nicely without the relay attachment if the distance were short. As the house is some distance from the station and an old iron telephone wire was used, the resistance was such that the main coils could not get enough current to operate them with success.—Contributed by H. S. Brink, Fort Des Moines, Iowa.

To Print on Tracing Cloth with a Rubber Stamp

Prepare the part of the tracing to be printed by scouring it good with pulverized French chalk to remove any grease spots and after dusting off all loose chalk apply the stamp in the usual manner, using any good brand or color of glycerine stamping ink.

After the stamp has been applied cover it again with pulverized French chalk, this time rubbing it lightly with the finger until the ink forming the letters has soaked up enough chalk to make them appear raised. Then dust off the loose chalk and the tracing is ready to use.—Contributed by E. W. Bowen, Denver, Colo.

Uniform Heat for Melting Brass

In melting brass or similar metals, too strong a heat is detrimental. Portions of the metal exposed will be melted and oxidized before the remainder is melted, says Brass World. The best practice is to have the metal melt as uniformly as possible so that all portions become liquid at about the same time. This avoids overheating any portion of it.

Transferring Punch Marks on Boiler Plate

The sketch shows a device for use in boiler shops, where, as it frequently happens, it is required to transfer a prick punch mark from one side of a marked plate to the other. Its application is shown. The two holes in the

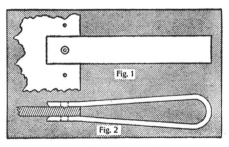

For Transferring Punch Marks

jaw are drilled in line and the one hole is placed so as to register with the punch mark (Fig. 1) and the spring of the jaws holds it in place, so that the plate may be turned over (Fig. 2) and the other center scribed or prick-punched, as may be desired. Any piece of flat steel may be used that has spring enough to adapt it to the thickness of the various plates.

What to Prevent in Building a Chimney

The settling of a chimney when built on a frame roof is not always taken in consideration and the result is that the ex-tended part of the chimney, shown at A in the sketch, is left to rest on the roof and the part below set-tles and leaves a crack through the mortar and brick. Many fires have been caused by this fault of con-struction. Enough space should be al-lowed for the settling at point A.

How to Repair Tire Casings

An old tire casing that may not be in a condition to warrant the repairing by a regular repair man can be put in condition to get several hundred miles of service from it, says The Motor Way. If it is blown out, carefully clean the inside of the cover with gaso-line for about 5 in. each side of the hole. Then take one of your covers that is in bad condition and cut a sec-tion, about 10 in. long, out of the best part of it; cutting the beads, A, Fig. 1, from it and trimming it with a sharp knife at the edges to a thin edge, as shown at B. Carefully clean the out-side with gasoline and when ready ap-ply three coats of solution to the in-side of the shoe to be repaired, allowing each coat to dry well, also about two

coats on the outside of the repair piece, and apply together as you would a patch on an inner tube.

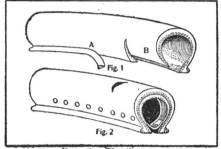

Repairing Tire Casings

Rivet the patch to the tire casing by using small copper rivets or split rivets in a single row, about 1 in. from the bead (Fig. 2), placing the rivets about $1\frac{1}{2}$ in. apart. After this is done canvas should be cemented to the inside of the casing, covering the entire patch, so as to make a smooth surface for the inner tube.

To Remove the Odor of Paint

Place a vessel of lighted charcoal in the middle of the room and throw two or three handfuls of juniper berries on it. Shut the doors, windows and all means of ventilation for about 24 hours and the smell will be entirely gone. This process will not injure curtains, carpets or furnishings.

How to Make an Adjustable Boring Bar

A quickly made adjustable boring-bar can be constructed as shown in the sketch, says the American Machinist. The adjustments of the bar, A, are

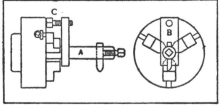

Adjustable Boring Bar

obtained by the screw, C, which passes through the plate, B, and bears against the face of the three-jawed chuck.

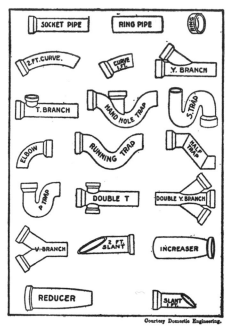

Courtesy Domestic Engineering.

Types of Sewer Pipe Joints

Emergency Tire-Testing Tank

The accompanying sketch shows what may be done with the ordinary materials that are carried in an automobile at any time. A traveling grip, emptied of its contents, with any water-proof garment pressed down into its mouth, can be filled with water, says a correspondent in The Motor Way. With this aid a puncture can be easily located. If there is no water at hand the water

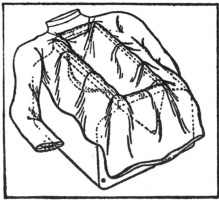

For Locating a Puncture

from the acetylene generator can be used, even though there is a small quantity, as the shape of the tank can be changed to fit the tube.

Changing Pulleys

In changing pulleys on line shafts or other places it may be desirable to know how much to cut out of or add to a belt, and have it come right. That is to say, if a belt runs over two pulleys 30 in. in diameter, and the pulleys were to be changed to 36 in., the belt would need to be as much longer as one pulley is larger around than the other.

The difference of the distance around two pulleys of unequal size is the same

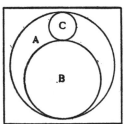

as the distance around a small pulley the diameter of which equals the difference between the diameters of the two, says Power and Transmission.

For instance: the distance around a 14-in. pulley is 44 in., and the distance around a 21-in. pulley is 66 in.; but, knowing the fact that the latter is the same as the distance around a 7-in. pulley, it is only necessary to determine that to get the correct result, 22 in.

The circumference A in the illustration equals the sum of the circumferences of the two, B and C.

Care of Paint Brushes

Always clean a new brush before putting it into paint. Work it briskly back and forth through the hand until most of the dust and loose bristles are out, soak in water until wet through and then swing and shake till dry.

For varnish and buggy paint the brush must be more thoroughly cleaned, until all loose hairs are out. Brushing it over sandpaper is good. Wash out in turpentine, not water. When not in use keep suspended in the varnish.

THE PROPER USE OF NAILS

One of the simplest details in correctly driving a nail is almost ignored by the ordinary workman. When a flooring or sheathing board is drawn in place the nail is set slanting and driven as shown in Fig. 1. If the board be lifted from the support about ¾ in., drive the nail through until it strikes the studding or joist, then finish driving the nail, taking along with it the board, as in Fig. 2, and the results are

ing and some methods that are more nearly correct.

Another point in locating the position for the nails, especially near the end of boards, is this: It should be remembered that the danger of splitting the board is limited to a well-defined field, the extent of which varies with different kinds of wood, but the general shape is about the same as indicated by the dotted line in Fig. 11,

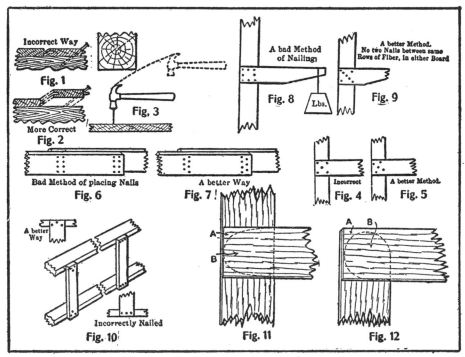

Advantageous Locating of Nails

much better, says a correspondent in Wood Craft.

To drive a nail in a confined place where a full swing of the hammer cannot be obtained the full force of the hammer can be obtained by moving the arm ahead at the time the blow is being struck, as in Fig. 3.

The location of nails should be placed staggered or zigzag, so as to be out of the line of the same fiber of wood. The illustrations Figs. 4 to 10 show some examples of incorrect nail-

which is supposed in this case to apply to a board 1 in. or less in thickness. A represents the area of risk, B the field of safety—so far as the splitting of the board is concerned. Fig. 12 shows a variation to fit another condition.

◆ ◆ ◆

Probably the heaviest chain ever made has been turned out by an English firm for the Japanese government. The common links weigh 200 lb. apiece, and the end link 300 lb.

A Home-Made Tinsmith's Window Jack

A window jack which can be used for a variety of purposes may be made at small expense by any mechanic. The

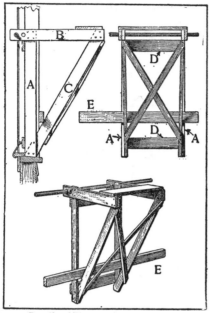

Details of Tinsmith's Window Jack

entire jack is built of strips of 1 in. by 4 in. wood and when completed it has strength enough to hold any reasonable weight, says The Metal Worker. The seat is made of 1 in. by 12 in. board 2 or 3 ft. long. The upright pieces, A, are 4 ft. long and may be left wide enough at the bottom for a notch to prevent slipping in too far on the window sill. The horizontal piece, B, is cut about 3 ft. long and should extend beyond A, with holes bored to receive a piece of ¾-in. gas pipe. The pieces C form the brace to which are nailed two strips of 1 in. by 2 in. material crossed. These strips will keep the jack from twisting. The pieces D are cut about 2 ft. long, but can be any length to suit the width of the jack. A loose piece of 2 in. by 4 in. material 2½ or 3 ft. long is used at the bottom to keep the jack from slipping in on the window sill.

As the jack is light, it is easily carried to the window and attached by setting the foot of the jack on the window sill and running the piece of gas pipe through the holes, so as to prevent it from falling out of the window. The loose piece of 2 in. by 4 in. material is then placed, as shown, across the window, so that the foot of the jack cannot slip in at the bottom. The weight of the jack will then hold it in position and it is a simple matter to climb out on the seat so that a tinner may flash around the top of a window or put in a new window head if desired. Two of these jacks extending out of two different windows with a plank across offer a very good scaffold for mounting a cornice or similar work. To avoid the use of the loose piece at the bottom the side pieces may be made 8 in. wide, notching the bottom 3 or more inches in from front to back and at least 4 in. deep to let the foot of the jack catch the window sill and to prevent it from slipping into the building at the bottom.

Repairing a Broken Cog

A cog in the main drive gear on our concrete mixer broke at a time when we could not afford to shut down, and as we were 70 miles from the shop, we made the repairs in a short time by threading two ¾-in. holes in the gear at the point where cog was broken and screwed in two steel bolts, riveted the bottoms and dressed up the bolts as shown in the cut. This worked nicely until a new gear could be made, which was several weeks.—Contributed by Frank L. Cash, Haralson, Ga.

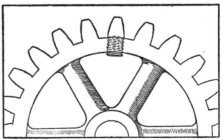

Showing Repaired Cog

A Handy Tool Holder

A handy light tool or screwdriver holder may be turned up from a piece of cold rolled steel. It is turned to the shape as shown in the cross section, Fig. 1, with a hole drilled in one end to insert different tools, while the other end is drilled, tapped and fitted with a

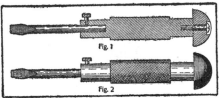

Turned from Cold Rolled Steel

screw which holds a rounded fiber handle loosely. The center part of the holder is knurled as in Fig. 2 and filled with a thumb screw to hold the tools.—Contributed by Frank Schwab, Geneva, N. Y.

Excellent Home-Made Muffler

The illustration shows a muffler for marine gasoline motors that has given great satisfaction. For 3 or 4 hp. it is made of a piece of 5-in. iron pipe, 12 in. long, with cast-iron heads. A bolt

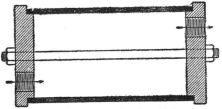

Muffler for Marine Gasoline Motors

running through the muffler holds these heads in place. The inside of this device is filled with old wire. Part of an old woven wire mattress makes an ideal filler. If there seems to be back pressure when the engine is running some of the wire may be removed, until the muffler is adjusted to get the best work out of the engine. Water may be pumped through the muffler if desired, in which case the amount of wire filler

can be greatly reduced. It has been found very satisfactory to make the outlet one size larger pipe than that through which the burned gases enter.—Contributed by "Boston."

Substituting a Shaper for a Power Hack-Saw

Where a number of angle irons had to be cut with a hack-saw and there was no power hack-saw in the shop, a shaper was used in its place. A bar of metal, long enough to reach the bench and turned in the shape of an L at one end, which was fitted in the tool post of the shaper, and a hand hack-saw clamped to

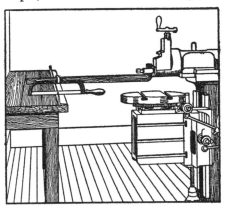

Substituting Shaper for Power Hack-Saw

the other end completed the arrangement. The angle iron was clamped to the bench at the right place and the shaper put in action. The bar of metal furnished the weight for the hack-saw to make the cut.—Contributed by C. F. H.

Cleaning Hot Brass

For cleaning hot brass cylinder heads and jackets try the following recipe, which a correspondent of the Practical Engineer says works fine:

Sift coal ashes fine and mix with kerosene oil to a thick paste; add as much air-slaked lime as can be conveniently mixed with it. Apply this polish to the bright parts, rubbing hard; wipe off and polish with dry slaked lime.

A Handy Ice Cream Freezer Shelf

Fasten a shelf, large enough for an ice cream freezer, the right height to a post or wall. On the surface of the shelf nail a cleat, A. Fasten two pieces of wood, BB, the same thickness as the cleat on the bottom of the freezer, leaving space enough between them to allow the cleat to fit in it. The cleat will

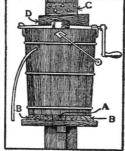

prevent rotation and movement of the freezer on the shelf. On the post or wall above the rim of the freezer nail another cleat, C. The freezer is then held firmly in position by the wedge, D.—Contributed by James H. Beebee, Rochester, N. Y.

To Keep Dirt from Sticking to a Shovel

Working on the levees in the rice fields, I had a good deal of trouble from the dirt sticking to the shovel. I drilled four small holes through the shovel,

Dirt Will not Stick to This Shovel

which made the shovel self-cleaning.— Contributed by William L. Walker, St. Charles, Ark.

A New Method of Putting Out a Fire

I was alone and a fire started in the roof of my house. There was no ladder at hand and it was too far to throw the water. I filled some corn cans with water and threw them one at a time on the spot where the fire was burning. The empty cans would roll down to be filled again. The location of the fire necessitated my throwing the cans against the wind. In this way I put out a fire that covered 10 sq. ft. in the center of the roof.—Contributed by Sim Harris, Boonville, Colo.

Repairing a Water Closet Trap Valve

Take down the box and disconnect the ball and rod from the plunger by removing the screw. Take out the plunger and put a little machine oil on the top of it and sprinkle with some fine emery. Turn the plunger over and drop into valve. As the plunger and valve are turned work a true bearing is made on the seat. Put a screwdriver into the screw that holds the disk and turn back and forth until a good seat is formed on the valve. Clean out the emery and put on a new disk and you have practically a new valve.— Contributed by William King, Cleveland, O.

A New Kink in Ladder Making

If the rungs of a ladder are made of wood that will split easily then it will be necessary to bore small holes for the nails or screws. To prevent the rungs from splitting when a heavy person mounts

the ladder a slanting notch is sawed where each one is fitted, as shown in the sketch. This will make it very light and strong.—Contributed by J. M. Myers, Davenport, Wash.

Melting Copper

It is important that none of the copper to be melted should project above the charcoal. Any copper not covered by charcoal will be oxidized or "burnt," and the casting will be weak and full of holes.

Utility Pipe Vise

Here is a kink that shows how a common vise will hold a pipe when

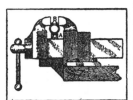

other ways fail. An old nut or piece of iron of the right size is placed in the vise at A, which will keep the pipe in position so that the corners of the jaws, B, will close on the pipe. This will not rough up the pipe as when a pipe vise is used.— Contributed by Willis Ferguson, Pisgah Forest, N. C.

To Assist in Making Forgings and Welds

Direct a jet of compressed air against the heated ends of the work. The air blast will cause a display of fireworks and will considerably raise the temperature of the metal just prior to making the forging or weld. By this means it is possible to revive the heat in a piece that has become cooled. The air jet will also blow off all dirt and scale. Try it on a bar of metal and see how it works, says Electric Traction Weekly. It will burn the metal faster, but it will increase the heat.

A Three-Horse Evener for Use without a Tongue

The accompanying sketch shows a three-horse evener for use on a plow or harrow where there is no tongue. The principle is the same as the one previ-ously described in these pages, but this plan makes a lighter evener and has less rigging. The equalizers as shown at A are of 2-in. by ⅜-in. iron about 18 in. long, with the holes punched one-third of the distance from the ends. An old singletree iron welded on the long end will be strong enough. On the short end a heavier hook is needed and this is supplied by a small clevis and a ring for the middle of the singletrees.

This arrangement can be attached to any two-horse whiffletrees in a few minutes, says a correspondent in The American Blacksmith. By using this plan and crossing the traces the inside horse will have plenty of room without chafing his legs on the traces.

Picture Wire for Belt Lacing

The accompanying sketch shows a novel way of using a picture wire for a

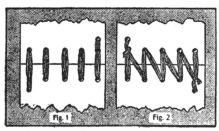

belt lacing. A 2-in. belt laced in this manner and running over a 24-in. wood pulley and a 6-in. iron pulley where the speed of the former is 247 r. p. m. has been in service for several months with best results. Fig. 1 shows the outside of the lacing and Fig. 2 the inside.—Contributed by J. E. Morris, Columbus, O.

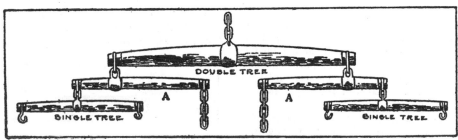

Three-Horse Evener where no Tongue is Used

A Home-Made Cement Block Mould

The lumber necessary to make this mould should be of selected white pine or hardwood free from knots and sap. The base board, A, Fig. 1, should be 14 in. wide by 24 in. long, well battened together. The sides are made as shown with a cleat on each end, which overlaps the end pieces and holds them in place. Both the ends and sides are fastened to the base with hinges, which permit them to be turned down to take out the completed block. On each end is placed a flat iron bar with a bend or notch in it to hold the sides together. These bars are the same as hooks with the ends extended to form a handle for convenience. The end pieces have a thin piece of board fastened in an upright position on their inner surface to form a key between the completed blocks.

The bottom board, Fig. 2, is to be fitted in the bottom of the mould loosely and can be blocked up from the bottom to make the right size block.

The plugs, Fig. 3, are made with a taper on both sides so that in removing them they will clear all the way out. The pins in the bottom of the plugs are to fit in holes in the bottom board, which will hold them in place.

When the plugs are to be removed take the board with the two square holes, Fig. 4, and place over the top of the mould and with the handle of the tamper bar, which is run through the rings in the top of the plugs, lift them upward, using the board as a guard to prevent the block from being broken. This board should not be used until the block is finished and ready to take out of the mould.

The tamper, Fig. 5, is made of a piece of iron rod about 18 in. long with a large nut threaded on one end,

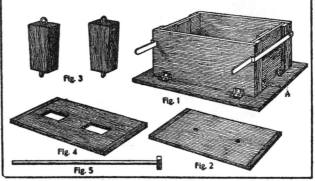

Mould for Cement Blocks

To make the blocks use one part of Portland cement and three parts of good, sharp sand. Mix well and put enough water on to simply dampen the whole mixture. Close up the mould and put in the plugs, and then fill the mould one-quarter full of the mixture and tamp down hard. Repeat this until the mould is filled and then scrape off the surplus material, remove the plugs, turn down the sides and lift out the finished block. The block should remain on the bottom board until it is hard enough to remove. It will be necessary to have a number of bottom boards. The finished blocks must be sprinkled with water from day to day for a duration of 15 to 30 days to properly cure them before using. A barrel of cement will make about 50 blocks.

A Pattern-Maker's Clamp

A very handy clamp for pattern makers' use can be made as shown in the illustration. The device consists of two levers, A, pivoted on the brace, B, which is threaded to receive the clamp screw, C. On this clamp screw is mounted a bushing, D, to which are connected the

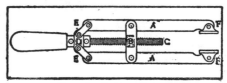

Clamp for Pattern-Makers

links, E. These links, in turn, are connected to the levers, A. The end of the levers are each fitted with a swivel jaw, F. The action of the clamp is readily seen and the clamping pressure is very great on thin work, due to the toggle action of the links.

Cleaning Machinery

Dissolve 1 lb. concentrated lye in about 2 gal. water, and with a mop saturate the engine with the liquid, being careful that it does not get into the oil holes of the journals and bearings. After the lye has eaten all the grease and gum from the surfaces, clean perfectly by scraping and brushing, and after the iron is dry and free from grease, apply a thin coat of lead paint, says Thresherman's Review. After this is thoroughly "set," paint the iron a deep black and varnish heavily. Coloring, striping or decorating should be done before varnishing. Then the engine can be easily and quickly cleaned with a dusting cloth, and escaped oil can be wiped off very easily.

How to Use Dividers for a Square

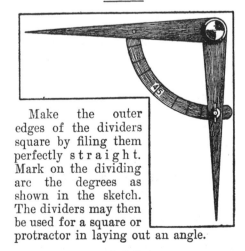

Make the outer edges of the dividers square by filing them perfectly s t r a i g h t. Mark on the dividing arc the degrees as shown in the sketch. The dividers may then be used for a square or protractor in laying out an angle.

Dusting finely ground emery upon paper or cloth that is coated with a thin glue makes emery paper and cloth.

Connecting Iron Pipe to Lead Pipe

Should it be necessary to repair a lead pipe and the tools for making a wiped joint are not at hand, or where

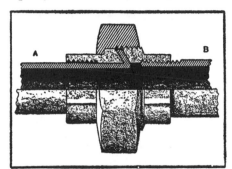

Use Union as Shown

an iron pipe must be attached to a lead pipe, the connection or repair may be made by using a union as shown in the sketch. The union must be of a size that the lead pipe, A, will just slip through the threads. After the parts of the union are on the lead pipe the latter is belled out, forming a flange. This flange makes the gasket for the union. The iron pipe, B, is screwed in to the other part of the union and the connection is made as shown.—Contributed by Alexander A. Gallich, Chicago.

Home-Made Cableway

The embankment on a railroad at a certain place was 70 ft. high and in building the concrete culvert through it at the base all materials had to be lowered from the tracks above, says Engineering-Contracting. A cableway was constructed by using a wire rope that passed through a double block at the top, attached to a post sunk in the embankment, the lower end of the rope being attached to another post at the site of the work. On this rope ran two boxes, having deep drop bottoms, and hung from the cables by small snatch blocks. These boxes were fastened to the cable by a 1¼-in. rope in such a way that when one box was at the top the other would be over the mixing board at the bottom. When the loaded box descended it pulled up the empty one. The speed was controlled by a brake stick.

How to Make a Commutator Press

A press is necessary in the building and rebuilding of commutators to firmly press the segments together so as to hold the mica securely and prevent oil and dust from getting between the segments, says Electric Railway Review. A home-made press can be cheaply made in almost any small repair shop, as shown in the sketch.

The press consists of a diagonally split steel shell, A, tapered toward both ends, the slope being about one in ten. The inside diameter of the shell is just a little larger than the diameter of the assembled commutator which it is desired to press together. Two heavy steel rings, BB, fitting the shell, A, can be drawn together by means of six or eight bolts, CC. The force with which the segments and mica can be pressed together is only limited by the strength of the rings, BB, which are made exceptionally heavy.

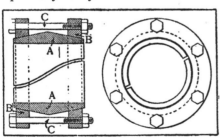

Plan and Section

The bolts CC and the rings BB are removed and one of the rings and the shell A are slipped over the assembled commutator bars and mica. The rings are then put in place and the bolts uniformly tightened. When sufficiently tight the whole can be put in a lathe and the commutator bars can be bored out true to receive the commutator shell and its insulation. When this insulation has been properly placed in posi-

tion, the clamping ring is warmed and put on over the end insulating ring and the bolts tightened. The clamp can now be removed and the assembled commutator placed in a lathe and the face turned.

Welding Wide Tires

Give the tire the right lap without scarfing. Heat it red hot and clip off the edges with a sharp chisel. This is a

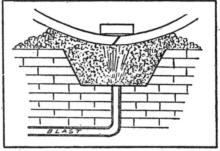

"Start with a Steady Blast"

great deal quicker and better than scarfing with a fuller, says the American Blacksmith. Stand the tire up in the fire and place a fire brick on top of the scarfs. A common building brick will do as well, only it does not last as long as the fire brick. Start with a steady blast, and if you find the edges getting hot before the center, stop the blast a few moments until it shows the same heat all over, and then blow up again and you will get a good heat. Any wide iron can be welded in this way in one heat if there are two good hammermen that know their work. Let the edges spread out as much as they will and trim with a chisel. The main point is, do not hurry. Give a steady blast and do not force it; coax it.

To Drill Tempered Steel

Sometimes it is necessary to drill out parts of a broken tap which is hard to make a drill take hold of it. Keep the drill and steel wet with spirits of turpentine and the drill will bite, where at other times it would wear the cutting edge.—Contributed by Wm. Rosenblohm, Brooklyn, N. Y.

A Ladder Made of Gas Pipe

A light and durable ladder can be made of ordinary gas pipe and fittings, as shown in Fig. 1. Use about 1-in.

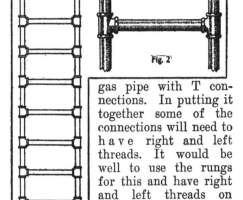

Fig. 2

Fig. 1

gas pipe with T connections. In putting it together some of the connections will need to have right and left threads. It would be well to use the rungs for this and have right and left threads on them. This will not make a heavy ladder and is lighter than some of the usual wooden ones, and is, of course, fireproof.

Equalizing Brush-Holder Springs

Many commutator troubles may be overcome by equalizing the tension on the brush-holder springs, says a correspondent in Electric Traction Weekly. Connect the brushes in pairs, as shown in the sketch, by small coil springs, which will keep the tension on the two

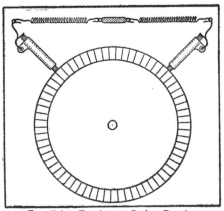

Equalizing Tension on Carbon Brushes

sets of brushes balanced and equalized. A small insulator should be placed in between the springs. This reduces the wear on the commutator and brushes, and will do away with grooves, rough places and burnt spots.

How to Make a Melting Ladle

A ladle for melting lead or babbitt metal that is made of wrought iron will not break like one made of cast iron, says a correspondent in The American Blacksmith. A wrought iron ladle can be made by cutting a piece of flat iron or steel in the shape as shown in sketch at A from about $\frac{1}{4}$-in. thick material. Weld or rivet a handle to this piece. Take a wide band about $1\frac{1}{2}$ in. smaller

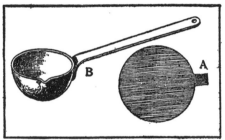

Wrought-Iron Melting Ladle

than the piece cut for the ladle. If you do not have a band of this description, make one. Heat the piece from which you intend to make the ladle until it is red hot. Take a round-faced hand hammer, lay the flat piece on the band, and hammer it down until you have it in the shape of a ladle. It may take several heats to do this, for it all depends on the size of the ladle. When completed it should be in the shape as shown at B.

A cement that will resist white heat may be made of pulverized fire clay, 4 parts; plumbago, 1 part; iron filings or borings free from oxide, 2 parts; peroxide of manganese, 1 part; borax, $\frac{1}{2}$ part, and sea salt, $\frac{1}{2}$ part. Mix these to a thick paste and use immediately. Heat up gradually when first using.

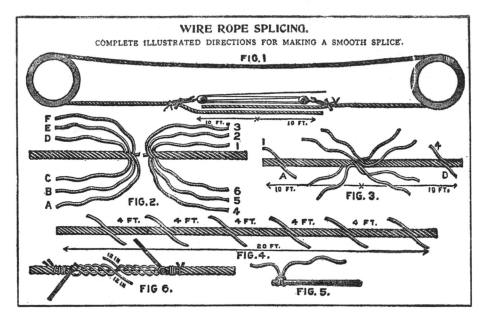

WIRE ROPE SPLICING.
COMPLETE ILLUSTRATED DIRECTIONS FOR MAKING A SMOOTH SPLICE.

Wire rope is susceptible of the most perfect splice; a better and smoother splice can be put in a wire rope than in any other 'ind of rope, for the simple reason that it is made with a view to this purpose. It has just the desired number of strands, namely, six, and a hemp core which provides place for fastening the ends. It is a plain, simple process, and but the work of an hour for anyone to learn.

In cases where an endless rope cannot be put on already spliced, the rope has to be put around the sheaves, hove taut by pulley blocks, and the splice made on the spot. See Fig. 1 in diagram of splices.

The necessary tools are a hammer and sharp cold chisel for cutting off ends of strands; a steel point or marlin spike for opening strands; two slings of tarred rope with sticks (see Fig. 5) for untwisting rope; a pocket knife for cutting the hemp core; a wooden mallet and block.

First—Put rope around the sheaves and heave it *tight* with good block and fall (see Fig. 1). The blocks should be hitched far enough apart so as to give room between to make a 20-ft. splice. A small clamp may be used to prevent the lashing from slipping on the rope where the blocks are hitched (see Fig. 1). Next see that the ropes overlap about 20 ft., about 10 ft. each way from the center, as shown by the double arrow in Fig. 1. Next mark the center on both ropes with a piece of chalk, or by tying on a small string. Now proceed to put in the splice, with the blocks remaining taut, when necessary; but the better way is to remove the blocks, throw off the ropes from the sheaves, let it hang loose on the shafts, and proceed with the splice on the ground or floor, or scaffold, as the case may be.

Second—Unlay the strands of both ends of the rope for a distance of 10 ft. each, or to the center mark, as shown in Fig. 2. Next cut off the hemp cores close up, as shown in Fig. 2, and bring the bunches of strands together, so that the opposite strands will interlock regularly with each other (see Fig. 3).

Third—Unlay any strand, A, and follow it up with strand 1 of the other end, lay it tightly in the open groove made by unwinding A, make twist of the strand agree exactly with the twist of the open groove. Proceed with this until all but 12 in. of 1 are laid in, or till A has become 10 ft. long. Next out off A, leaving an end about 12 in. long.

Fourth—Unlay a strand, 4, of the opposite end, and follow with strand D, laying it into the open groove as before, and treating this precisely as in the first case (see Fig. 3). Next pursue the same course with B and 2, stopping 4 ft. short of the first set. Next with 5 and E, stopping as before. Then with C and 3; and lastly with 6 and F. The strands are now laid in with the ends 4 ft. apart, as shown in Fig. 4.

Fifth and last—The ends must now be secured without enlarging the diameter of the rope. Take two rope slings or twisters (see Fig. 5) and fasten to the rope as shown in Fig. 6; twist them in opposite directions, thus opening the lay of the rope (see Fig. 6). Next, with the knife cut out the hemp core about 12 in. on each side. Now straighten the ends, and slip them into the place occupied by the core, then twist the sling back, closing up the rope, taking out any slight inequality with a wooden mallet. Next shift the slings and repeat the operation at the other five places, and the splice is made.

Home-Made Cooler

A cooling device that will keep things cold can be made at little cost and will work well in any place. I have used one that kept food cold, say 55°, on the desert with heat registering by the

thermometer 115° to 120°. The frame may be made as high as you wish and to hold the required number of shelves, as shown in Fig. 2. Cover this over on all sides with burlap as shown in Fig. 1, leaving a part of the upper end of the burlap to lay in a pan of water which is placed on top of the frame. The burlap will absorb the wa-

ter, which will run down the sides, keeping the enclosed contents cool. It is necessary to change the water every morning.—Contributed by H. C. Mayer, Venice, Cal.

Quickly Made Carpenter's Clamp

This is a handy device if anyone has a door to make or any cabinet work where tools are scarce. Take a board of sufficient length and nail a cleat on both ends, as shown in Fig. 1. The space

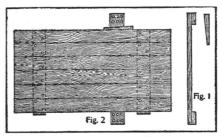

Clamp for Cabinet Work

between the cleats should be of a width that will just take in the door or cabinet work. The wedge is then driven in as shown in Fig. 2, which holds the boards together until they are nailed to the batten pieces or glued in cabinet work.

Annealing Novo Steel

If you have a piece of novo high speed steel and wish to soften it so it can be worked, take a barrel of slacked lime, and a piece of gaspipe about an inch larger in diameter and two or three inches longer than the steel you wish to anneal. Thread the pipe on both ends and fit a cap on one end, then put in about an inch of lime, drop in the steel and pack well with lime, keeping the steel in the middle of the pipe, and fill the other cap with lime and screw it on the other end. Put the pipe and its contents in the fire and heat slowly and evenly to a white, but not melting, heat and then take it out and quickly bury it in the middle of your barrel of lime and leave it for 12 or 14 hours. For ordinary sized pieces the time taken to heat will not be over 20 minutes and if a good sized forge is used, it will be considerably less. Be sure it is heated through before putting it in the lime barrel.— Contributed by E. V.

Wood Handle Without a Metal Ferrule

Make the handle the shape desired and bore a $\frac{1}{2}$-in. hole about $\frac{1}{2}$ in. deep in the end where the tool is to be inserted. Continue the hole to the required depth with a $\frac{1}{4}$-in. bit  or drill. The rim of the larger hole, A, as shown in the sketch, serves as a ferrule and will keep the wood handle from splitting.—Contributed by W. C. Loy, Rochester, Ind.

How to Make a Boiler Compound Feeder

The accompanying sketch shows a type of boiler compound feeder which depends for its action on the drop in pressure between two points in the feed water main to which it is connected, being evident that the greater the distance apart the points of connection are made the greater will be the tendency of the flow of feed water to follow the path offered through the feeder. The arrangement has the advantage of increasing the rate or amount of compound feeding to the boilers when the feed water being delivered to the boiler

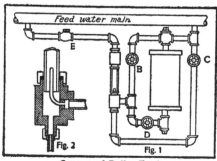

Compound Boiler Feed

is increased and *vice versa,* which tends to give automatic control within certain limits.

The difficulty of securing sight feed in handling boiler compounds has been overcome in this feeder in an ingenious manner and constitutes the improvement for which originality is claimed. Referring to the sketch, it will be seen that opening the valve C admits a flow of water which passes around the feeder and up through the glass, giving an independent circulation that maintains a clear view of the jet from which the boiler compound is flowing. The action prevents any coloring matter, used in mixing the compound, from diffusing, as the rapid circulation carries it beyond the jet before it has had time to blend with the circulating water.

The usual soda compounds are made more effective when a small quantity of tannic acid is used, as results from adding logwood during the period of dissolving the soda crystals, giving the solution a dark amber color that when feeding gives the appearance of a miniature column of smoke issuing from the jet. A mixture of this character will be heavier than water and should be fed from the bottom through valve D. A compound lighter than water may be fed equally as well by closing valve D and opening valve B.

The use of the check valve E is for the purpose of retarding the rebound of the water, due to the pump action, which would otherwise cause the water to surge in the glass, preventing a steady feed.

Fig. 2 shows an enlarged cross-section of the part where the compound comes in contact with the feed water.— Contributed by C. Everett Smith, Baltimore, Md.

In treatment of burns the main thing is exclusion of air and keeping the skin soft with some unguent. White of eggs beaten while castor oil is poured in until a thick creamy paste is formed makes a good application which is easily prepared.

SHOP NOTES

Home-Made Draft Spring

A draft spring for use on the evener or tongue of agricultural implements, to relieve the jerk on the horses' shoulders, may be made from any old

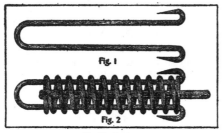

Draft Spring

corn plow or machinery spring. Two loops are formed as shown in Fig. 1 from $\frac{3}{8}$-in. round iron. Insert one loop from each end of the spring as in Fig. 2. The clevis or pulling trace may be fastened in either end.

Hot Tube Ignition Changed to Electric

Gas and gasoline engines are now made to use battery ignition as well as the hot tube, but some one may have an old style engine that is only provided with a hot tube. The accompanying sketch shows how a correspondent in The American Blacksmith fixed up an old engine of this kind. A $\frac{3}{4}$-in. hole was drilled through the water jacket into the ignition chamber and a $\frac{1}{2}$-in. pipe screwed into this hole. As $\frac{1}{2}$-in. pipe is seven-eighths of an inch on the outside a $\frac{7}{8}$-in. top was used

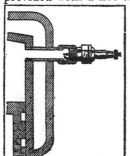

to cut the threads. A jump spark plug was screwed into a coupling and this coupling turned on the projecting pipe. This will give about $2\frac{1}{2}$ in. to compress the gas to the spark. A good jump spark coil, with a vibrator in connection with the battery, was used. As this requires a circuit to make the spark, one wire must be insulated from the engine so that it will come in contact at the right time, and the other fastened to the engine. Attach the insulated wire in such a way that it will come in contact with the exhaust cam just at the compression.

Handle for Hand Turning Tools

The handle, A, Fig. 1, is made from a piece of steel tube about 7 in. long and $\frac{1}{2}$ in. in diameter. With a few blows of the hammer form the tube

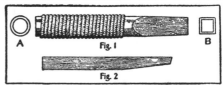

Handy Tool Handle

at one end into a square as shown in B. The tools (Fig. 2) are formed by grinding, and are made from $\frac{5}{16}$-in. tool steel. It will be found that the tool will fit securely in the handle when the latter is brought down quickly in a vertical position on an anvil or any solid piece of iron. This causes the angles at the base of the tool to jam into the circular part of the tubular handle. When it is required to release the tool, insert a small rod into the handle and strike the rod with a hammer. The tube may be wound with whipcord so as to increase the grip and to avoid handling the bare steel.

"Bramble Border—From the London Decorator"

A Tool for Shaping Wax Fillets

In the cut is shown a wax fillet tool that shapes the wax to a correct fillet instead of round as the usual way, says

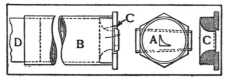

Makes Desired Shape

Machinery. The brass tube, B, is $1\frac{1}{4}$ in. by 8 in., threaded at one end to receive a brass plug, C. This plug has a dovetail cut in it as shown. In this dovetail may be fitted brass plates, as many as are required for the various sizes of fillets. These plates are cut out as shown at A. By placing the brass fillet plate required in the brass plug, and heating the tube in the regular way, a much better fillet is made than with the round wax. A wood plunger, D, is used to push the wax in the tube through the hole in the brass plate.

Sandpaper Block

Cut a block of wood triangular as shown at B, Fig. 1, with sides about 3 in. in length, making the corners

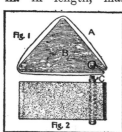

Fig. 1
Fig. 2

slightly round. Bore a hole in the block B and cut a slot leading f r o m the hole to a corner of the blcck. This slot must be wide enough to admit two sheets of sandpaper. Into the hole that is bored fit a kcv, C, Fig. 2, made of steel with a slot cut ir it the full width of the block. The sandpaper, A, is passed around the block and both ends inserted in the slot of the block and the slot of the key. Turning the key will make the sandpaper tight around the block.—Contributed by S. C. Bunker, West Orange, N. J.

Removing Stains From Marble

Blood stains may be removed by brushing with alabaster dust and distilled water, then bleaching with chlorine solution.

Iron mold or ink spots may be taken out in the following manner: Take $\frac{1}{2}$ oz. butter of antimony and 1 oz. oxalic acid; dissolve them in 1 pt. rain water; add enough flour to bring the mixture to a proper consistency. Lay it evenly on the stained part with a brush, and, after it has remained for a few days, wash it off and repeat the process, if the stain is not wholly removed.

To remove oil stains apply common clay saturated with benzine. If the grease has remained in long the polish will be injured, but the stain will be removed.

The following method for removing rust from iron depends upon the solubility of the sulphide of iron in a solution of cyanide of potassium. Make clay into a thin paste with ammonium sulphide, and smear the rust spot with the mixture, being careful to just cover the spot. After ten minutes wash off this paste and replace by one consisting of white bole mixed with a solution of potassium cyanide (1 to 4). After about $2\frac{1}{2}$ hours wash this off, also.

Should a reddish spot remain after washing off the first paste, a second layer may be applied for about five minutes.

Etching Zinc

Nitric acid will etch zinc. It will depend upon the kind of work as to the strength of the acid. Nitric acid must be diluted about one-half with water, and for some kinds of work will require more than this amount of water. Parts of the zinc that are not to be etched with the acid can be covered with asphaltum. Fine work must

How to Make a Carpenter's Tool Chest

The chest is made of cherry and maple strips. The arrangement may be made to suit the tools the builder may possess. The size of the chest illustrated is 18 in. square and 32 in. long inside. This length is sufficient to take in squares and saws. The saw rack resembles a drawer sliding vertically, the saws sliding through kerfs in the pieces which correspond to the sides of the drawer.

The swinging chisel rack is 1¾ in. shorter than the inside of the chest to

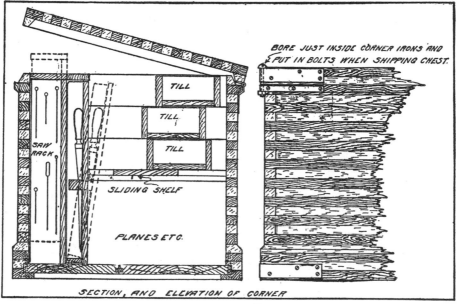

Details of Carpenter's Tool Chest

be done with a pen or brush using printers' ink diluted with benzine. The ink must be made thin enough to flow from a pen. While the ink is still wet, sift powdered dragon's blood on the zinc. Remove the surplus dragon's blood by turning the zinc over and shaking it. Dry the ink and dragon's blood by slightly heating it over a flame. The acid will then etch the parts uncovered. When the etching is complete wash the zinc to clean it from the acid and remove the ink or asphaltum by using alcohol.

allow it to swing out past the till runs, as shown by the dotted lines.

The sliding shelf below the tills forms a compartment, when the tills are pushed to one side, in which to put clothes and loose tools. The elevation of the outside corner shows the iron corner bands, also how a bolt may be put through each corner to take the strain from the lock and hinges when shipping. The construction of this chest makes it so that each class of tools has a place and all are protected from injury.

Courtesy Copper and Brass

First Wall Crane Ever Built for Brass Foundry

Silver Plating without a Battery

Dissolve eight silver quarters (money) or silver of equivalent amount in two ounces of nitric acid (strong), and to this add 4 oz. of common salt dissolved in as little water as possible. A heavy precipitate is silver chloride. Decant the liquid, add more salt solution to see if all the silver has been taken out. Wash the silver chloride precipitate with water and then dissolve it in a solution composed of 2 oz. potassium cyanide and 3 oz. sodium hyposulphate in 6 oz. of water. Filter the solution, if necessary, and make up to 2 qt. with pure rain water. You may, by the aid of this mixture, plate all sorts of things as watch chains, rings, medals, watches, ornaments, steel, iron and german silver articles as spoons, spectacles, etc. Hang the article to be plated in the solution suspended by a strip of lead or immerse the articles and boil them for ten to twenty minutes, according to the thickness of the plating desired. The articles to be plated must be free from grease, fat and dirt and by this method take a durable and handsome silver plating.

Temporary Wagon Wheel Nut

To keep a wagon wheel on the spindle after losing the nut is quite a thing to accomplish. Try wrapping heavy twine on the thread, pulling it tight in the winding, and greasing it well. It will be a surprise the distance that can be traveled without the wheel coming off from the axle.—Contributed by Leonard Graper, Greeley, Colo.

An Adjustable and Portable Electric Light Bracket

The use of an electric light over the bench always requires some little time to adjust and find something to hang the cord over to get the globe in the right place. A small light bracket or crane, constructed as shown in the sketch, will make a handy device to bring the electric globe in proper position quickly.

Cut a piece of wood, A, 2 by 4 in., 4 ft. long, and attach to it a horizontal piece of wood, B, $1\frac{1}{4}$ in. by 2 in., of any length desired, braced with a piece of the same material, C. Bend a $\frac{1}{8}$ in. by 1 in. band iron, D, in the shape of a U and drill a hole in the ends at E and

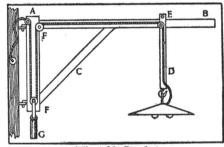

Adjustable Bracket

insert a roller that is just a little longer than the wood B is wide. At the other end, or the bottom end of the U band iron, fasten a hook or eye, to which is attached an adjustable cord connecting the lamp holder and shade. The points marked F are pulleys over which the flexible electric wire moves to take up the slack by the weight, G.

The piece of wood, A, is provided with two hinge hooks to hook into screw eyes that may be fastened in any convenient place on the wall or post near a vise or machine. A plug and a sufficient length of flexible wire will connect it to any near-by electric light socket.

The U-shaped band iron can be moved back and forth on the wood, B, and the bracket swung around in a semi-circle, giving access to different positions of the electric globe.

Locating Holes to be Drilled in a New Casting

In fitting a new casting on a machine it is not an easy matter to locate the holes to be drilled. If a large center punch or a round staking tool

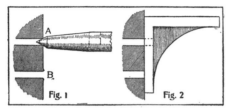

Locating Holes in a Casting

be driven in the holes as shown in sketch at A, Fig. 1, it will make a small ridge around the hole as shown in B. Take the new casting and chalk the side that is to be fitted to the machine. Place this chalked side at the proper place against the holes (Fig. 2) that have been rigged by the punch and strike the casting lightly with a hammer. This will make a small ring where the hole is to be drilled which can be centered with the dividers.

Metal Forms for Round Concrete Columns

Every cement contractor has encountered the difficulty of making wooden forms for circular concrete columns. The trouble may be overcome by using sheet metal, which gives a mold more handy than the old wooden type, and which is slightly less in cost.

Use two sheets of No. 16 gauge plate and bend each to a semi-circle of a radius equal to that of the column. Flange the two side edges about an inch and a quarter, and drill holes in these

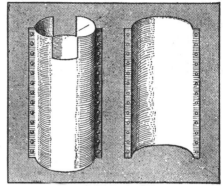

Concrete Molds for Pillars

at intervals of about $2\frac{1}{2}$ in. The two sheets can then be placed together and secured by fillister head bolts.

Holes are cut at the top to accommodate the various wooden floor beam forms. The inside of the sheet iron should be coated with oil to facilitate its removal after the concrete has set. Immediately after pouring the concrete the form should be braced by timbers to the floor, which will prevent the column from bulging or assuming an elliptical shape.

Removing a Broken Pump Rod

The bottom part of the broken pump rod is always hard to remove, and especially so if it is in a tubular well.

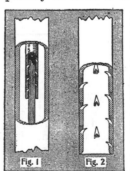

A tool for pulling this broken part out of the well can be made from a piece of gas pipe $1\frac{1}{4}$ in. in diameter. Place the gas pipe over a piece of shafting that will almost fill it and with a cold chisel cut triangular notches as shown in Fig. 2.

Bend the points out by driving the chisel under them. File the points sharp and drive them in with a punch. This will give them the position as shown in Fig. 2. Enough pipe can be attached to this pronged piece to make it reach the broken pump rod. Drive the pipe over the rod as shown in Fig. 1, and it is ready to be pulled out.

How to Make a Handy Wire Reel

Costs from $5 to $8

When an exchange manager has occasion to do some line work at a distance from the central office and the amount of material necessary for the job does not warrant using the time of the entire construction gang and the heavy double-team construction wagon, a small light pair of reels can be conveniently used. These can be economically constructed by anyone who has a little mechanical skill. Fig. 1 shows the completed stand with one of the pair of reels mounted thereon.

To an oak plank, 2 in. thick by 12 in. wide and 5 ft. long, a tapered axle or journal of cast iron— A, Fig. 2—is fastened 7 in. from each end. The reel is made from the same kind of wood, although any hard wood will do for either, by mortising two pieces 2 in. thick by 4 in. wide and 34 in. long and bolting them together with bolts through the bearing casting, B. The hole in the casting B is made tapering to fit the tapering part of the journal, A. The brake shoe is also made tapering with a flat interior side, G, which fits against a corresponding plane surface on the journal and prevents its turning with the reel. The spiral spring, D,

and the adjusting nut, E, complete the parts necessary, aside from the spreaders which are made of double end bolts bent over and fastened through holes bored in the reel arms. The customary guard is put on the reel to strengthen the arms and prevent the wire catching under them, but is not absolutely necessary.

The material which enters into this construction may all be secured locally at a low figure. When put together as described it makes a strong, light reel with a good bearing that will insure smooth running and good wearing qualities. This outfit weighs and costs only as much as one of the ordinary

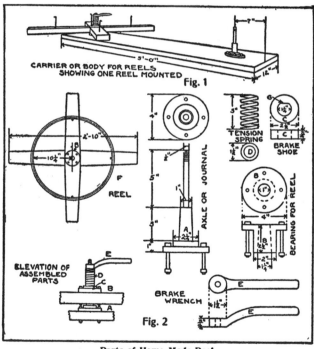

Parts of Home-Made Reel

pay-out reels, says The American Telephone Journal. The cost will run from five to eight dollars, according to the skill of the maker and the proximity of a foundry or a machine shop.

When stringing wire it can be easily fastened to the wagon box, or if put on the ground will not tip over and tangle up the coil if the wire gets caught, as often occurs with some types of reel.

Planing Large Timbers

Few planing mills other than those connected with saw mills have planers that will take the timbers larger than about 8 in., yet many mills where jobbing is done, or those in connection with lumber yards, are often called upon to dress large timbers. A

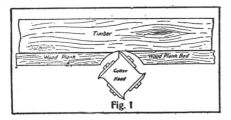

Fig. 1

small planer may be used to dress large timbers by attaching an extra bed, says the Wood-Worker.

In the accompanying sketches, Fig. 1 shows the side of a large timber being dressed, also a section of the cutterhead and the plank forming the bed on which the timber travels while being dressed. The sketch shows about all that is done to transform the planing machine temporarily into a jointer or hand planer. Fig. 2 is a view across the machine, with the end of the timber shown. It is easy to rig a temporary bed upon any planer where the feed rolls do not extend higher above the bed than the cutting circle of the head. If the tops of the rolls are above the cutting line, and cannot be lowered, they must be removed.

In view of the fact that many timbers become warped in seasoning, it is well to make the wood bed a trifle high

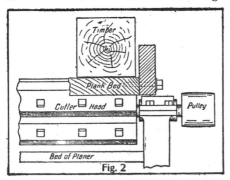

Fig. 2

at the cutting center, in order that the hollow side of the timbers can be dressed without cutting off the ends to get at the hollow part, as would be the case if the timbers were passed over a regular jointing machine.

The top rolls on the planer can in many instances be so raised that the timber rests upon them, and they act as the feedworks for moving the stock over the cutters. Another good way to move very heavy timbers over the cutters without too much hand labor is to have a rope with a loop or hook to catch the timber, a pulley to pass the rope over, and use the feed rolls as a capstan. The plank bed can be well made, and in most instances put in place in a short time, and when the work is done, set aside for future use.

Under-Water Exhaust for Motor Boats

To muffle the exhaust from a motor boat engine it is better to lead the discharge horizontally from the stern than to point it directly down, which causes back pressure. The plan illustrated in Amateur Work is a good one, and is 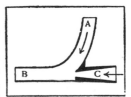 made of bent pipe. The exhaust from the engine enters at A and passes down and out into the wake at B. Movement of the discharge is facilitated by the enlarged mouth, C, which faces forward, the water moving from C to E and out, thus causing a partial vacuum at A. In the case of small engines it is better to exhaust into the air until the boat is under fair headway.

On the subject of under-water exhaust the Motor Boat says: If the exhaust pipe be carried direct from the motor through the hull below the water line, without the use of a muffler or expansion chamber, and the pipe opens out flush with the outer skin of the boat, the resultant action of the exhaust is somewhat similar to the familiar phenomenon of the gun barrel bursting when the muzzle of the gun has been obstructed in some way. The gun barrel does not burst because the obstruction at the muzzle is held there with strength sufficient to withstand the force of the explosion but because the pressure on the gun barrel in the vicinity of the exploding charge becomes great enough to rend it before this pressure can be communicated through the medium of the air to the slight obstruction at the muzzle, and so displace it. In the same way, when the exhaust valve begins to lift, the pressure of the water at the outer mouth of the exhaust pipe is much less than the pressure of the outgoing charge of burnt gas, but this sudden explosive discharge through the valve does not have time to communicate its full pressure to the lower resistance of the water, and it spends its force in the immediate vicinity of the valve, most of it working back against the piston on its upward exhaust stroke. In other words, this explosive discharge, like most other explosive phenomena, does not seek the path of least resistance at the moment of discharge but spends its force on the nearest resisting media.

Turning on a Planer

A certain large fly wheel that was broken had to be turned in order to shrink a band on the hub. The shop did not have a lathe that would take the wheel in the swing, and it was decided to do the work on a planer, says a correspondent in American Machinist. A flange bushing, B, was bolted to the planer table C, and the fly wheel placed on this bushing. The fly wheel was driven, by means of a quarter-turn belt, from a pulley, D, placed on a piece of shafting in a lathe set in front of the planer. An extension planer,

tool, E, was used so as to reach out to the center of the fly wheel. The cut was set with the cross feed, and the down feed was worked by hand.

How to Make a Cement Coping

In the sketch Fig. 1 shows how to construct a form to make a cement coping on brick walls. Use two 6-in. boards, AA, and nail on a 1 by 2-in.

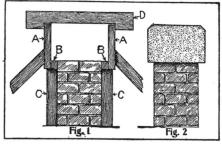

Fig. 1--Form   Fig. 2--Cast

strip, BB, on the bottom of each to form the projection of the stone. The strips may be of any width to show the thickness of the stone desired, but 4 in. thick is about right for 8 and 12-in. brick walls. Under the side boards put strips, CC, perpendicular to the ground, to hold the form at the proper height. Brace the form as shown to keep it from spreading when the ce-

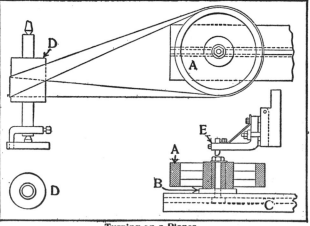

Turning on a Planer

ment is put in. Short forms will not need bracing, but any form 6 or 8 ft. long should have at least one brace on

each side. A board, D, notched just right to fit over the top of the mold, will do for a brace in some places, says Cement World.

After the mold is put in place take some thick cement mortar and stop all cracks where the mold does not fit the bricks. This should be well done so the water will not drip through and deface the brick work. As soon as the mold is ready mix the sand and cement in proportions of 1 part cement and 2 or 3 parts of sand. Mixing 1 part cement and 3 parts sand will make a good job, but 1 part cement and 2 parts sand will be extra good. Mix the cement and sand dry before putting any water with it.

Put the cement into the mold and with a trowel work it down well along the sides and fill the mold as you go, and rather quickly. After the mold is full, level the cement off on top and trowel to an even surface. After the cement has set sufficiently to stand without running, then, with a trowel, clip the top corners and smooth them down.

To Prevent Lead Pencil Point from Breaking

A small shell partly filled with a piece of lead, steel or shot, and forced on the end of a drawing pencil, may

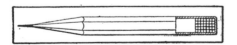

To Save Pencil Point

appear to be a queer contrivance, says Machinery; but this end being the heaviest will naturally fall to the floor first, and will prevent the lead point from breaking.

A method of bluing small steel goods by dipping is to melt saltpetre in an iron pot, then immerse the previously polished and cleaned articles until sufficiently blued. Remove and cool at once in paraffin oil and afterwards dry out in sawdust.

How to Make a Temporary Tire Repair

It may interest some readers to know how to make a temporary repair of a rim cut in a tire which causes the inner tube to blow through the casing, as shown at A in the sketch. After the

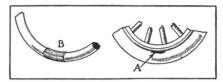

Temporary Tire Repair

inner tube is repaired, wrap a heavy piece of leather, about 10 in. long and wide enough to more than cover the hole in the casing, around the tube, B, covering the patch, says a correspondent in Motor Talk. This will encircle the inner tube about one and one-half times, but after being placed in the casing, the inflating of the inner tube will press it back tight against the walls of the casing, so that when fully inflated it will lap about 2 in. By lapping the leather it prevents pinching the inner tube.

How to Make Gold Leaf Stripes on Glass

Sign writers often have calls for a glass sign with one or more gold leaf stripes around the sign. These stripes can be quickly made by using a tool shaped like a paddle cut from a piece of soft pine or basswood. Dress the edge of the paddle down with sandpaper to a straight sharp edge, and cut notches, as shown in Fig. 1, suitable to the size and number of stripes de-

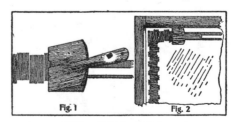

Making Gold Leaf Stripes

sired. Soak the paddle in water until it is thoroughly wet. Lay the gold leaf in the usual way, and with the wet paddle make the stripes by cutting away the gold leaf, as shown in Fig. 2, using a straightedge as a guide.—Contributed by H. E. Mangold, Compton, Calif.

How to Make a Handy Wrench

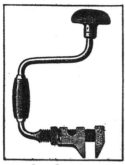

Take an old monkey wrench and remove the wood handle and weld the metal part of the handle to a piece of ⅝-in. round iron and shape in the form of a bitstock. This will be found a very handy wrench.

How to Tighten Loose Wagon Wheel Spokes

When wagon wheel spokes become loose or the tenons are worn where they are fitted into the felloe, lift the felloe from the spoke with a lever, A, and a post, B, as shown in the sketch, and either place a leather washer around the tenon at point C, or invert the wheel and run melted lead or babbitt around it.

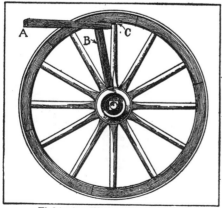

Tightening Wagon Wheel Spokes

How to Make a Durable Whitewash

When lime slakes, if the thing is properly done with hot water and a cover over the vessel, it will boil fiercely, and as soon as the slaking is done the wash should be used. If some tallow be added to the boiling lime, says the Master Painter, it will make a wash that will wear like paint. Salt tends to harden the lime, and is useful for doing damp places. There are two kinds of lime, the magnesian lime being the proper one for whitewashing purposes

Ladder on Wheels for Oiling

The accompanying sketch will need no explanation to the oiler. It will enable him to transform his present lad-

Very Handy—Lasts for Years

der into something better, says a correspondent in American Miller, or give the hint for constructing one that is vastly more convenient than the ordinary means of reaching overhead machinery.

How to De-Magnetize a Watch

Hang the watch to a string and twist the string so as to rotate the watch rapidly near the pole of a strong magnet. While it is whirling, gradually take it away from the magnet. This will produce the desired effect, says a correspondent in Southern Machinery.

The method used for de-magnetizing with alternating current consists of a coil of wire with a hole in the center large enough to admit a watch, the coil being connected to a source of alternating current, and when the watch is dropped in and pulled out, it is de-magnetized.

Extension Bit Used for Cutting Leather Washers

A very accurate and satisfactory tool for cutting leather washers of any size under 3 in. is to use a common extension or expansive bit. If the stationary cutter is not as large as the hole desired, cut the outside rim of the washer with the lip of the sliding cutter and then set at the proper position and cut the hole. Use the bit in a bitstock the same as in boring.

Making Core-Prints

It is a common occurrence to find patterns with core-prints on them so short that it is almost impossible to set the core. A pattern of this kind is shown in Fig. 1. The core-prints are left very short and much difficulty is experienced in obtaining a good bearing surface in the nowel when the core is set, says The Brass World.

Short core-prints should be avoided. They only serve to produce bad castings. The core is more apt to shift and it cannot be set as accurately as one which is made with core-prints of sufficient length. In setting the core,

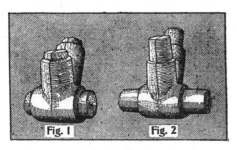

Making Core-Prints

short core-prints usually result in the breaking of the sand away from the edge of the mold. In Fig. 2 is shown a pattern with core-prints of a better length.

Holding a Trestle Leg up While Working under It

A description was given in a paper read before the American Society of Civil Engineers of a method used by the contractors in holding up one leg of a viaduct, the masonry under which came directly in the new sewer. The viaduct carried the street traffic. Traf-

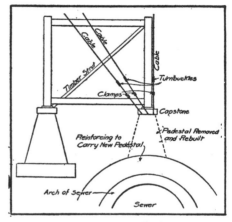

Supporting Leg of Viaduct

fic on the viaduct was not interrupted except by erecting barriers so as to deflect the traffic to the other side of the roadway where the weight would be carried directly to the undisturbed foundations. The post which rested upon the pier to be removed was suspended by passing a cable from the foot of the post diagonally upward to the top of the opposite post, and other cables to the tops of both posts composing the next pair of the trestle bents. By means of turn-buckles, the weight of the columns and the capstone of the pedestal attached was lifted free from the pedestal. Timber struts were also put in along with the cables in order to take up vibration. The arrangement of the cable and struts is shown in the sketch. The construction of the sewer was carried forward as near as practicable to the pier to be removed, and the excavation and the foundations at the sides were carried forward a short distance on either side and beyond the pedestal. The pedestal was then removed, leaving the capstone hanging to the foot of the viaduct column, and the sewer structure was carried through to completion without interference underneath. After the arch had been completed, the upper portion of the pedestal was rebuilt upon the back of the arch, and, after the arch had sufficiently hardened, the turn-buckles were gradually loosened and the weight brought to bear upon the new structure.

How to Make Wooden Stave Pipe

On account of the high prices of cast iron, wrought iron and steel, engineers have been constructing wooden stave pipe for a number of years. A certain stave pipe 30 in. in diameter which is used for power purposes has been in service for 45 years. The construction of such a pipe is shown in Fig. 1. It is made of staves with concentric inner and outer surfaces and radial edges. The ends of the stave are scarfed about ¾ in. deep, and a steel plate of No. 12 or No. 14 gauge, and slightly longer than the width of the stave, is inserted as shown at S, Fig. 1. The staves are held in place by round or oval steel bands, the spacing of the bands depending upon the pressure. Sometimes a small bead is left on the edge of the stave, which, being forced against the adjoining stave edge, will fill any slight depression or irregularity of the surface, thereby reducing the chance of leakage, says Wood Craft.

The bands are secured by a coupling shoe, the more common form of which

is shown by Fig. 2. The band has a T-head which locks into the under slot of the shoe, and the other end is threaded and provided with a washer and nut. Shoes are usually made of cast or mal-

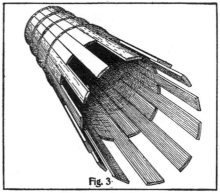

Fig. 3

"The Joints Are Broken"

leable iron and rods of soft or medium steel. The rod is swelled just below the head to prevent danger of breaking at that point; and the thread-

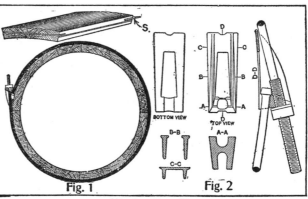

Fig. 1   Fig. 2

Wooden Stave Pipe

ed end is either upset so that the diameter at the base of the thread is about as large, or slightly larger than that of the rod, or else the thread is pressed or rolled.

In constructing the pipe, staves are placed over a form, care being taken to break joints at least 18 in., as shown in Fig. 3. The bands are spaced uniformly, and then held in place by turning up the nut, and at the same time rapping the band smartly with a mallet so

Nominal diameter Inches.	Stock sizes for staves Inches.	Thickness of staves Inches.	Economic sizes of bands Inches.
10	1½ x 4	1 1/16	5/16 x 7/16
12	1½ x 4	1⅛	5/16 x 7/16
14	1½ x 4	1 3/16	5/16 x 7/16
16	2 x 6	1 7/32	5/16 x 7/16
18	2 x 6	1⅜	5/16 x 7/16
20	2 x 6	1⅜	5/16 x 7/16
22	2 x 6	1⅜	⅜
24	2 x 6	1⅜	⅜
27	2 x 6	1 7/16	⅜
30	2 x 6	1½	½
36	2 x 6	1 9/16	½
42	2 x 6	1⅝	½
48	2 x 6	1 11/16	½
54	2½ x 8	2⅛	⅝
60	3 x 8	2½	⅝
66	3 x 8	2 9/16	¾
72	3 x 8	2⅝	¾

Economic Proportions for Pipe Design

as to secure the necessary indentation of the staves. Curves are made by forcing the pipe up or down or sideways after the bands are placed and holding it in the desired position while turning up the nuts on the bands. The lasting qualities of the pipe depend upon the complete saturation of the staves, and the thorough protection of the bands, saddles, etc., by an asphalt or similar coating. So long as the staves are kept saturated, they will last indefinitely. The life of the bands will depend upon the coating.

A Novel Exhaust Heater

An old oil barrel was placed on the roof of a boiler room to be used for the purpose of an exhaust heater, says a correspondent in Engineers' Review. The exhaust pipe from a deep well and a boiler feed pump were conducted into the barrel which was filled with rocks and broken pieces of iron, as shown in the sketch. The water ran down over the stone and iron and was thus heated when it passed out of the bottom to the boiler feeder.

Shoemaker's Wax

Take 4 oz. pitch, 1 oz. resin, ¼ oz. good tallow, heat well over a slow fire in an old saucepan. As the composition is combustible, great care must be used in keeping the flames away from it. Stir the mixture until the resin melts and mixes with the others. Then pour into a pail of cold water. When cool enough to handle put one hand underneath the wax and turn the edges to the center to form a ball. Take it out, make it into a roll and pull like taffy until it is of the color of pale resin. Lay on a slab, taking care that it does not stick. Roll out and cut into strips 1 in. wide and 1½ in. long. The wax must be hard in warm weather and soft in cold weather. To make it hard use more resin; to make it soft use more tallow. Keep the wax in water.

A Rear Number and Light for Automobiles

Substituting a square frosted glass for the usual round one on the rear lamp and painting it black leaving the number and letters plain makes a fine number card and lamp combined. During the day the frosted figures will show nicely, while at night the light will shine through them.—Contributed by F. J. Yorke, Chicago, Ill.

How to Clean Tile Floor

Use clean soap suds to which sufficient lye has been added to make it strong in attacking dirt, but not so strong as to injure the fiber of the scrubbing brush. Wipe the soap suds up and sprinkle fine white sand over the parts that still show grime. Use a soft pine board in rubbing the sand on the tile, says Building Management. The sand that will stick to the board should be removed from time to time. If necessary, a second scrubbing with suds and lye is to follow the treatment with sand. Ink spots and stains will not be removed in this way, but they can be taken out by a treatment with dilute solution of muriatic acid made stronger than that commonly used for removing cement from the surface of the tile after they have been set. This strong acid should be wiped up and not allowed to remain on the tile too long. As the lye is quite strong, it is necessary for the workman to wear rubber gloves.

Animated Electric Signs

A new field has been opened to builders of electrical signs in producing characteristic displays such as a kicking mule, an eagle flapping his wings, or, in fact, any idea wished for, an animated picture advertisement that is simple enough to be built of electric lights.

The kicking mule device, for instance, is built on a perfectly black background large enough to accommodate effectively the necessary number of lights. By working the flash machine, which has a speed of 150 contacts a minute, the mule is made to wag its ears and tail and go through many other movements as a darkey approaches and tickles him, finishing the display by kicking the darkey over backwards.

As less than half the lamps are burning at the same time the cost of operation is moderate. The flashers for some figures are very expensive and for others nominal. The kicking mule flasher would cost about $125 and the flapping eagle $40.

Threading Faucet Stems

A skeleton frame of cast iron is made, as shown in Fig. 1, which contains the die and is bolted to the platen or table of the drill press. A steel bushing, B, is fitted on top of the die to be used to guide the stem. Fig. 2 shows the faucet stem which has al-

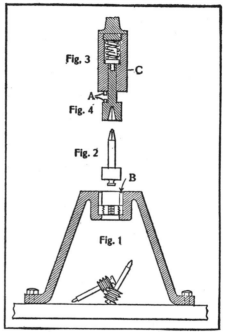

Threading Faucet Stems

ready been turned to the proper size. The upper end of the faucet stem has a square taper, designed to fit the handle with which the faucet is opened and closed, says American Machinist. This is particularly useful for driving the stem when threading.

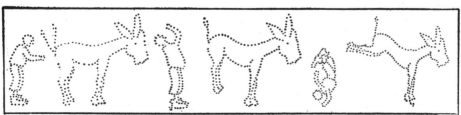

Showing Three of the Progressive Flash Movements

It will be noticed that Fig. 4 contains a square hole which slips over the square end of the stem the instant the drill press handle is pulled down. It is unnecessary to stop the press to connect, as the collet, C, and the drive are so arranged that it does not revolve after the square hole has engaged with the square end of the faucet stem, until the two pins, A, come together. Then, by pulling down the handle of the drill press, the stem will be forced into and through the die, dropping down out of the way as soon as the threaded end is clear.

The top of the drill press spindle is set so that the stem will be forced down far enough to clear the die, but the driver will not come in contact with the fixture in any way.

The Cause of Cracks in Aluminum Castings

The most frequent source of the cracking of aluminum castings is caused by overheating or "burning" the aluminum while melted. The demand for aluminum castings has now become so large and many of them are so thin and complicated, that founders continually have trouble in making them. The aluminum alloy most generally used for casting is one which contains aluminum and zinc. The presence of the zinc renders the casting difficult and far more liable to crack than when not used, says The Brass World. The brass must be employed to obtain the highest strength.

There are several rules that must be firmly obeyed in making aluminum castings, and they are, to melt the aluminum with a slow fire so that the top of the metal will not become "burnt" before the remainder of the metal is melted, to avoid overheating the metal after it has once melted, and pack the ingots in the crucible as compactly as possible so that portions will not stick up and become exposed to the action of the flame. Do not have the aluminum melted before the mold is ready. This is one of the most common sources of trouble.

How to Make an Adjustable Spar

The accompanying sketch shows how to make a spar that can be laid down over the cabin of the boat when not in use. The side pieces should be made of oak, carried down below the cabin top, C, securely fastened by $\frac{3}{8}$-in. bolts to a squared post, A, which may be stepped in the usual manner. A forged band placed around these side pieces and the post will give added strength, says Motor Boat. The spar is fastened by one large bolt, B, and a removable pin, D. Two large washers, W, are inserted between the spar and the oak side pieces. It may also be advisable to put brass plates on the spar where the bolt passes through it. This will prevent any wear to the hole in the spar.

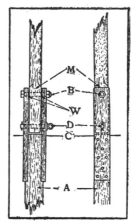

Making Stove Pipe

A certain stove dealer sells and uses his own make of stove pipe, which he claims is a better quality, both in material and workmanship, than he could purchase, says the Metal Worker. A blank pattern of each size of pipe is

"Turn a Sliver to Hold"

kept to set the gauges on the squaring shears. A quantity of material is cut each time. The pieces of metal are then folded for about a $\frac{5}{16}$-in. lock in a common iron folder. The metal is formed in rolls, then swaged by a hand groover or machine. The small end of the pipe is slightly drawn in over the end of a stake. Either put a small rivet through the lock at this end, or turn a sliver over the lock to prevent the collapse of the seam as shown in sketch. The pipe should not be crimped, as it will not stay in place as well as a good fitting telescope joint. A bead may be made on each end of the pipe the depth of the joints.

Lining an Engine Up with Shafting

If an engine is not in line with the shaft, the operation of the belt on the driving pulley will never be satisfactory. Fig. 1 shows a method of lining up an engine and shaft when it is impossible to place the line against the side of the rims of the pulleys. Two

ley, the line AB must be placed a short distance from the plumb lines CD, but at an equal distance from both lines.

In case it is impossible to line up from the flywheel to the plumb lines, the line EF may be run through the opening in the wall as shown, which touches or is placed at an equal distance from the rim of the wheel on each side of the line shaft. Then plumb lines are dropped so as to touch the line EF. If the plumb lines also touch the flywheel rim at both top and bottom where it crosses the edge of the rim, the pulleys are in line.

If the pulleys are of different widths of face, the distance, E and F (Fig. 2), between the rim of the pulley and the lines should be evenly divided on both sides of the pulley.

If the line touches the rim of the flywheel on one side of the crankshaft and

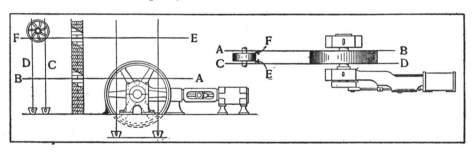

View at Left—Lining Engine and Shaft Vertically   View at Right—Lining Engine Horizontally

plumb lines are placed close to the rim of the driven pulley, so that they merely touch the rim, the lower ends of the plumb bobs being submerged in pails of water, which is to prevent vibration, says a correspondent in Engineers' Review. The line AB is run close to the plumb lines so that it just touches them, the ends being carried to a point beyond the driven pulley and also beyond the engine flywheel. The distance between the line AB and the flywheel on the engine shaft will of course indicate the amount the engine must be moved in order to bring both pulleys in line.

In case the engine flywheel has a greater face width than the driven pul-

is $\frac{3}{8}$ of an inch distant on the other side of the shaft, it indicates that the opposite end of the engine must be swung around to equal one-half the distance, or $\frac{3}{16}$ of an inch.

Figure 2 shows a simple method by which an engine may be lined up with a line shaft. The first thing to do is to stretch a line, AB and CD, from a point beyond the pulley on the line shaft to a point beyond the flywheel of the engine. If both pulleys have the same width of face the line should just touch the side of the pulley on both sides of the shaft, and if the engine is in line, the line will also just touch the rim of the flywheel on both sides of the crankshaft.

Rules for Concrete

Many rules are given for concrete, some of which are very good and others unreliable, and what holds good in one situation may not in another, says the Cement Era. To the engineer it can only be said, study carefully your material and the use to which it is to be put. Don't put railroad arch concrete under a country pavement, or vice versa, or use the same mixture for a reservoir wall that you would for a retaining wall.

In preparing concrete the sand and cement should be mixed dry first; then add water, and then subsequently add the crushed stone, gravel or whatever the aggregate is to be, and then thoroughly mix the mass. All mechanical mixing also, by whatever machine, should follow this rule. It should be transferred in as large quantities as possible to the work in dump wagons, wheelbarrows, or carriers, and dumped as nearly as possible in position in a 6-in. layer, as shoveling and rolling tends to roll out the stone, thereby making an excess of aggregate at one point and pure mortar at another. It should then be tampered to an even surface by a smooth iron tamper, preferably square, with 6 to 8-in. square surface, and weighing 25 to 30 lb. Do not attempt to deposit concrete under water when there is any way to avoid it. If used in this way at all place in coarse jute bags and deposit them in layers as close together as possible and tamp hard; this prevents the loss of the strength of the concrete, and enough cement comes through the bags to bind the mass.

No rule for composition of concrete can be laid down that will fit all cases, but we have found the following successful:

For arches and watertight work, 1 cement; 1 sand; 3 stone. For heavier walls, requiring bulk and strength, but a lesser degree of permeability, 1 cement; 2 sand; 4.5 stone. For ordinary uses in abutments, heavy walls paving, foundations, etc., 1 cement; 3 sand; 6 stone. A good common concrete in gravel is, 1 cement; 2 sand; 5 gravel.

Concrete has a great advantage over rough masonry for all work required to be watertight, as the mortar fills in all interstices and prevents the passage of water. The recent experience with the Jerome Park Reservoir, New York, would have been avoided if the reservoir wall had been of concrete.

The cost and often almost impossibility of ramming concrete to a solid mass is a weighty argument in favor of wet concrete. After considerable experience in this line and examination of many works of magnitude we conclude that a mixture wet enough to pour is the thing. Hand tamping depends for efficiency on the "location of the boss" and the "personal equation" of the tamper.

Shoveling is a poor way to transport concrete; the larger bulk the batch is moved in the better; large barrows, carts, carriers, etc., should be employed and the concrete landed as nearly as possible in position. All work should be tamped well to place, and if the laying is interrupted the set surface should be well wet and given a coat of neat cement before fresh material is applied. Do not attempt to fill or brush over joints, as they will break out in jagged lines the first winter. A neat joint made by a jointing tool is better. The same principle applies to brush wash. The writer has never seen a neat job of work where it was patched up by brush wash.

In freezing weather concreting work may be carried on with fair results, but it is more expensive and requires eternal vigilance on the part of the engineer or inspector. The sand should be hot and dry, the aggregate heated, the water warm and about a pail of salt used in each barrel of water, or about the proportion of one to fifteen. If the work is carried on as above and not interrupted it will set properly, but if you stop at night, or for any other reason, and the work freezes there will be a line of separation where the fresh work is added.

Some Boiler Room Ideas

One of the requisites for a good steaming boiler is a well fitted, well proportioned smokebox and stack, says a correspondent of the Practical Machinist. The poor proportioning of stack used and breeching has injured many a good boiler's reputation. As an instance I have in mind a 150-hp. tug boat boiler which was considered a hard steamer. According to the usual way of rating boilers it should have furnished steam without forcing, but did not. It was found that the total cross section area of the tubes was about 8 per cent more than that of the stack. A new stack and breeching enabled the doing away with forced draft. Too large a stack injures the draft, as well as does one too small. The happy medium for natural draft seems to be a stack having a cross section area equal to the combined area of the tubes.

It is well to keep an eye on the brickwork around the boilers to see that they are not getting air where they should not. A lighted candle held close to the cracks will indicate if there is an air suction that should not exist.

Many firemen are in the habit of opening the furnace doors when the steam pressure becomes too high. This scheme of opening the furnace doors to hold down the steam should be anything but recommended. If the dampers will not keep the safety valve from blowing, let it blow. The very fact that the pressure needs holding down shows that the boiler is hot and to let a continuous current of cold air pass through the warmest parts is conducive to leaking tubes and joints and will certainly cause trouble.

Some boiler men hold that steam flue blowers furnish the satisfactory method to clean tubes—others that to scrape them is the only way. A tube even if thoroughly blown at the regular cleaning periods will show scale with a brush or scraper after a day or so of steaming. If not scraped for some time it will be found difficult to force a hand cleaner through it which would readily pass through the same tube if freshly scraped. I have found a combination of the two methods to be most satisfactory. The daily dry steam blowings, with a weekly scraping seems to keep them in the right condition.

Portland Cement in House Repairs

Buy a sack of Portland cement, keep it in a dry place, and here are some of the many uses you can make of it; in fact, you will soon find it a household necessity, says a correspondent of Concrete. The writer had occasion to repair a wooden cap around a sink, the only defect being around the water-pipe, where the hot and cold water had caused the wooden cap to rot out. After cutting away the defective part, cutting the finished edge under to form a bevel edge or dove-tail, and wetting the surface well, he filled the cavity with neat Portland cement mixed with water to the consistency of putty. Then he worked the mixture into the crevices by pounding lightly on the wooden cap, thus jarring the mixture to the consistency of jelly by bringing the air-bubbles and water contained in the voids of the mixture to the surface. This made a dense close-grain stone when crystallized. He then troweled the surface smooth to a finish. The result was a perfectly water-tight joint around the pipe. The neat cement also adhered to the newly trimmed edges of the woodwork, leaving it neat and clean in appearance. This system of repairing decayed woodwork will be found especially valuable in repairing old wooden buildings, as it can be employed in the renewal of steps, floors, posts, walks, etc., without the necessity of the high-priced mechanics and expensive lumber.

How to Make Soldering Stick

The following formula will make up a soldering stick or paste that will give a good surface to which the solder will adhere and hold firmly. It will be well to avoid getting the acid mixture on one's hands, while in the liquid state, as it is liable to burn and cause some discomfort, says American Telephone Journal:

Put 1½ pt. muriatic acid in a stone jar having straight sides, and to this add as much zinc as you think will combine with it, and immediately light the gas which will be given off during the process of combination. Keep this gas burning as long as it exists, after which allow the solution to cool and filter it to remove the remaining zinc. To this solution add 1 oz. of sal ammoniac and stir until dissolved. Then make a combination of 1½ lb. of olive oil, 1½ lb. of tallow and 12 oz. of pulverized rosin. Mix them well and boil them. When the mixture is just about cool add the acid mixture and stir the entire solution until it becomes stiff, at which time you will have secured a most reliable soldering stick or paste. We would caution you, however, against the danger of spilling this mixture on your clothing, as it will burn holes in cloth very quickly. The completed stick should be wrapped in tinfoil.

◆ ◆ ◆

The first mention of a coal mine in the United States is found in the journal of Father Hennepin, a Jesuit missionary, who in 1679 discovered a "Cole" mine on the Illinois river. Coal was discovered in Ohio in 1755, but not produced as far as records show until 1838. The first records of production in Virginia were in 1822 when, according to one authority, 50,000 tons were mined.

◆ ◆ ◆

Slide Wire Bridge

The slide wire bridge is very useful for measuring low resistances, which is

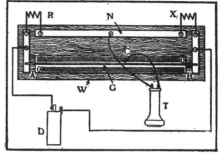

Slide Wire Bridge

as important sometimes as measuring high resistances. It is easy and simple to construct an instrument, as is shown in the cut, of which G is a German silver wire and may be any length so long as the scale beneath, which is made of paper and pasted to the wood base, W, is divided into 1,000 equal parts from right to left, and left to right, and the readings are read from above and below the wire, which result is the ratio of its length and, as a consequence, a ratio to the unknown resistance, X. The known resistance, R, for this style of bridge is 1 ohm, 5 ohms and 10 ohms each. Two brass or copper strips cross the ends of the wood base with a like strip, N, which is longer and is fastened lengthwise of the base. A telephone receiver is connected with one wire to the strip N and the other to slide along the German silver wire G. Place receiver to the ear and slide wire C along the German silver wire, and when no sound is heard it is then in balance and the readings are taken on the scale. A cell of dry battery is connected as shown and must not be left in circuit when not in use. Example: Say we have a 10-ohm coil at R and we wish to find the resistance of the unknown resistance X. After finding balance and after readings are taken we find that we have from A to C 605 on the lower scale and on the upper scale from B to C 395. Then the value of the unknown resistance may be found by the following formula:

$$X = R \times \frac{C\,A}{C\,B} = 10\,R\,\frac{605}{395} = \frac{6050}{395} = 15.31\ \text{Ohms.}$$

To Brighten Linoleum

The linoleum must be cleaned by using equal parts of milk and water. After wiping dry apply the following mixture by means of a cloth: Yellow wax, 5 parts; turpentine oil, 11 parts; varnish, 5 parts.

Simple Angular Projection

A very simple problem in third angle projection that the ordinary draftsman and amateur frequently bumps into is the laying out of the different views of some angular casting or forging, and the most common way it is done is to make something that looks like it or something that is intended to look like it and leave the blacksmith or pattern maker to do the studying and then if a mistake is made, he is to blame and the company has to stand the cost.

I have arranged a very simple problem, using as an illustration a hexagon prism, tipping it up into different positions, as shown in Figs. 1 and 2.

Starting with view A, the plan view in Fig. 1, we project to view B, the

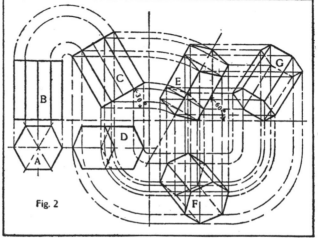

Fig. 2

Fig. 1

elevation; then following the construction lines to view C, we tip the hexagon prism up into one corner, making an angle of 60° between the base line and the edges of the prism; this is projected, following with construction lines to plan view D, thus giving a plan view of C as it would look pulling out the plane from the bottom. Turning the prism view C on the corner on which it rests to an angle of 20° with the center line and again taking a plan view of it, we have a view as shown in E, now projecting from both plan view E and elevation view C; we have a view at F showing the result of turning a hexagon prism into the two different angles, as shown in C and E.

In Fig. 2 the views A, B, C and D are the same as views A, B, C and D shown in Fig. 1.

From the view C following the construction lines project to view E the heights as given in view C.

View E shows an end elevation of view C, tipped over to bring the sides to an angle of 60° with the base line.

Now projecting from both the elevation, as shown in view E, and the plan view of C, as shown in view D, we find the plan view of view E at view F.

View G shows a side elevation of view E and is the result of the projection as shown by the construction lines projected from views E and F.

With view G we have completed the three views; the side and elevation and plan, that may be shown to carry the idea of the angles, the hexagon prism or other object being drawn is bent.

This is intended to show the manner in which any casting or forging may be correctly drawn, no matter to what angle or shape it is bent.—Contributed by E. W. Bowen, Denver, Colo.

Uses of Powdered Soapstone in the Draughting Room

Ordinary powdered soapstone, such as may be procured almost anywhere for about 10c a pound, is a most useful article for the draughting room. When used on tracing cloth it makes an excellent sizing and may be rubbed in freely without any danger of cutting or scratching the surface, as it contains no grit.

After rubbing out on tracing cloth a little soapstone sprinkled on the injured surface and rubbed with the fingers, will quickly restore the gloss and prevent the adherence of dirt to the spot which has been erased.

During the summer months many draughtsmen roll their sleeves up to the elbows, but some cannot work in this way, as the perspiration from the arms spoils the surface of the tracing cloth and makes it opaque. To prevent this, sprinkle a little soapstone in each hand and rub on the arms. This will absorb the perspiration and prevent the arms from sticking to the tracing cloth.

When making an intricate drawing, which may require several weeks for its completion, it is sometimes a good idea to sprinkle a little powdered soapstone on the paper and rub it in the same as in sizing tracing cloth. This renders the paper less absorbent and prevents dirt adhering to it, which would otherwise hide the lines. Hard paper is better adapted to this treatment than soft, and if it is found difficult to rub out, give the eraser an occasional rub on clean paper to remove the glaze.

Probably the most convenient way to keep powdered soapstone is in a large tin salt shaker, as it is then always ready for use.—Contributed by E. W. Davis, 897 Hamilton Ct., Chicago.

How to Slag the Cupola

The tap-hole for iron and for slag should be of such size that a continuous stream will run throughout the heat, says Obermayer's Bulletin. Just as soon as slag comes out with the iron, or blast comes out of either hole, you will know that it is too large. It is not an easy matter to keep either of these streams continuous. If the bottom of your tuyere is about 12 in. above the sand bottom the slag-hole should be about 4 in. below the tuyere, and should be about 1 in. in diameter made hard with fire clay.

Fill the hole with ordinary molding sand and stop the inside and outside with about $\frac{1}{2}$ in. thick of fire clay. In charging use about 40 lb. of limestone to each ton of iron charged and place it on the coke. Do not use any lime on the first two or three charges and do not open the slag-hole until you have taken out about 10 ton of iron.

Work a hole through for the slag and have it run over a clay-lined trough to the ground so as not to be in the way of the bottom when it is drawn out—after the slag has run a little while a crust will form on the top of the stream. Raise this crust with a bar an inch or so, and hold until it stays there. This will form a covered stream of slag which will run for hours, and even if this blast does come out it will make no noise, for it will be under this cover. If it is necessary to break the crust near the hole it will soon bridge over again.

It takes about half the amount of fluor spar as lime, and it is a better flux; but there is so little difference between oyster's shells, marble chips, limestone, or fluor spar that whichever is cheapest is best.

STANDARD SYMBOLS FOR WIRING PLANS
AS ADOPTED AND RECOMMENDED BY
THE NATIONAL ELECTRICAL CONTRACTORS ASSOCIATION OF THE UNITED STATES and THE AMERICAN INSTITUTE OF ARCHITECTS.

Copies may be had on application to the Sec'y of The Nat. Elec. Cont. Assoc'n, Utica, N. Y., and the Sec'y of The American Instit. of Architects. Washington, D. C

Ceiling Outlet, Electric only. Numeral in center indicates number of Standard 16 C. P. Incandescent Lamps.

Ceiling Outlet; Combination. ⅘ indicates 4-16 C. P. Standard Incandescent Lamps and 2 Gas Burners. If gas only

Bracket Outlet; Electric only. Numeral in center indicates number of Standard 16 C. P. Incandescent Lamps.

Bracket Outlet; Combination. ⅘ indicates 4-16 C. P. Standard Incandescent Lamps and 2 Gas Burners. If gas only

Wall or Baseboard Receptacle Outlet. Numeral in center indicates number of Standard 16 C. P. Incandescent Lamps.

Floor Outlet. Numeral in center indicates number of Standard 16 C. P. Incandescent Lamps.

Outlet for Outdoor Standard or Pedestal; Electric only. Numeral indicates number of Stand. 16 C. P. Incan. Lamps.

Outlet for Outdoor Standard or Pedestal; Combination. ⅚ indicates 6-16 C. P. Stand. Incan. Lamps; 6 Gas Burners.

Drop Cord Outlet.

One Light Outlet, for Lamp Receptacle.

Arc Lamp Outlet.

Special Outlet, for Lighting, Heating and Power Current, as described in Specifications.

Ceiling Fan Outlet.

S^1 S. P. Switch Outlet.

S^2 D. P. Switch Outlet.

S^3 3-Way Switch Outlet.

S^4 4-Way Switch Outlet.

S^D Automatic Door Switch Outlet.

S^E Electrolier Switch Outlet.

Show as many Symbols as there are Switches. Or in case of a very large group of Switches, indicate number of Switches by a Roman numeral, thus; S^1 XII; meaning 12 Single Pole Switches. Describe Type of Switch in Specifications, that is, Flush or Surface, Push Button or Snap,

Meter Outlet.

Distribution Panel.

Junction or Pull Box.

Motor Outlet; Numeral in center indicates Horse Power.

Motor Control Outlet.

Transformer.

———————— Main or Feeder run concealed under Floor.

———————— Main or Feeder run concealed under Floor above.

— — — — — Main or Feeder run exposed.

———————— Branch Circuit run concealed under Floor.

———————— Branch Circuit run concealed under Floor above.

— — — — — Branch Circuit run exposed.

–●–––●–– Pole Line.

●   Riser.

Telephone Outlet; Private Service.

Telephone Outlet; Public Service.

Bell Outlet.

Buzzer Outlet.

Push Button Outlet; Numeral indicates number of Pushes.

Annunciator; Numeral indicates number of Points.

Speaking Tube.

Watchman Clock Outlet.

Watchman Station Outlet.

Master Time Clock Outlet.

Secondary Time Clock Outlet.

Door Opener.

Special Outlet; for Signal Systems, as described in Specifications.

Battery Outlet.

————·— { Circuit for Clock, Telephone, Bell or other Service, run under Floor, concealed. Kind of Service wanted ascertained by Symbol to which line connects.

———··— { Circuit for Clock, Telephone, Bell or other Service, run under Floor above, concealed. Kind of Service wanted ascertained by Symbol to which line connects.

NOTE—If other than Standard 16 C. P. Incandescent lamps are desired, Specifications should describe capacity of Lamp to be used.

SUGGESTIONS IN CONNECTION WITH STANDARD SYMBOLS FOR WIRING PLANS.

It is important that ample space be allowed for the installation of mains, feeders, branches and distribution panels.

It is desirable that a key to the symbols used accompany all plans.

If mains, feeders, branches and distribution panels are shown on the plans, it is desirable that they be designated by letters or numbers.

Heights of Centre of Wall Outlets (unless otherwise specified)

Living Rooms	5' 6"
Chambers	5' 0"
Offices	6' 0"
Corridors	6' 3"

Height of Switches (unless otherwise specified)

4' 0"

SHOP NOTES FOR 1908